ENERGY SCIENCE, ENGINEERING AND TECHNOLOGY

CONCENTRATING SOLAR POWER

DATA AND DIRECTIONS FOR AN EMERGING SOLAR TECHNOLOGY

ENERGY SCIENCE, ENGINEERING AND TECHNOLOGY

Additional books in this series can be found on Nova's website
under the Series tab.

Additional E-books in this series can be found on Nova's website
under the E-book tab.

RENEWABLE ENERGY: RESEARCH, DEVELOPMENT AND POLICIES

Additional books in this series can be found on Nova's website
under the Series tab.

Additional E-books in this series can be found on Nova's website
under the E-book tab.

ENERGY SCIENCE, ENGINEERING AND TECHNOLOGY

CONCENTRATING SOLAR POWER

DATA AND DIRECTIONS FOR AN EMERGING SOLAR TECHNOLOGY

BURT J. ALEXANDER

AND

TED F. RICHARDSON

EDITORS

Nova Science Publishers, Inc.

New York

For permission to use material from this book please contact us:
Telephone 631-231-7269; Fax 631-231-8175
Web Site: http://www.novapublishers.com

NOTICE TO THE READER

The Publisher has taken reasonable care in the preparation of this book, but makes no expressed or implied warranty of any kind and assumes no responsibility for any errors or omissions. No liability is assumed for incidental or consequential damages in connection with or arising out of information contained in this book. The Publisher shall not be liable for any special, consequential, or exemplary damages resulting, in whole or in part, from the readers' use of, or reliance upon, this material. Any parts of this book based on government reports are so indicated and copyright is claimed for those parts to the extent applicable to compilations of such works.

Independent verification should be sought for any data, advice or recommendations contained in this book. In addition, no responsibility is assumed by the publisher for any injury and/or damage to persons or property arising from any methods, products, instructions, ideas or otherwise contained in this publication.

This publication is designed to provide accurate and authoritative information with regard to the subject matter covered herein. It is sold with the clear understanding that the Publisher is not engaged in rendering legal or any other professional services. If legal or any other expert assistance is required, the services of a competent person should be sought. FROM A DECLARATION OF PARTICIPANTS JOINTLY ADOPTED BY A COMMITTEE OF THE AMERICAN BAR ASSOCIATION AND A COMMITTEE OF PUBLISHERS.

Additional color graphics may be available in the e-book version of this book.

Library of Congress Cataloging-in-Publication Data

Concentrating solar power : data and directions for an emerging solar technology / editors, Burt J. Alexander and Ted F. Richardson.
       p. cm.
  Includes index.
  ISBN 978-1-62081-423-9 (hardcover)
  1. Solar concentrators. 2. Solar thermal energy. 3. Solar radiation--Measurement. I. Alexander, Burt J. II. Richardson, Ted F.
  TJ810.C575 2011
  621.47'2--dc23
                                        2012008878

Published by Nova Science Publishers, Inc. † New York

CONTENTS

PREFACE

As the world looks for low-carbon sources of energy, solar power stands out as the single most abundant energy resource on Earth. This book focuses on the capacity value of concentrating solar power plants and presents detailed information about solar resource data and the resulting data products needed for each stage of the concentrating solar power project, from initial site selection to systems operations. It also examines the degree to which concentrating solar power may be complimentary to solar photovoltaic via its use of thermal energy storage.

Chapter 1- This *Handbook* was developed in response to a growing need by the Concentrating Solar Power community for a single document addressing the key aspects of solar resource characterization. The material was assembled by scientists and engineers who have many decades of combined experience in atmospheric science, radiometry, meteorological data processing, and renewable energy technology development. In essence, this *Handbook* represents the culmination of more than 30 years of research and development investment by the US Department of Energy and the National Renewable Energy Laboratory to advance the authors' understanding of the nation's renewable energy reserves.

You are encouraged to provide feedback to the authors for future revisions and expansion of the *Handbook* scope and content.

Chapter 2- This study estimates the capacity value of a concentrating solar power (CSP) plant at a variety of locations within the western United States.

This is done by optimizing the operation of the CSP plant and by using the effective load carrying capability (ELCC) metric, which is a standard reliability-based capacity value estimation technique. Although the ELCC metric is the most accurate estimation technique, the authors show that a simpler capacity-factor-based approximation method can closely estimate the ELCC value.

Without storage, the capacity value of CSP plants varies widely depending on the year and solar multiple.

The average capacity value of plants evaluated ranged from 45%–90% with a solar multiple range of 1.0–1.5. When introducing thermal energy storage (TES), the capacity value of the CSP plant is more difficult to estimate since one must account for energy in storage.

The authors apply a capacity-factor-based technique under two different market settings: an energy-only market and an energy and capacity market. The authors' results show that adding TES to a CSP plant can increase its capacity value significantly at all of the locations.

Adding a single hour of TES significantly increases the capacity value above the no-TES case, and with four hours of storage or more, the average capacity value at all locations exceeds 90%.

Chapter 3- Falling cost of solar photovoltaic (PV) generated electricity has led to a rapid increase in the deployment of PV and projections that PV could play a significant role in the future U.S. electric sector. The solar resource itself is virtually unlimited compared to any conceivable demand for energy (Morton 2006); however, the ultimate contribution from PV could be limited by several factors in the current grid. One is the limited coincidence between the solar resource and normal demand patterns (Denholm and Margolis 2007a). A second is the limited flexibility of conventional generators to reduce output and accommodate this variable generation resource.

At high penetration of solar generation, increased grid flexibility will be needed to fully utilize the variable and uncertain output from PV generation and shift energy production to periods of high demand or reduced solar output (Denholm and Margolis 2007b). Energy storage provides an option to increase grid flexibility and there are many storage options available or under development.[1]

Chapter 4- The US Department of Energy (DOE), National Renewable Energy Laboratory (NREL), and Sandia National Laboratories hosted a workshop on thermal energy storage for concentrating solar power (CSP) on May 20, 2011, at NREL in Golden, Colorado. The objective for this workshop was to engage the university and laboratory research communities to identify and define research directions for developing new high-temperature materials and systems that advance thermal energy storage for CSP technologies. Desired outcomes for the workshop were to 1) inform the workshop participants of CSP technology challenges, specifically with respect to materials, and 2) generate and document new ideas for advancing materials development for CSP thermal energy storage.

Chapter 5- Concentrating solar power (CSP) technologies continue to mature and are being deployed worldwide. Power towers will likely play an essential role in the future development of CSP due to their potential to provide dispatchable solar electricity at a low cost.

This Power Tower Technology Roadmap has been developed by the U.S. Department of Energy (DOE) to describe the current technology, the improvement opportunities that exist for the technology, and the specific activities needed to reach the DOE programmatic target of providing competitively-priced electricity in the intermediate and baseload power markets by 2020.

As a first step in developing this roadmap, a Power Tower Roadmap Workshop that included the tower industry, national laboratories, and DOE was held in March 2010. A number of technology improvement opportunities (TIOs) were identified at this workshop and separated into four categories associated with power tower subsystems: solar collector field, solar receiver, thermal energy storage, and power block / balance of plant.

In this roadmap, the TIOs associated with power tower technologies are identified along with their respective impacts on the cost of delivered electricity. In addition, development timelines and estimated budgets to achieve cost reduction goals are presented.

The roadmap does not present a single path for achieving these goals, but rather provides a process for evaluating a set of options from which DOE and industry can select to accelerate power tower R&D, cost reductions, and commercial deployment.

In: Concentrating Solar Power
Editors: Burt J. Alexander and Ted F. Richardson

ISBN: 978-1-62081-423-9
© 2012 Nova Science Publishers, Inc.

Chapter 1

CONCENTRATING SOLAR POWER: BEST PRACTICES HANDBOOK FOR THE COLLECTION AND USE OF SOLAR RESOURCE DATA[*]

Tom Stoffel, Dave Renné, Daryl Myers, Steve Wilcox, Manajit Sengupta, Ray George, and Craig Turchi

FOREWORD

This *Handbook* was developed in response to a growing need by the Concentrating Solar Power community for a single document addressing the key aspects of solar resource characterization. The material was assembled by scientists and engineers who have many decades of combined experience in atmospheric science, radiometry, meteorological data processing, and renewable energy technology development. In essence, this *Handbook* represents the culmination of more than 30 years of research and development investment by the US Department of Energy and the National Renewable Energy Laboratory to advance our understanding of the nation's renewable energy reserves.

You are encouraged to provide feedback to the authors for future revisions and expansion of the *Handbook* scope and content.

---

[*] This is an edited, reformatted and augmented version of a National Renewable Energy Laboratory Technical Report NREL/TP-550-47465 publication, dated September 2010.

PREFACE

As the world looks for low-carbon sources of energy, solar power stands out as the single most abundant energy resource on Earth. Harnessing this energy stands forth as the challenge for this century. Photovoltaics (PV) and concentrating solar power (CSP) are two primary forms of electricity generation using sunlight. These two solar power generation approaches use different technologies, collect different fractions of the solar resource, and have different siting and production capabilities. Although PV systems are most often deployed as distributed generation sources, CSP systems favor large, centrally located systems. Accordingly, large CSP systems require a substantial investment, sometimes exceeding $1 billion in construction costs. Before such a project is undertaken, the best possible information about the quality and reliability of the fuel source must be made available. That is, project developers need to have reliable data about the solar resource available at specific locations, including historic trends with seasonal, daily, hourly, and (preferably) subhourly variability to predict the daily and annual performance of a proposed CSP plant. Without these data, no financial analysis is possible.

In September 2008, the US Department of Energy (DOE) hosted a meeting of prominent CSP developers and stakeholders. **One purpose was to identify areas where the DOE's CSP** Program should focus its effort to help the industry develop and deploy projects. At the top of the priority list was the need to provide high-quality solar resource data and recommend to industry the best way to use these data for site selection and estimating plant performance. The direct result is the National Renewable Energy Laboratory's (NREL) *Concentrating Solar Power Best Practices Handbook for the Collection and Use of Solar Resource Data*. The content is based on the experiences of scientists and engineers from industry, academia, and DOE for identifying the sources, quality, and methods for applying solar and meteorological data to CSP projects.

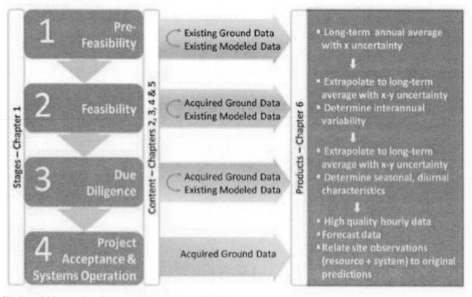

Credit: David Renné and Connie Komomua, NREL.

This handbook presents detailed information about solar resource data and the resulting data products needed for each stage of the project, from initial site selection to systems operations. It is not meant to be read from cover to cover, but to be used as a reference during each project stage. The figure below lists these stages and shows which sections contain information about the corresponding available data and resulting products.

Project developers, engineering procurement construction firms, utility companies, energy suppliers, financial investors, and others involved in CSP plant planning and development will find this handbook a valuable resource for the collection and interpretation of solar resource data.

ACRONYMS

AC	alternating current
AM	air mass
AOD	aerosol optical depth
AU	astronomical unit
BSRN	Baseline Surface Radiation Network
C	circumsolar brightness 0.3 degrees to 3.2 degrees from the center of the solar disk
CSP	concentrating solar power
COV	coefficient of variation
DEM	digital elevation model
DHI	diffuse horizontal irradiance
DIF	diffuse horizontal irradiance
DISC	direct solar insolation code
DNI	direct normal irradiance
DOE	US Department of Energy
ESRA	European Solar Radiation Atlas
ETR	extraterrestrial radiation
FOV	field of view
GHI	global horizontal irradiance
GIS	geographic information system
GOES	Geostationary Operational Environmental Satellite
GUM	Guide to Measurement Uncertainty
ISCCP	International Satellite Cloud Climatology Project
ISIS	Integrated Surface Irradiance Study
ISO	International Standards Organization
JRC	Joint Research Council
K	Kelvin
$kWh/m^2/day$	kilowatt hours per square meter per day
MBE	mean bias error
MCP	measure-correlate-predict
MESoR	Management and Exploitation of Solar Resource
METEONORM	commercial data product of Meteotest, Bern,

	Switzerland
METSTAT	meteorological-statistical transfer model
MSG	METEOSTAT Second Generation
NCAR	National Center for Atmospheric Research
NCDC	National Climatic Data Center
NCEP	National Center for Environmental Prediction
NIP	The Eppley Laboratory, Inc. Model Normal Incidence Pyrheliometer
NM	nanometer
NOAA	National Oceanic and Atmospheric Administration
NREL	National Renewable Energy Laboratory
NSRDB	National Solar Radiation Database
NWS	National Weather Service
POA	plane of array
POWER	Prediction of Worldwide Energy Resources
PV	photovoltaics
PVGIS	photovoltaic geographical information system
QA	quality assurance
R&D	research and development
RRDC	Renewable Resource Data Center
Rs	responsivity
RSR	rotating shadowband radiometer
S	solar brightness 0.0 degrees to 0.3 degrees from the center of the solar disk
SI	International System of Units
SOLEMI	Solar Energy Mining
SOLMET	Solar and Meteorological hourly dataset
SRB	Surface Radiation Budget
SRRL	Solar Radiation Research Laboratory
SSE	surface meteorology and solar energy
SUNY	State University of New York
SURFRAD	Surface Radiation Network
SWERA	solar wind energy resource assessment
SZA	solar zenith angle
TOA	top of atmosphere
TSI	total solar irradiance (formerly solar constant)
TMM	Typical Meteorological Month
TMY	Typical Meteorological Year
TMY2	Typical Meteorological Year (Version 2)
TMY3	Typical Meteorological Year (Version 3)
UPS	uninterruptible power supply
USI	upwelling shortwave irradiance
WCRP	World Climate Research Programme
W/m^2	watts per square meter
WMO	World Meteorological Organization
WWC	World Radiation Center
WRR	World Radiometric Reference

1. WHY SOLAR RESOURCE DATA ARE IMPORTANT TO CONCENTRATING SOLAR POWER

Sunlight is the fuel for all concentrating solar power (CSP) generation technologies. Like any generation source, knowledge of the quality and future reliability of the fuel is essential to accurate analysis of system performance and financial viability of a project. With CSP systems, the variability of the supply of sunlight probably represents the single greatest uncertainty in a plant's predicted performance. Solar resource data and modeling factor into three elements of a CSP project's life:

- Site selection
- Predicted annual plant output
- Temporal performance and operating strategy.

The first two items are interrelated. Site selection includes numerous factors, but a top priority is a good solar resource. For site selection, a representative annual solar resource is required to make comparisons with alternative sites and estimate plant output. Because site selection is always based on historical solar resource data and changes in weather patterns from year to year, more years of data are better for determining a representative annual dataset. Defining a typical meteorological year (TMY) dataset is not a trivial exercise and is described in section 5. TMY data are used to compare the solar resource at alternative sites and to define the probable annual performance of a proposed CSP plant. Data from individual years are useful to assess the annual variability that can be expected for the proposed location.

Note: Because they rely on reflecting collectors, all CSP technologies use direct normal irradiance (DNI). In this context, discussion of the solar resource for CSP plants implies the analysis of DNI.

Development of TMY data for large regions requires the use of models that rely on satellite imagery. In regional terms, the identification of prime solar resource areas is fairly simple. The southwestern United States, for example, has broad areas of excellent solar resource. However, narrowing down the data to a specific few square kilometers of land requires consideration of local impacts; although satellite data are very useful in mapping large regions, individual sites should be vetted with ground monitoring stations. Local measurements can be compared with same-day satellite data to test for bias in the satellite model. Any correction in the satellite model can then be applied to the historical datasets.

Once a plant is built, resource data are immediately required to complete acceptance testing. The owner and financiers will insist on verifying that the plant output meets its design specifications for a specific solar input. Often the acceptance tests will be for a short duration, perhaps a few days, but the owners will want to extrapolate the results to estimate annual performance. Annual performance estimates can be improved by comparing locally measured ground data to the satellite-derived data for the same time interval. Correcting any bias in the satellite data will allow the modeler to more accurately apply multiple years of satellite data to generate an improved TMY dataset for the site. Accurate resource data will remain essential to the plant's efficient operation throughout its service life. Comparison of plant output as a function of solar radiation resource is one global indicator of plant performance. A drop in overall efficiency implies a degradation of one or more plant components and indicates that maintenance is required. Lastly, the realm of resource forecasting is becoming more important for plant dispatch as higher penetration of solar power is planned for the electric grid. An accurate forecast can increase plant profits by optimizing energy dispatch into the time periods of greatest value. Although not explicitly covered in this handbook, forecasting requires the same principles described here for historical resource assessment—proper use of satellite- and ground-based data sources and models.

2. OVERVIEW OF SOLAR RADIATION RESOURCE CONCEPTS

Introduction

Describing the relevant concepts and applying a consistent terminology are important to the usefulness of any handbook. This section uses a standard palette of terms to provide an overview of the key characteristics of solar radiation, the fuel source for CSP technologies. Beginning with the sun as the source, we present an overview of the effects of the Earth's orbit and atmosphere on the types and amounts of solar radiation available for energy conversion. An introduction to the concepts of measuring and modeling solar radiation is intended to prepare the reader for the more in-depth treatment in Sections 3 and 4. The overview concludes with an important discussion of the estimated uncertainties associated with solar resource data based on measurements and modeling methods used to produce the data.

Properties of Extraterrestrial Solar Radiation

Any object with a temperature above absolute zero emits radiation. With an effective temperature of approximately 6000 K, the sun emits radiation over a wide range of wavelengths, commonly labeled from high-energy shorter wavelengths to lower energy longer wavelengths as gamma ray, x-ray, ultraviolet, visible, infrared, and radio waves. These are called *spectral regions* (Figure 2-1). Most (97%) of solar radiation is in the wavelength range of 290 nm to 3000 nm. Future references to broadband solar radiation refer to this spectral range.

Before continuing our discussion of solar radiation, it is important to understand a few basic radiometric terms. Radiant energy, flux, power, and other concepts used in this handbook are summarized in Table 2-1.

The total radiant power from the sun is remarkably constant. In fact, the solar output (radiant emittance) has commonly been called the *solar constant,* but the currently accepted term is *total solar irradiance* (TSI) to account for the actual variability with time. There are cycles in the number of sunspots (cooler, dark areas on the sun) and general solar activity of approximately 11 years.

Figure 2-2 shows a composite of space-based measurements of the TSI, normalized to 1 astronomical unit (AU), since 1975, encompassing the last three, 11-year sunspot cycles (see De Toma et al. 2004).

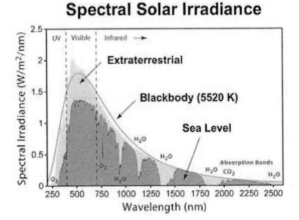

Figure 2-1. The atmosphere affects the amount and distribution of solar radiation reaching the ground.

Table 2-1. Radiometric Terminology and Units

Quantity	Symbol	SI Unit	Abbreviation	Description
Radiant energy	Q	Joule	J	Energy
Radiant flux	φ	Watt	W	Radiant energy per unit time (radiant power)
Radiant intensity	I	Watt per steradian	W/sr-1	Power per unit solar angle
Radiant emittance	M	Watt per square meter	W/m-2	Power emitted from a surface
Radiance	L	Watt per steradian per square meter	W/sr-1/ m-2	Power per unit solid angle per unit of projected source area
Irradiance	E, I	Watt per square meter	W/m-2	Power incident on a surface
Spectral irradiance	Eλ	Watt per square meter per nanometer	W/m-2 nm-1	Power incident on a surface per wavelength

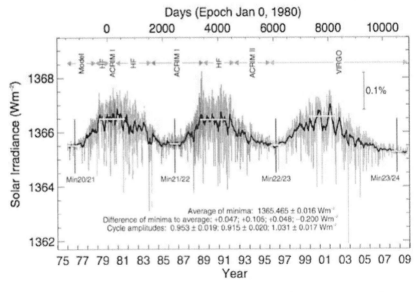

Figure 2-2. Three solar cycles show the variations of TSI in composite measurements from satellite-based radiometers (color coded) and model results produced by the World Radiation Center (www.pmodwrc.ch/pmod.php?topic=tsi/composite/Solar Constant) (Used by permission of Physikalish-Meteorologisches Observatorium Davos World Radiation Center).

The measured variation in TSI resulting from the sunspot cycle is ± 0.2%, only twice the precision (repeatability, not total absolute accuracy, which is about ± 0.5%) of the most accurate radiometers measuring the irradiance in space. There is, however, some large variability in a few spectral regions, especially the ultraviolet (wavelength less than 400 nm), caused by solar activity.

The amount of radiation exchanged between two objects is affected by their separation distance. The Earth's elliptical orbit (eccentricity 0.0167) brings us closest to the sun in January and farthest from the sun in July. This annual variation results in variation of the Earth's solar irradiance of ± 3%. The average Earth-sun distance is 149,598,106 km (92,955,953 miles), or 1 AU. Figure 2-3 shows the Earth's orbit in relation to the northern hemisphere seasons, caused by the average 23.5-degree tilt of the Earth's rotational axis with respect to the plane of the orbit. The solar irradiance available at the top of atmosphere (TOA) is called the *extraterrestrial solar radiation* (ETR). ETR (see Equation 2-1) is the power per unit area, or flux density in Watts per square meter (W/m^2), radiated from the sun and available at the TOA. ETR varies with the Earth-sun distance (r) and annual mean distance (r0):

$$\text{ETR} \quad = \quad \text{TSI} \cdot (r0/r)^2 \qquad\qquad (2\text{-}1)$$

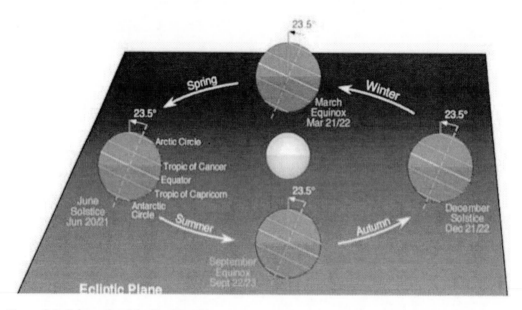

Figure 2-3. Schematic of the Earth's orbit.

As measured by multiple satellites over the past 30 years, the TSI is 1,366 ± 7 W/m^2 at 1 AU. According to astronomical computations, such as NREL's solar position software, the variation in the Earth-sun distance causes the ETR to vary from about 1,415 W/m^2 around January 3 to about 1,321 W/m^2 around July 4.

From the Earth, the sun appears as a very bright disk with an angular diameter of about 0.5 degrees. This means that a point on the Earth intercepts a cone of light from the hemisphere of the sun facing the Earth with an angle of 0.5 degrees at the apex, and a divergence angle from the center of the disk of 0.25 degrees (half the apex angle). Because the divergence angle is very small, the rays of light from the sun are considered parallel for most applications, and are called the *solar beam* or *direct normal irradiance* (DNI).

Solar Radiation and the Earth's Atmosphere

The Earth's atmosphere is a continuously variable filter for the solar ETR as it reaches the surface. Figure 2-1 illustrates the "typical" absorption of solar radiation by ozone, oxygen, water vapor, and carbon dioxide. The amount of atmosphere the solar photons must traverse, also called the *atmospheric path length or air mass* (AM), depends on the relative solar position of the observer (Figure 2-4). By convention, air mass one (AM1) is defined at the amount of atmospheric path length observed when the sun is directly overhead from a location at sea level. AM is geometrically related to the solar zenith angle (SZA) as AM = secant of SZA, or 1/Cos(SZA). Because SZA is the complement of the solar elevation angle, AM is also equal to 1/Sin (solar elevation angle). Air mass two (AM2) occurs when the SZA is 60 degrees and has twice the path length of AM1. Weather systems, specifically clouds and storm systems, are the major elements that modify the extraterrestrial solar radiation on its way to the surface or to a solar collector. The cloudless atmosphere also contains gaseous molecules, dust, aerosols, particulates, etc., which reduces the ETR as it moves through the atmosphere. This reduction is due to absorption (capturing the radiation) and scattering (essentially a complex sort of reflection).

Absorption removes radiation from the DNI, converting that radiation to heat and raising the temperature of the absorber. The longer the path length through the atmosphere, the more radiation is absorbed. Scattering redistributes the radiation in the hemisphere of the sky dome above the observer, including reflecting part of the radiation back into space. The probability of scattering—and hence of geometric and spatial redistribution of the solar radiation—increases as the path (AM) from the TOA to the ground increases.

Part of the radiation that reaches the Earth's surface will be reflected back into the atmosphere. The actual geometry and flux density of the reflected and scattered radiation depend on the reflectivity and physical properties of the ground and constituents in the atmosphere.

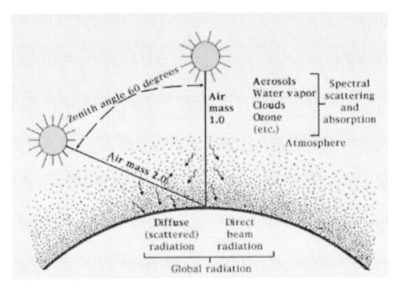

Figure 2-4. Scattering of the direct-beam photons from the sun by the atmosphere produces diffuse radiation that varies with AM (from Marion et al. 1992).

Research into the properties of atmospheric constituents, ways to estimate them, and their influence on the magnitude of solar radiation in the atmosphere at various levels and at the ground continues, and is of great importance to those who measure and model solar radiation fluxes (see sections 3 and 4).

Solar Resources: The Solar Components

Radiation can be transmitted, absorbed, or scattered by an intervening medium in varying amounts depending on the wavelength (see Figure 2-1). Complex interactions of the Earth's atmosphere with solar radiation result in three fundamental broadband components of interest to solar energy conversion technologies:

- Direct normal irradiance (DNI)–Solar (beam) radiation available from the solar disk (of particular interest to CSP)
- Diffuse horizontal irradiance (DHI) – Scattered solar radiation from the sky dome (not including DNI)
- Global horizontal irradiance (GHI) – Geometric sum of the DNI and DHI (total hemispheric irradiance).

These basic solar components are reacted to the SZA by the expression,

$$GHI = DNI \times Cos\ (SZA) + DHI \tag{2-2}$$

These components are shown in Figure 2-6.

Direct Normal Irradiance

The World Meteorological Organization (WMO) defines DNI as the amount of radiation from the sun and a narrow annulus of sky as measured with a pyrheliometer designed with about a 5-degree field of view (FOV) full angle. In the absence of scattering by the atmosphere, the sun would appear to have a diameter subtending a 0.5-degree FOV. Therefore, DNI includes the forward-scattered radiation near the solar disk (also called circumsolar radiation).

The effects of this scattering are as variable as the composition of the atmosphere at the time of observation. A sample of cloudless sky measurements from a circumsolar telescope illustrating this effect is shown in Figure 2-7 (see Grether et al. 1975).

The five momentary measurements of relative DNI brightness from Barstow, California, and Atlanta, Georgia, are plotted as a function of angle from the center of the solar disk. The FOVs for two commonly used pyrheliometers are indicated for convenience (*cavity radiometer* refers to the electrically self-calibrating instrument used to maintain the measurement standard; *NIP pyrheliometer* refers to the field instruments used to monitor DNI [see section 3]).

The ratio C/S is computed from the energy available from the circumsolar brightness (C = 0.3 degrees to 3.2 degrees from the center of the solar disk) and the solar disk (S = 0.0 degrees to 0.3 degrees from the center of the solar disk). These ratios can range from a few percent to several tens of percent of the total (C + S). More information about circumsolar radiation is available from http://rredc.nrel.gov/solar/ old_data /circumsolar/ and Major (1994). With the resurgence of interest in concentrating solar technology, there is a renewed interest and research in the amount of circumsolar radiation, or sunshapes, as affected by the variable properties of the atmosphere.

Relative Motions of the Earth and Sun

The amount of solar radiation available at the TOA is a function of the TSI and the Earth-sun distance at the time of interest. The slightly elliptical orbit of the Earth around the sun was briefly described above and shown in Figure 2-3. The Earth rotates around an axis through the geographical north and south poles, inclined at an average angle of about 23.5 degrees to the plane of the Earth's orbit. The resulting yearly variation in the solar input results in the climate and weather at each location. The axial tilt of the Earth's rotation also results in daily variations in the solar geometry over the course of a year.

In the northern hemisphere, at latitudes above the Tropic of Cancer near midday, the sun is low on the horizon during the winter and high in the sky during the summer. Summer days are longer as the sun rises north of east and sets north of west. Winter days are shorter as the sun rises south of east and sets south of west. Similar transitions take place in the southern hemisphere. All these changes result in changing geometry of the solar position in the sky with respect to a specific location (see Figure 2-5 generated for Denver, Colorado, by the program available from the University of Oregon at http://solardat.uoregon. edu/SunChartProgram. php). These variations are significant and are accounted for in analysis and modeling of solar radiation components using solar position calculations such as NREL's solar position or Solar Position Algorithm (see www.nrel.gov/rredc/models_tools.html).

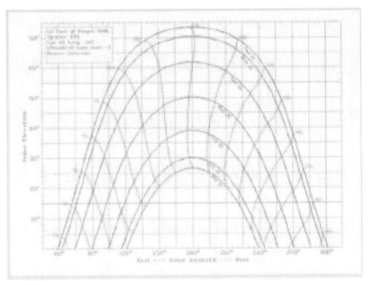

Credit: Tom Stoffel, NREL.

Figure 2-5. Apparent sun path variations during a year for a northern hemisphere location.

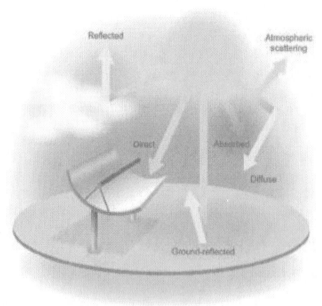

Credit: Al Hicks, NREL.

Figure 2-6. Solar radiation components resulting from interactions with the atmosphere.

Part of the DNI can be reflected by the Earth's surface and local clouds. The magnitude and direction of this reflected radiation depend on the optical properties of the surface. Some of this radiation can also be reflected upward, and is subject to scattering and reflection by the atmosphere, resulting in a small additional contribution to the diffuse horizontal, or sky irradiance, discussed in the next section.

Diffuse Horizontal Irradiance

A cloudless atmosphere absorbs and scatters radiation as the DNI penetrates to the ground. Parts of the DNI radiation are absorbed (removed) and reflected (scattered) in many other directions away from the path of this beam radiation. It is the scattered radiation we see as the sky radiation in the hemisphere above the ground. Lord Rayleigh (1871), Mie (1908), and Young (1981) developed theories for the mechanism of scattering in the atmosphere. These theories explain why the sky radiation appears blue (short wavelength, or blue light, is scattered more efficiently by atmospheric gases) and the solar disk tends to appear yellow and red at sunrise and sunset (the blue wavelengths are scattered a great deal out of our line of sight, but the longer red wavelengths from the solar disk come through unscattered). The sky radiation in the hemisphere above the local horizontal is called the DHI. A more technical definition of DHI is that it represents all radiation from the sky dome except the DNI (considered to be the quasi-parallel ray radiation from the solar disk). This includes radiation reflected or scattered by clouds (if present) and ground-reflected radiation is re-reflected downward by the atmosphere or clouds. Sky-reflected radiation is difficult to model because the photon interactions with the atmosphere are complex, clouds have varying compositions, and the ground has complex optical properties.

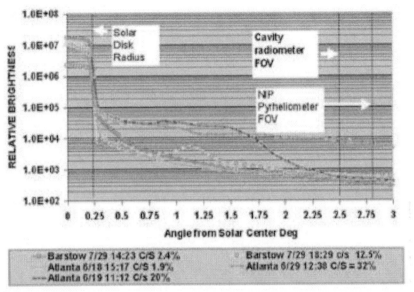

Credit: Daryl Myers, NREL.

Figure 2-7. Sample measurements from a circumsolar telescope at Barstow, California, and Atlanta, Georgia (circa 1977).

Global Horizontal Irradiance

The total hemispherical solar radiation on a horizontal surface is the sum of the flux density resulting the DNI at the given SZA, and the additional DHI:

$$\text{GHI} \quad = \quad \text{DNI} \cdot \text{Cos (SZA)} + \text{DHI} \tag{2-3}$$

SZA is the solar zenith angle computed from the date and time of measurement at a specific location.

This fundamental equation is the basis of most solar radiation measurement system designs, data quality assessments, and atmospheric radiative transfer models addressing the needs for solar resource data.

Solar Radiation Resources for Solar Energy Conversion

Determining the solar radiation components—GHI, DNI, or DHI, or some combination— that are applicable to a conversion system is the first step in evaluating design criteria and performance. Systems with concentrating optics rely on DNI availability. Low concentration systems may be able to use DHI radiation by light trapping techniques. Flat-plate collectors, fixed or variable in their mounting, can use all radiation components. GHI is most often the only available measured, or modeled, solar radiation data. In this case, conversion models are used to derive estimates of the appropriate quantities (Perez et al. 1987). The solar radiation scientific research community, peer-reviewed publications, and published reports are presently used to evaluate, validate, and assess the quality of these conversion algorithms. Models for estimating solar radiation are constantly appearing and being evaluated (Badescu 2008). A few classic examples are discussed in the next sections.

Model inputs are limited to site location, hour of interest, and GHI for the hour. We describe a quasi-physical model, based on the following premises:

- A physical model is used to calculate clear sky limits for the direct normal atmospheric transmittance.
- An exponential function of AM, similar in form to physical equations used to calculate energy transmission or propagation losses, is used to calculate deviations from clear sky transmittance values, based on atmospheric composition.
- The equations for computing Kn and other direct normal coefficients are continuously variable relative to Kt and AM and reproduce real-world variations in the relationship between DNI and GHI over monthly intervals.

The model is not a rigorous physical algorithm because the coefficients for computing clear sky transmittance values were derived from empirical regression analyses of measured DNI and GHI data from Atlanta, Georgia. Hourly average and thermopile radiometer data were used to derive the model. Applicability to higher time resolution (subhourly) data and solid-state (photodiode) radiometers that are subject to spectral effects, which do not sense the entire solar spectrum, is an open research question (see Maxwell 1987).

Estimating Direct Horizontal Irradiance From Global Horizontal Irradiance or Direct Normal Irradiance

Under clear and partly cloudy conditions, DHI is often a relatively small part (< 30%) of the GHI. Under overcast conditions, the GHI and DHI should be identical. When DHI measurements are not available, estimates of the diffuse may be needed in conjunction with GHI data to estimate DNI (as in the DISC model). DHI is also useful for daylighting applications.

Many models based on empirical correlations between GHI and DHI data have been developed. Liu and Jordan (1960) developed a model for estimating monthly average hourly diffuse. Erbs et al. (1982), Orgill and Hollands (1977), Iqbal (1983),

Spencer (1982), and many others have developed algorithms for estimating hourly DHI. These algorithms generally use correlations of global and diffuse clearness indices, Kt and Kd:

Kt   =   Clearness index or global horizontal transmittance of the atmosphere
$$GHI/[TSI \cdot (r_0/r)^2 \cdot Cos(SZA)]$$

Kd   =   Diffuse transmittance of the atmosphere

$$DHI/[TSI \cdot (r_0/r)^2 \cdot Cos(SZA)]$$

Estimating Direct Normal Irradiance From Global
Horizontal Irradiance

One of the few models for estimating DNI from GHI is the Maxwell DISC (Direct Solar Insolation Code) and the Perez variation on this approach, DIRINT (Perez et al. 1990). This model is based on empirical relations between clearness indices Kt and Kn (Liu and Jordan 1960):

Kt = Clearness index or global horizontal transmittance of the atmosphere
$= GHI/TSI \cdot (r_0/r)^2 \cdot Cos\ (SZA)$
Kn = Direct normal transmittance of the atmosphere
$= DNI/TSI \cdot (r_0/r)^2$

where

TSI = Total solar irradiance (mean TSI, ~$1366.7\ Wm^{-2} \pm 7\ Wm^{-2}$)
r0 = mean Earth-sun distance (149,598 km)
r = Earth-sun distance at the time of interest
SZA = Solar zenith angle at the time of interest.

Modeled Datasets

As mentioned above, long-term measured datasets are rare, have variable periods of record, and inconsistent ease of access. Measurement networks or stations providing high-accuracy, up-to-the-minute measured data are rare. A wide variety of agricultural research station solar radiation data of highly variable quality are available. These types of data require careful evaluation and comparison with other sources of data, perhaps estimated or modeled data, to establish appropriateness of use. There are many sets of modeled solar radiation, typically GHI, sometimes with DNI, and DHI. A few examples are the National Solar Radiation Database (NSRDB), the Swiss Meteotest METEONORM dataset, the *European Solar Radiation Atlas, the* NASA *SSE,* and the European Community *Solar Data (SoDa)* datasets (see section 5 for more details about these and other sources of data).

A popular modeled dataset is the TMY for a specific location. TMY datasets were originally designed for simplified building heating and cooling load calculations. The TMY consists of 8,760 hourly data records for one year. A TMY is the concatenation of 12 Typical Meteorological Months (TMMs) of data selected from a long-term period based on an optimized (weighted parameters) match of frequency distribution characteristics for the target month relative to the longer term. The TMM selection algorithm takes into account the distributions of solar radiation and several meteorological parameters. Thus, the resulting mean of a TMY parameter will be near (but not equal to) the mean of the parameter in the long-term dataset represented by the TMY. By design, a TMY does not include extremes of the dataset. The representative months may come from different years but are spliced together to give the continuous one-year time series. These datasets are used mainly to evaluate relative performance of different conversion system designs with respect to a standard dataset, and may not be appropriate for optimizing performance. Many software applications, however, use the TMY data to predict the typical performance of a solar conversion system.

Individual detailed descriptions of the properties of specific datasets will be discussed in section 5.

Uncertainty Measurements and Models

Measurements of solar radiation are among the most uncertain in any measurement discipline. Empirical models developed from measured solar radiation data, and validation of any model with measured data, always include the measurement uncertainties in addition to the inherent model accuracy. Solar radiation models based on physics are impossible to validate to an overall accuracy better than the uncertainty of the measured data. Measurement uncertainty analysis has been formalized by several organizations, including the International Bureau of Weights and Measurements (French acronym BIPM) and published by the International Standards Organization (ISO) as the *Guide to the Expression of Uncertainty in Measurements* (BIPM 1995).

Measurement Uncertainty

Uncertainty in measurements begins with the uncertainty in calibration references, calibration processes, and sensor design characteristics. As summarized in Figure 2.8, the resulting uncertainty in calibration factors must then be combined with the influence of additional sources of uncertainty in the field measurement instrumentation, installation methods, data acquisition, and operations and maintenance (O&M) processes. (More detailed information is provided in section 4.)

Calibration Reference and Direct Normal Irradiance Uncertainty

The internationally accepted System Internationale (SI) traceable reference for the measurement of terrestrial solar radiation is the World Radiometric Reference (WRR). This internationally recognized measurement reference is a detector-based standard maintained by a group of electrically self-calibrating absolute cavity pyrheliometers at the World Radiation Center (WRC) maintained by the Physical Meteorological Observatory, Davos (PMOD), in Switzerland (see section 3). The present accepted inherent uncertainty in the WRR is ± 0.30%. Reference cavity pyrheliometers used as national and institutional standards are calibrated against the WRR at international pyrheliometer comparisons conducted by the WRC once every five years. Transfer of calibration from WRR to national standards results in an expanded uncertainty[1] for these measurement standards of ± 0.45%. The annual transfer of calibration from national reference absolute cavity radiometers to pyrheliometers for field measurements results in absolute uncertainty (in the calibration factors) of ± 1.0%, mainly because of the environmental influences on the performance of field pyrheliometers. The calibration stability of commercially available pyrheliometers is generally < 1% change in responsivity (Rs) per year (see Figure 2-8). Results of a field pyrheliometer calibration for clear sky comparisons with an absolute cavity are shown in Figure 2-9. When finally deployed in the field, factors such as accuracy of solar tracking, data logger accuracy, cleanliness of the windows, frequency of recalibration, etc., may contribute more sources of uncertainty resulting in typical uncertainties of ± 2.0% to ± 2.5% (or greater) in DNI measurements from a very carefully conducted, high-quality measurement system (see section 3 for more details).

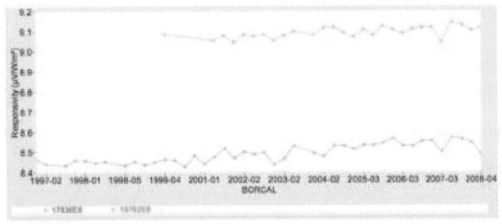

Credit: Daryl Myers, NREL.

Figure 2-8. Calibration histories for two pyrheliometer control instruments spanning 12 years (arrows are ± 1% error bars).

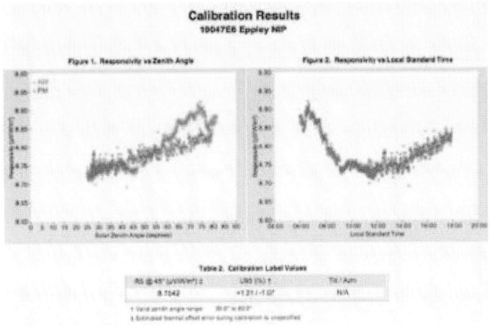

Credit: Daryl Myers, NREL.

Figure 2-9. Pyrheliometer calibration results summarizing Rs versus SZA (left) and versus local standard time (right).

Uncertainty in Pyranometer Calibrations and Global Horizontal Irradiation Measurements

The WRR is also the reference for calibration of pyranometers used to measure GHI and DHI. Physically, it is assumed the hemispherical detectors in a pyranometer respond only to the vertical component of the DNIVertical based on the SZA at the time of measurement:

$$DNI_{Vertical} \quad = \quad DNI \cdot Cos\,(SZA).$$

The pyranometer detector is assumed to have no response to the horizontal component of $DNI_{Horizontal}$

$$DNI_{Horizontal} \quad = \quad DNI \cdot Sin\,(SZA).$$

Using the relationship described in section 2.5.3 for GHI, DNI, DHI, and SZA:
$$GHI \quad = \quad DNI \cdot Cos\,(SZA) + DHI \text{ we can compute the DNI as:}$$

$$DNI = \quad (GHI - DHI)/Cos\,(SZA).$$

The GHI and DHI are measured by unshaded and shaded pyranometers, respectively (see section 3). Thus, we can use the above relationship to calibrate a single pyranometer.

By alternately shading and unshading the detector surface of a pyranometer on a clear day, the difference in output signal between shaded $_{(Vshade)}$ and unshaded $_{(Vunshade)}$ conditions can be compared with the reference DNI measurement to compute the Rs of the pyranometer under test:

$$Rs\,(Volts/W/m^2) \quad = \quad [(Vunshade - Vshade)/Cos\,(SZA)]/DNI.$$

This is called the *shade/unshade* calibration technique, and is described in more detail by Reda et al. (2003).

Alternatively, the radiometer can be calibrated by using a reference pyrheliometer to measure DNI and a continuously shaded pyranometer (calibrated using the above shade/unshade technique) to compute a reference GHI. The Rs of pyranometer(s) under calibration can be computed from their unshaded signal (Vunshade):

$$Rs\,(Volts/W/m^2) = \quad Vunshade/(DNI \cdot cos\,(SZA) + DHI).$$

Computing the Rs in this way is called the *component summation calibration technique.*

The shade/unshade and component summation techniques, when conducted over a range of SZA, demonstrate pyranometers, which by design have differing non-Lambertian, or nonideal response as a function of the SZA (or incidence angle) of the DNI. The differences in Rs as a function of SAZ are like fingerprints or signatures for each individual (not just type) of pyranometer detector. Figure 2-10 shows that variations of pyranometer Rs can be symmetrical with respect to solar noon, or highly skewed, depending on the mechanical alignment of the pyranometer detector, the detector surface structure, and the detector absorber material properties.

Typical calibration uncertainty for any sensor with respect to a WRR reference cavity radiometer is about 0.5% at any one very narrow range (± 2 degrees to ± 5 degrees) of zenith angle. Over a wide range of zenith angles (0 degrees to 85 degrees), the Rs can vary by 10 to 20 times that over a narrow range, or from ± 3% to ± 10% or even more. These effects then need to be combined with the field measurement influences, just as with the DNI measurement uncertainty estimate (e.g., include pyranometer installation, data logger accuracy, and cleanliness).

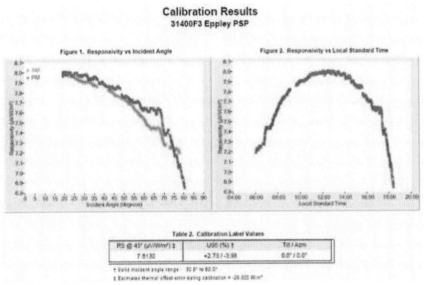

Credit: Daryl Myers, NREL.

Figure 2-10. Pyranometer calibration results summarizing Rs versus SZA (left) and local standard time (right).

These larger high zenith angle-related uncertainties occur over parts of the day (morning and afternoon) when the available solar resource is much smaller than typical midday resources, when the zenith angles are smaller. Because the maximum elevation (minimum zenith) angles vary through the seasons, the uncertainty in hemispherical radiation data will vary as well.

Even in the good measurement regime of midday, hemispherical field measurement uncertainty is typically two to three times that of direct-beam measurements, or ± 4% to ± 5%, over a year, mainly because of these seasonal uncertainty variations. Better instrumentation design and careful applications of correction factors as a function of zenith angles are ways to improve (reduce) the uncertainty in GHI measurements. The alternative is to use high-quality DNI and DHI measurements using a tracking shading disk/ball to compute GHI. The measurement uncertainties for GHI then approach that of the DNI (± 2%) for clear sky measurements.

Figure 2-11 shows the calibration traceability for pyrheliometers used to measure DNI and pyranometers used to measure GHI or DHI and indicates how measurement uncertainties accumulate from calibration to field deployment. Broad arrow boxes show accumulated uncertainty at each phase of the process. The resulting field deployment uncertainties for pyrheliometers used for measuring DNI is ± 2.0%. Measurement uncertainties for pyranometers used to measure GHI in the field range from ± 3.0% for SZA between 30 degrees and 60 degrees and up to ± 7% to ± 10% for SZA greater than 60 degrees.

An overview for estimating the measurement uncertainty of DNI is available in section 3.

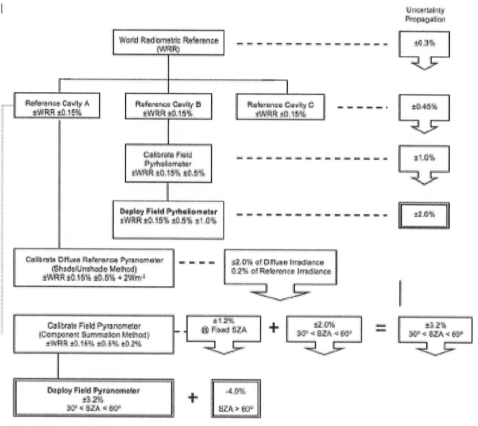

Credit: Daryl Myers, NREL

Figure 2-11. Calibration traceability and accumulation of measurement uncertainty for pyrheliometers and pyranometers.

Model Estimate Uncertainties

Empirical models derived from measured data correlations with independent parameters inherently carry measurement uncertainty embedded in the ultimate model accuracy. Models based on 2% or 5% or 10% accurate measurements can be no more accurate than the data used to generate the model.

Typically, scatter about model regression lines increases the random component of uncertainty further. Models based on first principles of physics and radiation transfer cannot be validated or verified to a level of accuracy greater than that of the measurements. Beware of claims of high accuracy in models or measurements without a thoroughly documented uncertainty analysis (Gueymard and Myers 2009).

Spatial and Temporal Variability of Solar Resources

We described earlier the variation of the ETR as a function of the 11-year sunspot cycle (less than ± −0.2%), and the annual variation of the Earth-sun distance (± −3%). These are minor variations compared with the influences of the atmosphere, weather, climate, and geography on the variation of solar resources at the Earth's surface. Variations in solar radiation from month to month, especially in the latitudes outside the tropics, follow an annual pattern, generally during the summer, with lower values during the winter. The year-to-year variation in these patterns is called the *interannual variability*. The coefficient of variation (COV), or ratio of the standard deviation to the mean of a set of given averages, can be used to quantify this variability. Studies of GHI and DNI distributions in the United States show the range of GHI interannual variability is typically 8%–10%. This is generally about half, or less, of the variability of DNI, which can be 15% or more at the 66% confidence interval (Wilcox and Gueymard 2010).

A typical measure of variability is the COV, defined as the standard deviation of a dataset (e.g., annual averages for several years) divided by the average of the dataset. Studies show the COV for annual averages of DNI can approach 10%, depending on climate stability (NSRDB Daily Statistics Files indicate COV for Daggett, California, is 6.2%). Interannual COV for annual averages GHI is typically 5%. The COV is based on a single standard deviation, and is typically about one-third the range of data in a sample.

Differences between radiation resources in the same months in different years are generally larger during the winter and smaller during the summer in the continental United States. Variations in weather and natural events such as forest fires, volcanic eruptions, dust clouds from drought regions, and agricultural activity all can contribute to interannual variations. Figure 2-12 compares the mean and maximum and minimum monthly average daily total GHI from the 1961–1990 NSRDB (modeled from meteorological data) with eight individual years of estimates based on satellite data (1998–2005) for Daggett, California. Variations much greater or somewhat smaller than this can be seen for locations with more or less variable weather patterns.

Spatial variations in solar resources often come into question, especially if nearby or neighboring measured data are available for a site without measured data. Mountainous terrain or highly variable urban, agricultural, or other microclimate influences may contribute to high spatial variability of the solar resource. Analysis of measured and modeled data correlations with distances between stations has generally shown that correlations decrease with increasing station spacing and higher time resolution (e.g., 15 minute versus hourly) data integration periods. One study of 17 sites in Wisconsin showed that correlations for hourly data fall from 0.995 to 0.97 as spacing increases from 5 km to 60 km. For 15-minute data, the correlations fall from 0.98 to less than 0.75 at more than 100 km (see section 6).

Prevailing winds and cloud motion patterns can also affect both spatial and temporal variability over distances from a few to hundreds of kilometers. A study of a dense solar measurement network in Oklahoma showed correlations between stations degrade from 95% or better for nearby stations to less than 45% for stations greater than 300 km away, depending on the geographical relationship (east, west, northwest, etc.) between the stations. Barnett et al. (1998) provided a correlelogram for these analyses. Attempts to interpolate between stations to estimate solar resources should be used with caution. Attention to the data sample period, geography, terrain, weather patterns, and spacing is important and requires careful analyses.

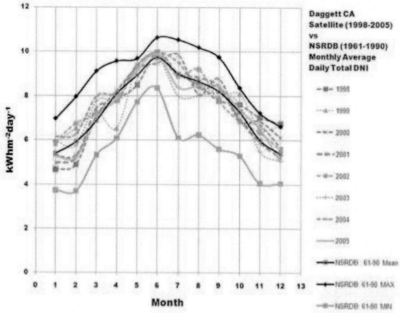

Credit: Steve Wilcox, NREL.

Figure 2-12. Example of direct-beam monthly average daily total (kWh/m2/day) interannual variability from 1961 through 2005 for Daggett, California (Data from NSRB).

3. MEASURING SOLAR RADIATION

Accurate measurements of DNI are essential to CSP project design and implementation. Because DNI data are relatively complex, and therefore expensive compared with other meteorological measurements, they are available for only a limited number of locations. Increasingly, developers are in need of DNI data for site resource analysis, system design, and plant operation. DNI measurements are also used to develop and test models for estimating DNI and other solar irradiance components based on available surface meteorological observations or satellite remote sensing techniques. DNI measurements will also play an important role in developing solar resource forecasting techniques.

This section focuses on the instrument selection, installation, design, and O&M of measurement systems suitable for collecting DNI resource measurements.

Instrumentation Selection Options

Before considering instrumentation options and the associated costs, the user must first evaluate the data accuracy or uncertainty levels that will satisfy the ultimate analyses based on the DNI measurements. This ensures the best value can be achieved after the available various measurement and instrumentation options are considered (see the Appendix for a list of radiometer manufacturers and distributors).

By first establishing the project needs for DNI accuracy, the user can base instrument selection and the levels of effort for operating and maintaining the measurement system on an overall cost-performance determination. Specifically, "first-class" instrumentation should not be purchased if the project resources cannot support the maintenance required to ensure measurement quality consistent with the radiometer design specifications and manufacturer recommendations.

Redundant instrumentation is another important consideration to ensure confidence in data quality. Multiple radiometers within the project location and/or providing for the measurement of all three solar irradiance components (GHI, DHI, and DNI), regardless of the primary measurement need, can greatly enhance opportunities for post-measurement data quality assessment (see page 39).

Instrument Types

Instruments designed to measure any form of radiation are called radiometers. In this section, we will summarize the types of radiometers most commonly used to measure solar radiation resources for application to CSP technology needs.

Pyrheliometers and Pyranometers

Pyrheliometers and pyranometers are two types of radiometers used to measure solar irradiance. Their ability to receive solar radiation from two distinct portions of the sky distinguishes their designs.

As described in section 2, pyrheliometers are used to measure DNI and pyranometers are used to measure GHI, DHI, or plane-of-array (POA) irradiances. Table 3-1 summarizes some key attributes of these two radiometers.

Pyrheliometers and pyranometers commonly use either a thermoelectric or photoelectric detector for converting solar flux (W/m^2) into a proportional electrical signal (μVdc). Thermoelectric detectors have an optically black coating that allows for a broad and uniform spectral response to all solar radiation wavelengths between about 300 nm and 3,000 nm (Figure 3-1).

Due to the relatively large thermal mass of this detector design, the time-response characteristics are typically 1–5 s.[2] That is, the output signal lags the changes in solar flux.

Table 3-1. Solar Radiation Instrumentation

Radiometer Type	Measurement	FOV (full angle)	Installation
Pyrheliometer	DNI	5.7 degrees to 6.0 degrees	Mounted on automatic solar tracker for alignment with the solar disk
Pyranometer	GHI	2 π steradians	Mounted on stable horizontal surface free of local obstructions*
Pyranometer	DHI	2 π steradians	Mounted on automatic solar tracker fitted with shading mechanism or on a manually adjusted shadowband platform for blocking DNI from detector surface*
Pyranometer	POA	2 π steradians	Mounted in the POA of the flat plate solar collector*

* Optionally installed with powered ventilator to reduce contamination of optical surfaces.

Photoelectric detectors, however, generally respond to only the visible and near infrared spectral regions from about 400 nm to 1,100 nm (Figure 3-2). These detectors have very fast time-response characteristics—on the order of microseconds. For either detector, as installed in commercially available instruments, the electrical signal generated by exposure to solar irradiance levels of about 1,000 W/m^2, is on the order of 10 mVdc (assuming no amplification of the output signal). This rather low-level signal requires proper electrical grounding and shielding considerations during installation (see section 5).

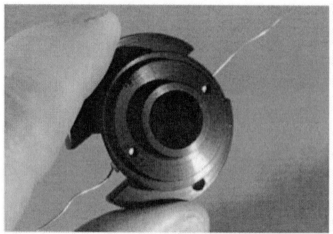

NREL/PIX 03962.

Figure 3-1. Thermopile assembly used in The Eppley Laboratory, Inc. Model PSP.

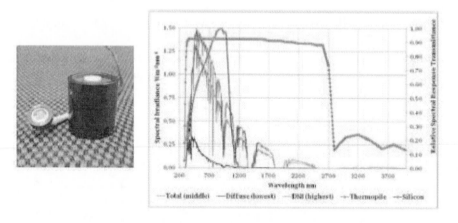

Figure 3-2. Typical photodiode detector (left) and spectral response of LI-COR pyranometer (right). Used by permission of LI-COR Biosciences, Inc.

Because of their narrow FOV (typically 5.7 degrees or 6.0 degrees full-angle), pyrheliometers are mounted in automatic solar trackers to maintain the instrument's alignment with the solar disk and fully illuminate the detector from sunrise to sunset (Figures 3-3 and 3-4). Alignment of the pyrheliometer with the solar disk is determined by a simple diopter, or sighting device in which a small spot of light (the solar image) falls on a mark in the center of a target located near the rear of the instrument (Figure 3-5). By convention and to allow for small variations in tracker alignment, view-limiting apertures inside a pyrheliometer allow for the detection of radiation in a narrow annulus of sky around the sun (WMO 2008). This circumsolar radiation component is due to the forward scattering of radiation near the solar disk caused by atmospheric aerosols and other constituents that can scatter solar radiation. Depending on the FOV and tracker alignment, pyrheliometer measurements include varying amounts of circumsolar irradiance contributions to the DNI.

The most accurate measurements of DNI are accomplished using an electrically self-calibrating absolute cavity radiometer (see Figure 3-6). Described in section 2, this type of pyrheliometer is the basis for the WRR, the internationally recognized detector-based measurement standard for DNI as shown in Figure 3-7 (Fröhlich 1991). By design, absolute cavity radiometers have no window and are therefore generally limited to fully attended operation under clear sky conditions to protect the integrity of the receiver cavity (Figure 3-8). Removable windows and temperature-controlled "all-weather" designs are available for automated continuous operation of these pyrheliometers.

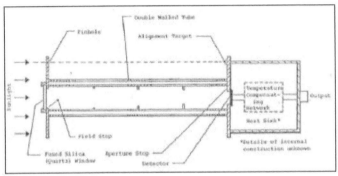

Credit: ERDA (now DOE)

Figure 3-3. The Eppley Laboratory, Inc. Model NIP (normal incidence pyrheliometer) schematic (Bahm and Nakos 1979).

Credit: Tom Stoffel, NREL.

Figure 3-4. Pyrheliometers mounted on automatic solar tracker.

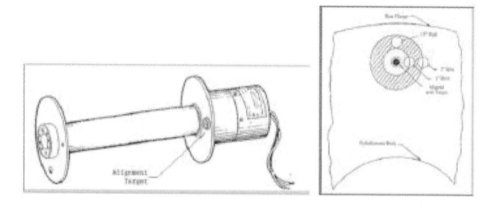

Figure 3-5. Pyrheliometer alignment diopter configuration (Micek 1981) (Used by permission of Leonard Micek.)

However, the installation of the protective window nullifies the "absolute" nature of the DNI measurement. The window introduces additional measurement uncertainties associated with the optical transmittance properties of the window (made from either quartz or calcium fluoride) and the changes to the internal heat exchange due to the now sealed system.

Credit:Tom Stoffel, NREL.

Figure 3-6. Multiple electrically self-calibrating absolute cavity radiometers mounted on solar trackers with control and data acquisition electronics.

NREL/PIX 08087.

Figure 3-7. The World Standard Group of six absolute cavity radiometers is used to define the WRR or DNI measurement standard.

A pyranometer has a thermoelectric or photoelectric detector with a hemispherical or "fisheye" FOV (360 degrees or 2π steradians) (see Figure 3-9). This type of radiometer is generally mounted on a horizontal platform for measuring GHI. In this orientation, the pyranometer has a complete view of the sky dome. Ideally, the mounting location for this instrument is free of natural or artificial obstructions on the horizon. The pyranometer detector is mounted under a protective precision-ground quartz (or other material) dome or a diffuser. Both designs protect the detector from the weather and provide optical properties consistent with receiving hemispheric solar radiation.

To reduce the potential for contaminating the pyranometer optics caused by dust, dew, frost, snow, ice, insects, or other material, pyranometers can be fitted with ventilators that constantly blow air—sometimes heated— from under the instrument and over the dome (Figure 3-10).

These ventilation devices can, particularly when heated, require a significant amount of electrical power, adding to the required capacity for on-site power generation in remote areas. Ventilators also affect the thermal offset characteristics of pyranometers with single-black detectors (Vignola et al. 2009).

Consistent with their low-cost design based on a photodiode detector, these pyranometer designs employ a diffuser above the detector (Figure 3-11). Acrylic diffusers can be more dust tolerant than optical glass domes (Maxwell et al. 1999).

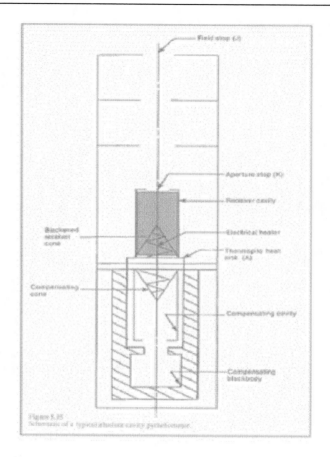

Credit: NREL.

Figure 3-8. Schematic of The Eppley Laboratory, Inc. Model AHF absolute cavity pyrheliometer (after Reda 1996).

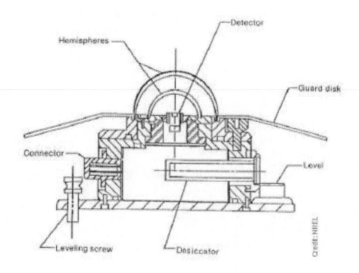

Credit: NREL.

Figure 3-9. Schematic of The Eppley Laboratory, Inc., Model PSP (precision spectral pyranometer).

Credit: Tom Stoffel, NREL.

Figure 3-10. Kipp & Zonen Model CM22 pyranometers installed in CV2 ventilators.

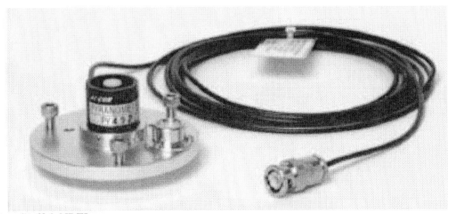

Credit: Tom Stoffel, NREL.

Figure 3-11. LI-COR Model 200SA pyranometer with photodiode detector and acrylic diffuser fore optic (from www.licor.com).

Pyrheliometer and Pyranometer Classifications

The ISO and the WMO have established classifications and specifications for the measurement of solar irradiance (ISO 1990; WMO 2008). We encourage the reader to review these documents in more detail as part of the project planning for solar resource measurements before acquiring pyrheliometers or pyranometers.

Estimated measurement uncertainty is the basis for these pyrheliometer and pyranometer classifications. The WMO (2008) recognizes the difficulties associated with measuring solar irradiance:

It may be said generally that good quality measurements are difficult to achieve in practice, and for routine operations they can be achieved only with modern equipment and redundant measurements. Some systems still in use fall short of best practice, the lesser performance having been acceptable for many applications. However, data of the highest quality are increasingly in demand.

The WMO characteristics of operational pyrheliometers and pyranometers are presented in Tables 3-2 and 3-3. The ISO specification lists for these radiometers are presented in Tables 3-4 and 3-5. Our purpose for providing these classifications is to address questions about differences in data quality and to give the reader a better understanding of the data quality afforded by particular instrument classes.

Table 3-2. WMO Characteristics of Operational Pyrheliometers for Measuring DNI

Characteristic	High Quality	Good Quality
Response time (95% response).	< 15 s	< 30 s
Zero offset – response to 5 K/h change in ambient temperature.	2 W/m^2	4 W/m^2
Resolution – smallest detectable change in W/m^2.	.051	1
Stability – change per year, percentage of full scale.	.01	.05
Temperature response – percentage maximum error due to any change of ambient temperature within an interval of 50 K.	1	2
Nonlinearity – percentage deviation from the responsivity at 500 W/m2 due to any change of irradiance within the range 100 to 1100 W/m^2.	.02	.05
Spectral sensitivity – percentage deviation of the product of spectral absorptance and spectral transmittance from the corresponding mean within the range of 300 to 3000 nm.	.05	1.0
Tilt response – percentage deviation from the responsivity at 0 degrees tilt (horizontal) due to change in tilt from 0 degrees to 90 degrees at 1000 W/m^2.	.02	.05
Achievable uncertainty (95% confidence level):		
1-min totals		
Percent	0.9	1.8
kJ/m2	0.56	1
Wh/m2	0.16	0.28
1-h totals		
Percent	0.7	1.5
kJ/m^2	21	54
Wh/m^2	5.83	15.0

**Table 3-3. WMO Characteristics of Operational Pyranometers
for Measuring GHI or DHI**

Characteristic	High Quality	Good Quality	Moderate Quality
Response time – 95% response	< 15 s	< 30 s	< 60 s
Zero offset Response to 200 W/m2 net thermal radiation (ventilated) Response to 5 K/h change in ambient temperature	7 W/m2 2 W/m2	7 W/m2 2 W/m2	7 W/m2 2 W/m2
Resolution – smallest detectable change	1 W/m2	5 W/m2	10 W/m2
Stability – change per year, percentage of full scale	.08	1.5	3.0
Directional response for beam radiation – the range of errors caused by assuming that the normal incidence Rs is valid for all directions when measuring, from any direction, a beam radiation whose normal incidence irradiance is 1000 W/m2	10 W/m2	20 W/m2	30 W/m2
Temperature response – percentage maximum error due to any change of ambient temperature within an interval of 50 K	2	4	8
Nonlinearity – percentage deviation from the Rs at 500 W/m2 caused by any change of irradiance within the range of 100 to 1000 W/m2	.05	1	3
Spectral sensitivity – percentage deviation of the product of spectral absorptance and spectral transmittance from the corresponding mean within the range 300 to 3 000 nm	2	5	10
Tilt response – percentage deviation from the Rs at 0 degrees tilt (horizontal) caused by change in tilt from 0 degrees to 90 degrees at 1000 W/m2	0.5	2	5
Achievable uncertainty – 95% confidence level Hourly totals Daily totals	3% 2%	8% 5%	20% 10%

Even among the instrument classifications and specifications, there can be some measurement uncertainty variations.

The user should research various instrument models to gain familiarity with the design and measurement characteristics in view of a particular application (Myers and Wilcox 2009; Wilcox and Myers 2008).

Table 3-4. ISO Specifications Summary for Pyrheliometers Used To Measure DNI

Pyrheliometer Specification List			
Specification	Class of Pyrheliometer		
	Secondary Standard	First Class	Second Class
Response time – 95% response	< 15 s	< 20 s	< 30 s
Zero offset – Response to 5 K h-1 change in ambient temperature	± 2 Wm-2	± 4 Wm-2	±8 Wm-2
Resolution – smallest detectable change in Wm-2	± 0.5 Wm-2	± 1 Wm-2	± 5 Wm-2
Stability – percentage of full scale, change/year	± 0.5%	± 1%	± 2%
Nonlinearity – percentage deviation from the responsivity at 500 W/m2 due to change in irradiance within 100 Wm-2 to 1000 Wm-2	± 0.2%	± 0.5%	± 2%
Spectral selectivity – percentage deviation of the product of the spectral absorptance and the spectral transmittance from the corresponding mean within 0.3 µm and 3.0 µm	± 0.5%	± 1%	± 5%
Temperature response – total percentage deviation due to change in ambient temperature within an interval of 50 K	± 1%	± 2%	± 10%
Tilt response – percentage deviation from the responsivity at 0 degrees tilt (horizontal) due to change in tilt from 0 degrees to 90 degrees at 1000 W/m-2 irradiance	± 0.2%	± 0.5%	± 2%
Traceability – maintained by periodic comparison	With a primary standard pyrheliometer	With a secondary standard pyrheliometer	With a first class pyrheliometer or better

Rotating Shadowband Radiometers

Rotating shadowband radiometers (RSRs) use a pyranometer that is periodically shaded by a motorized shadowband that moves across the detector's FOV (Figure 3-12). By design, the instrument measures GHI when unshaded and DHI when shaded. Using the following equation relating GHI, DHI, and DNI, the DNI is calculated from GHI, DHI, and the solar position at the time of band rotation (Figure 3-13). Although this instrument is motorized and requires energy for electronics necessary to operate the system, the electrical power requirements of some commercially available units is low enough to be powered by a small photovoltaic (PV) panel and storage battery. Such a design is well suited for remote installations where conventional power is not available. Most models incorporate some type of postprocessing where the measurements are corrected for known errors, such as effects of shade band geometry and pyranometer response characteristics for temperature and solar spectral distributions. Sometimes the corrections are site-specific, requiring empirical testing to establish their magnitude.

Users should inquire of the manufacturer about whether such postprocessing is part of the instrument package and is readily available.

Table 3-5. ISO Specifications Summary for Pyranometers Used To Measure of GHI and DHI

Pyrheliometer Specification List			
Specification	Class of Pyrheliometer*		
	Secondary Standard	First Class	Second Class
Response time – 95% response	< 15 s	< 30 s	< 60 s
Zero offset Response to 200 Wm-2 net thermal radiation (ventilated) Response to 5 K h-1 change in ambient temperature	+ 7 Wm-2 ± 2 Wm-2	+ 15 Wm-2 ± 4 Wm-2	+ 30 Wm-2 ± 8 Wm-2
Resolution – smallest detectable change	± 1 Wm-2	± 5 Wm-2	± 10 Wm-2
Stability – percentage change in responsivity per year	± 0.8%	± 1.6%	± 2%
Nonlinearity – percentage deviation from the responsivity at 500 W/m-2 due to change in irradiance within 100 Wm-2 to 1000 Wm-2	± 0.2%	± 0.5%	± 2%
Directional response for beam radiation (the range of errors caused by assuming that the normal incidence responsivity is valid for all directions when measuring, from any direction, a beam radiation whose normal incidence irradiance is 1000 Wm-2	± 10 Wm-2	± 20 Wm-2	± 30 Wm-2
Spectral selectivity – percentage deviation of the product of the spectral absorptance and the spectral transmittance from the corresponding mean within 0.3 μm and 3.0 μm	± 2%	± 5%	± 10%
Temperature response – total percentage deviation due to change in ambient temperature within an interval of 50 K	2%	4%	8%
Tilt response – percentage deviation from the responsivity at 0 degrees tilt (horizontal) due to change in tilt from 0 degrees to 90 degrees at 1000 W/m-2 irradiance	± 0.5%	± 2%	± 5%

* The highest category for pyranometers is the secondary standard, because the most accurate determination of GHI has been suggested to be the sum of the DNI as measured by an absolute cavity radiometer and the DHI as measured by a secondary standard pyranometer shaded from the DNI by a disk.

$$DNI = \frac{(GHI - DHI)}{Cos\ (SZA)}$$

Credit: Tom Stoffel, NREL.

Figure 3-12. Two commercially available RSRs: Irradiance, Inc. Model RSR (left) and Yankee Environmental Systems, Inc. Model SDR-1 (two units shown on right).

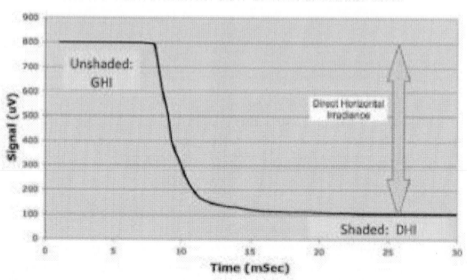

Credit: Tom Stoffel, NREL.

Figure 3-13. Time-series data concept for RSR measurements illustrating the difference between the two measured quantities (GHI and DHI) is proportional to the vertical component (direct horizontal or DH) of the DNI (DNI = DH/Cos (SZA).

Measurement Uncertainty

Every measurement only approximates the quantity being measured, and is incomplete without a quantitative statement of uncertainty. Each element of a measurement system contributes to the final uncertainty of the data. Accurate measurements of solar irradiance depend on the radiometer design, hardware installation scheme, data acquisition method, measurement system O&M, calibration method and frequency, and possible real-time or a posteriori corrections to the data. A successful measurement uncertainty analysis produces no properly measured data that exceed the expected range of uncertainty.

This overview of measurement uncertainty is based on Myers et al. (2002), Reda et al. (2007), Stoffel et al. (2000), and Wilcox and Myers (2008).

Terminology

Historically, uncertainty analysis treated sources of uncertainty in terms of "random" and "bias" error types. Random sources were related to the standard deviation or variance of measured datasets. Biases were estimates of deviations from a "true value" primarily based on engineering judgments of the measurement system performance. Total uncertainty (UT) was computed as the square root of the sum of the squares for these two error types:

$$UT = \quad [\Sigma \, (\text{Bias})^2 + \Sigma (2 \cdot \text{Random})^2]^{1/2}$$

where the factor of 2 in the random term was necessary to "inflate" the random component to provide approximately a 95% confidence interval for the computed value of UT, assuming the data were normally distributed (i.e., random).

The WMO (2008) is currently the accepted guide for measurement uncertainty (BIPM et al. 1995). GUM defines Type A uncertainty values as derived from statistical methods, and Type B sources as evaluated by "other means," such as scientific judgment, experience, specifications, comparisons, and calibration data. GUM defines the concept of a *standard uncertainty* (U_{std}) for each uncertainty type, which is an estimate of an *equivalent* standard deviation (of a specified distribution) of the error source. The *combined uncertainty* (U_C) is computed from the Type A and Type B standard uncertainties summed under quadrature. The GUM replaces the historical factor of 2 with a *coverage factor*, k (which depends on the known or assumed statistical distribution of uncertainties) and computes the *expanded uncertainty* (U_E) as:

$$U_E = [\Sigma \, (\text{Type B})^2 + \Sigma \, (k \cdot \text{Type A})^2]^{1/2}$$

For small samples (n < 20) from a normal distribution, k may be selected from the Student's t-distribution. The coverage factor (k) is usually in the range of 2 to 3 for confidence intervals of 95% and 99%, respectively (Taylor and Kuyatt 1987). For a 95% confidence interval, UE is twice the value of U_C.

When a result, R, is functionally dependent on several variables x_i, where i = 1 to n, the propagation of error is used:

$$U_R = [\Sigma_i \, (\partial X_i R \cdot e \, X_i)^2]^{1/2}$$

where

    U_R = Uncertainty in the resultant
    ex_i = estimated uncertainty in variable x_i
    $\partial x_i R$ = the partial derivative of the response R with respect to x_i
    (sensitivity function for variable x_i).
    The GUM procedure can be summarized in four steps:

1. Determine the process measurement equation.
2. List or estimate the standard uncertainty for each variable in the measurement equation and for each component (curve fitting uncertainty, environmental conditions uncertainty, etc.) that might introduce uncertainty to the measurement process.
3. Calculate the combined standard uncertainty using the root-sum-of-squares method of all standard uncertainties in step 2.

Calculate the expanded uncertainty by multiplying the combined standard uncertainty by the coverage factor, typically by applying Student's "t" analysis to determine the appropriate coverage factor (typically 2 for 95% and 3 for 98% confidence, respectively, for large datasets).

Estimating Direct Normal Irradiance Measurement Uncertainty

There are two measurement processes applicable to DNI measurement uncertainty analysis:

- Pyrheliometer calibration
- Field measurements.

Estimating the Uncertainty of Pyrheliometer Calibrations

The pyrheliometer responsivity (Rs_i) is computed as the microvolts (μV) per W/m^2 at each measurement comparison (i) typically made at 1-s to 60-s intervals with a reference or transfer standard radiometer (typically an electrically self-calibrating absolute cavity radiometer traceable to the WRR) and the output signal from the pyrheliometer under calibration:

    Rs_i = V_i/REF_i

where

    V_i =   Pyrheliometer output voltage (μV)
    REF_i =   Reference DNI (W/m^2)

Table 3-6. Estimated Pyrheliometer Calibration Uncertainties in Rsi

Type A Error Source	Ustd(%)	Type B Error Source	Ustd(%)
WRR transfer	0.200	WRR uncertainty (UE, k=2)	0.3
Absolute cavity responses to environmental conditions	0.013	Absolute cavity bias responses to environmental conditions	0.013
Data logger precision	0.0025	Data logger bias (9µV/10mV)	0.09
Pyrheliometer detector temperature response	0.25	Pyrheliometer detector temperature response	0.25
Pyrheliometer detector linearity	0.100	Event to event temperature bias (10°C)	0.125
Solar tracker alignment variations	0.125	Solar tracker alignment bias	0.125
Pyrheliometer window spectral transmittance	0.500	Pyrheliometer window spectral transmittance	0.5
Electromagnetic interference and Electromagnetic field	0.005	Electromagnetic interference and electromagnetic field	0.005
TOTAL Type A*	0.615	TOTAL Type B*	0.665

*Summed under quadrature.

Applying the GUM procedure to the pyrheliometer calibration, Table 3-6 summarizes the uncertainties for 95% confidence interval for the individual pyrheliometer responsivity results.

The *combined* uncertainty, UC, can be determined from the above standard uncertainties for Type A and Type B errors:

$$UC = \quad [(0.615)^2 + (0.665)2]^{1/2} = 0.906\%$$

The *expanded* uncertainty (UE) with a 95% confidence interval can therefore be computed based on the effective degrees of freedom (greater than 100 for pyrheliometer calibrations that can be based on more than 1000 measurements over the course of a day) and a coverage factor, k, of 2.0:

$$U_E = \quad 2 \cdot UC = 1.8\%$$

Therefore, the expanded uncertainty of the *calibration* for each Rs_i is ± 1.8%.

With this in mind, the reader can review the radiometer calibration certificate issued for each instrument and contact the manufacturer for additional information about the calibration process. NREL assigns a single value for Rsi, Rs, corresponding to SZA = 45 degrees and values of Rs for each 2-degree interval in the range of SZA encountered during the outdoor calibrations (additional information is available from www.nrel.gov/ solar_radiation).

Estimating the Uncertainty of Direct Normal Irradiance Field Measurements

Accounting for this calibration uncertainty and other sources of measurement errors (condition of radiometer optics and the relevant issues similar to those considered for the calibration measurement uncertainty estimates), the expanded measurement uncertainty for subhourly DNI measurements is ± 2.5% for a well-maintained measurement station equipped with a thermopile-based pyrheliometer and ± 5% for a photodiode-based RSR (Wilcox and Myers 2008).

Table 3-7 identifies the error sources used for our uncertainty analysis of DNI measurements from two types of radiometers.

Table 3-7. Estimated Direct-Normal Subhourly Measurement Uncertainties (Percent)

Type A Error Source	Ustd(%) [TP#]	Ustd(%) Si^	Type B Error Source	Ustd (%)	Ustd(%) Si^
"Fossilized" calibration error	0.615	0.615	"Fossilized" calibration error	0.665	0.665
Data logger precision (± 50 µV/10 mV)*	0.5	0.5	Data logger bias (1.7 µV/10 mV)*	0.02	0.02
Si detector cosine response	0	0.5	Si detector cosine response	0	1.5
Pyrheliometer detector temperature response (D20°C)	0.25	0.05	Detector temperature response	0.25	0.05
Pyrheliometer detector linearity	0.100	0.10	Day-to-day temperature bias (10°C)	0.125	0.10
Solar alignment variations (tracker or shade band) and pyranometer level for Si)	0.2	0.10	Solar alignment variations (tracker or shade band) and pyranometer level for Si)	0.200	0.20
Pyrheliometer window spectral transmittance	0.1	1.0	Pyrheliometer window spectral transmittance	0.5	1.0
Optical cleanliness (blockage)	0.2	0.1	Optical cleanliness (blockage)	0.25	0.1
Electromagnetic interference and electromagnetic field	0.005	0.005	Electromagnetic interference and electromagnetic field	0.005	0.005
TOTAL Type A**	0.889	1.382	TOTAL Type B**	0.934	1.938

\# Thermopile detector used for a pyrheliometer.

^ Silicon diode pyranometer detector used for an RSR.

* Typical manufacturer specified accuracy: ± 0.05% of full scale range (typically 50 mV) –25°C to 50°C; assume 10 mV signal so ± 50 microvolts (µV) (0.5%) with 1.67 µV resolution (0.02%).

** Summed under quadrature.

The *combined* uncertainty, UC, can be determined from the above standard uncertainties for Type A and Type B errors for each detector type:

$$U_{CTP} \quad = \quad [(0.889)^2 + (0.934)^2]^{1/2} \quad = \quad 1.29\%$$
$$U_{CSi} \quad = \quad [(1.382)^2 + (1.938)^2]^{1/2} \quad = \quad 2.38\%$$

The UE with a 95% confidence interval can therefore be computed based on the effective degrees of freedom (greater than 100 for pyrheliometer measurements that can be based on several thousand measurements over the course of a day) and a coverage factor, k, of 2.0:

$$U_{Etp} \quad = \quad 2 \cdot U_{CTP} = \quad 2.58\%$$

$$U_{ESi} \quad = \quad 2 \cdot U_{CSi} = \quad 4.76\%$$

The expanded uncertainty estimate of DNI from a thermopile pyrheliometer or silicon photodiode-based RSR is ± 2.6% and ± 4.76%, respectively. Measured data should be examined carefully and periodically checked against field reference radiometers to identify conditions that exceed these limits, in which case, problems with the radiometers, data acquisition systems, or other supporting equipment could be affecting the measurements.

Measurement Station Design Considerations

To collect useful DNI resource data, the successful design and implementation of a solar resource measurement station or network of stations requires careful consideration of the elements summarized in this subsection.

Location
The primary purpose of setting up a solar resource measurement station is to collect data that allow an analyst to accurately characterize the solar irradiance and relevant meteorological parameters at a particular location. Ideally, the instruments would be collocated with the targeted analysis area, but in some cases, separation distances may be tolerated depending on the complexities of local climate and terrain variations. Lower variability in terrain and climate generally translates to lower variability in the solar resource over larger spatial scales; however, these effects should be well understood before determining the final location of a measurement station. The proximity to the target area must also be weighed against operational factors, such as availability of power, communications, and access for maintenance as discussed below. One should also consider the possible effects of local sources of pollution or dust, for example traffic on a nearby dirt road that could degrade the measurements.

When measurement stations are constructed in metropolitan or industrial areas, consideration should be given to possible sources of radio frequency signals that could impart unwanted noise in sensors or cables. For example, the same high building that would provide an attractive unobstructed site for solar measurements may also be the ideal location for radio or television broadcast towers, or some other communication apparatus. Such sites should also be investigated for harmful effects of electromagnetic radiation on the health of station maintenance workers.

Instrument selection is a fundamental consideration, as measurements with greater accuracy will better reflect the actual resource; however, instrument placement is also an important consideration. If nearby objects—such as trees or buildings—shade the instruments for some period of time during the day, the resulting measurement will not truly represent the available solar resource. Distant objects—especially mountains—may be legitimate obstructions, as the shadows they cast are likely to produce an influence beyond the area local to the instruments. Conversely, nearby objects can potentially *reflect* solar radiation onto the instruments, likewise resulting in measurements that do not represent the local natural environment. Such cases could include a nearby wall, window, or other highly reflective object. The best practice is to locate instruments away from any objects that are in view of the instrument detector.

The easiest way to determine the quality of solar access is to scan the horizon for a full 360 degrees of azimuth and note the elevation of any objects protruding into the sky above the local horizon. Look for buildings, trees, antennae, power poles, and even power lines. Most locations will have *some* obstructions, but you must determine whether they will be significant in the context of the necessary measurements. Generally, pyranometers are very insensitive to sky blockage within 5 degrees or so elevation above the horizon. Pyrheliometers, however, will be more sensitive because they can completely block the DNI, depending on the daily path of the sun throughout the year. The amount of blockage time each day will be related the object's width and height above the horizon. The number of blockage days each year will depend on where along the horizon the object lies. To be a concern, it must be in the area of the sun near sunrise or sunset, the time and azimuth of which vary throughout the year. For most of the horizon, objects blocking the sky will not be a factor because the sun rises in a limited range in the east and sets likewise in the west during sunset (e.g., at 40 degrees N latitude, sunrise near the summer solstice occurs at about 60 degrees from true north). However, the further north in latitude the site is located, the greater the range of these sunrise and sunset areas of interest. A solar horizon mapping, or even a sketch of obstructions by elevation and azimuth, will help determine the areas where horizon objects will affect the measurement (see Figure 2-4).

Considerations for locating a station should also include environmental concerns, such as wildlife habitat, migratory paths, drainage, and antiquities or archeological areas.

Station Security and Accessibility

Measurement stations can comprise equipment worth tens of thousands, or even hundreds of thousands of dollars. Although this equipment is typically not the target of thieves seeking property for resale, it is still subject to theft and should be protected. Vandalism may be even more likely than theft. Unlike thieves, vandals typically care less about *what* they're vandalizing and more about their ability to destroy property with high value to its owner. The less visible and accessible the station is to the public, the less likely it will be the target of theft or vandalism. For example, instruments mounted on a rooftop are less likely to attract unwanted attention than those unprotected beside a highway. Lack of visibility is the best defense against vandalism, including damage from bullets or rocks.

Security fences should be used if people or animals are likely to intrude. Fencing should be at least 6 feet tall, topped with barbed wire, and fitted with locking gates in high-profile areas where intrusion attempts are likely. Less elaborate fences may suffice in areas that are generally secure and only the curious need be discouraged from meddling with the equipment. In remote venues with few human hazards, cattle fence paneling (about 4 feet tall) may be advisable if large animals roam the area. The fencing should be sturdy enough to withstand the weight of a large animal that may rub against the compound or otherwise be pushed or fall against the fence. It may not be possible to keep smaller animals out of the station compound, and precautions should be taken to ensure the equipment, cabling, supports, etc., can withstand encounters with these animals. Coyotes, rodents, rabbits, birds, and other wildlife may be able to move through the wires or jump over or burrow under fences. In particular, signal cabling between modules or sensors at or near ground level is prone to gnawing by rodents and should be run through a protective conduit or buried. Any buried cable should either be specified for use underground or run through conduit approved for underground use. Underground utilities and other objects should be investigated before postholes are dug or anchors sunk.

If fences are used, the radiometers must be positioned above the fence line (including barbed wire), if only by a few millimeters, to prevent any shading of the sensor. This assumes that the pyranometer is mounted in a horizontal position and the pyrheliometer is installed in a solar tracker. POA pyranometers should have an unobstructed view of the ground and sky in front of them. If nearby towers are unavoidable, the station should be positioned between the tower and the equator (e.g., to the south of the tower in the northern hemisphere) to minimize shading. The radiometers should be positioned as far as possible from the tower— at least several meters—so the tower blocks as little of the sky as possible (radiometer signal cables should be shorter than 50 meters to avoid losses caused by line resistance). The tower should also be painted a neutral gray to minimize strong reflections that could contaminate the solar measurement. These guidelines assume the tower is part of the measurement station proper and the site operator has control over placement or modification of the tower. Absent that control, the radiometers should be moved as far as possible from the tower.

Access to the equipment must also be part of a station construction plan. Because routine maintenance is a primary factor affecting data quality, provisions must be made for reasonable and easy access to the instruments. Factors here could include ease of access to cross-locked property, well-maintained all-weather roads, and roof access that might be controlled by other departments. Safety must also be a consideration. Locations that present hazardous conditions—such as rooftops without railings or that require access using unanchored ladders—must be avoided.

Power Requirements

Ongoing measurements require a reliable source of electrical power to minimize system downtime from power outages. In some areas, power from the utility grid is reliable, and downtime is measured in minutes per year. In other areas, multiple daily power interruptions are routine. Depending on the tolerance of the required analysis to missing data, precautions should be taken to ensure gaps in the data stream from power outages do not seriously affect the results. The most common and cost-effective bridge for power outages is an uninterruptible power supply (UPS). A UPS can also filter out unwanted or harmful line voltage fluctuations that can occur for a variety of reasons. It has internal storage batteries that are used as a source of power in the event of an alternating current (AC) power interruption. When the AC power is interrupted, internal circuitry makes an almost seamless switch from grid-connected AC power to AC provided through an inverter connected to the battery bank. When power is restored, the UPS recharges the internal battery from AC line power. Power loss is detected quickly, as is switching to battery, and is measured in milliseconds or partial line cycles. Some equipment may be particularly susceptible to even millisecond power interruptions during switching and should be identified through trial and error to avert unexpected downtime despite use of the UPS.

The UPS is sized according to:

- Operating capacity (amount of power—Watts. It can continuously supply either on or off grid-connected AC power).
- Longevity of battery power (how long the battery can last under anticipated maximum load).

Users should estimate the longest possible power outage and size the UPS for the maximum load of attached devices and the maximum period of battery capacity. Batteries should be tested regularly to ensure the device can still operate per design specifications. Internal battery test functions sometimes report errors only when batteries are near complete failure and not when performance has degraded. A timed full power-off test should be conducted periodically to ensure the UPS will provide backup power for the time needed to prevent measurement system failure.

In remote locations where utility power is not available, local power generation should be devised. Options for on-site electrical power generation include PV or small wind turbine systems (or both) and gasoline- or diesel-fueled generators with battery storage. The renewable energy systems should be sized to provide enough energy for the maximum continuous load and power through several days of cloudy weather when solar generation would be minimal. This would include sites prone to persistent ground fog. The sizing is a function of the extremes of the solar climate and should consider the longest gap during reduced generation, the shortest recharge period available after discharge, and the generation capacity and storage necessary to provide uninterrupted power for the target location. Some oversizing is necessary to accommodate degradation of PV panels and battery storage, and consideration should be given to ambient temperature, which affects the ability of a battery to deliver energy. Sizing calculators are available to help with this effort (e.g., www.nrel.gov/eis/imby/).

Equipment should be specified and tested for self-power-on capability in the event of a power outage. This ensures that when power is restored, the equipment will automatically resume measurements and logging without operator intervention. This is an important consideration for remote locations where considerable downtime might occur before personnel could be dispatched to restart a system.

Grounding and Shielding

Station equipment should be protected against lightning strikes and shielded from radio frequency interference that could damage equipment or reduce the validity of the measurements.

Several books are available that describe techniques for grounding and shielding low-voltage signal cables (e.g., Morrison 1998). The reader is urged to consult available references or seek expert technical advice during the design of a solar resource measurement system.

In general, these steps should be taken when designing and constructing a measurement station:

1. Use a single-point ground (e.g., a copper rod driven several feet into the ground) for all signal ground connections to prevent ground loops that can introduce noise or biases in the measurements.

2. Use twisted pair, shielded cables for low-voltage measurements and connected as double-ended measurements at the data logger. Double-ended measurements require separate logger channels for "+" and "−" signal input conductors. These inputs do not share a common signal ground and therefore significantly reduce the possibilities for electrical noise introduced in the signal cable.

3. Physically isolate low-voltage sensor cables from nearby sources of electrical noise, such as power cables (do not run signal cables in the same bundle or conduit as AC power cables). If a power cable must be near a signal cable, always position the two at right angles to each other. This limited contact will minimize the possibility of induced voltages in the signal cable.

4. Metal structures such as masts and tripods should be connected to the ground to provide an easy path to ground in the event of a lightning strike. This will help protect sensitive instruments. Electronic equipment often has a special ground lug and associated internal protection to help protect against stray voltages from lighting strikes. These should be connected with a heavy gauge wire to ground (12 American wire gauge or larger). Metal oxide varistors, avalanche diodes, or gas tubes can be used to protect signal cables from electrical surges such as lightning. These devices must be replaced periodically to maintain effectiveness. The replacement frequency is a function of the accumulated energy dissipated by the unit.

Data Acquisition

Data logging equipment should have performance specifications that do not degrade the potential measurement of the radiometer signals (e.g., analog-to-digital conversion of low-level direct current voltages, temperature response coefficients, and environmental limits of operation).

Most radiometers output a voltage, current, or resistance that is measured by a voltmeter, ammeter, or ohmmeter. The measured value is subsequently converted to engineering units through a multiplier and/or an offset determined by calibration to a recognized measurement standard. Data loggers should be chosen so that the measurement signal is consistent with the uncertainty of the sensor; e.g., a much smaller uncertainty, perhaps 3 to 10 times smaller than the estimated measurement uncertainty associated with the radiometer. This is the accuracy ratio between the data logger and the radiometer. For example, typical specifications for a good data logger measuring a 10 mV output from the radiometer accurate to 1%, or 0.1 mV (100 μV) are on the order of total uncertainty (accuracy) of better than (less than) 0.1% of reading (or full scale) for the parameter in question, which would be 0.010 mV, or 10 μV. The logger should also have a range that can measure the voltage or resistance at near full scale to best capture the resolution of the data. For example, a sensor with a full-scale output of 10 mV should be connected to a logger with a range that is at least, but not below, 10 mV. A logger with a 1-V range may be able to measure 10 mV, but not with the desired precision. Most modern data loggers have several range selections, allowing the user to optimize the match for each instrument. Because of the nature of solar radiation, radiometers can sometimes produce 200% or more of clear sky readings under certain passing cloud conditions, and the logger range should be set to prevent over-ranging under unusual sky conditions.

Some radiometers use amplifiers to raise the instrument output to a higher range to better satisfy signal range matching requirements. However, such amplifiers require power and will add some uncertainty to the data with nonlinearity, noise, temperature dependence, or instability. High-quality amplifiers may minimize these effects and allow a reasonable tradeoff between logger cost and data accuracy. Calibrations must be made of these radiometer systems by including the pyranometer or pyrheliometer and its uniquely associated amplifier.

The logging equipment should also have environmental specifications that are compatible with the environment where the equipment will be used. Loggers used inside an environmentally controlled building could have less stringent environmental performance specifications than one mounted outside in a desert or arctic environment. Equipment enclosures can create an internal environment several degrees above ambient air temperature because of solar heating (absorption by the enclosure materials), heat generated by electronic devices mounted inside, and lack of ventilation to help purge heat. Gore Tex vent plugs are available to provide ventilation openings and prevent insects and water from entering the enclosure.

The sampling frequency and time statistics of the solar resource data should be determined from the desired data analysis requirements. For example, monthly means, daily totals, hourly, minute or sub-1-min data records can be useful. Data loggers can generally be configured to produce output of instantaneous or integrated values at any reasonable time period consistent with the radiometer time-response characteristics. The design should consider the current requirements and, if convenient and practical, future needs for additional analyses. A high-temporal resolution data logging scheme can be down-sampled or integrated to longer time periods than the other way around. For example, transforming hourly data to 1-min data with any certainty and accuracy is impossible if a specific data time-series must be reproduced. Data logging equipment, data transfer mechanisms, and data storage can generally handle 1-min data resolution, and this time realm should be considered as the fundamental resolution in the data logger. Because most applications address the solar energy available over time, integrated data of subminute samples within the data logger (e.g., 1-s signal sampling) is a common method of data output regardless of the final data resolution required by the analysis. The output of instantaneous samples is much less likely to represent the available energy and should be avoided when configuring a data logger. If the size of a measured dataset is a defining issue (e.g., limited data communications throughput), the user can determine the lowest temporal resolution necessary for the application and optimize the data collection accordingly.

Data Communications

Provisions should be made for transferring data from the data logger to a data processing facility. Historically, data have been captured, transferred, and processed in various ways. The manual transfer of data recorded on strip charts physically carried or shipped from the observing station to a data center has been replaced by advances in electronics and telecommunications that allow remote data collection from nearly any location. A telephone modem link that uses conventional dial-up phone lines to connect between station and data center can now be replaced with cellular telephone technology, obviating the need for a physical connection between logger and phone line. The cell phone network is configured to provide virtual Internet links between a measurement station and the data center. Satellite up- and down-links are also available for data transfers in areas that are not served by either wire- or cell-based phone service. Within the area of an observing station, short-distance wireless communications such as Wi-Fi connectivity may be useful to minimize the need for long cables between radiometers and data loggers. (See the Appendix for sources of more detailed information.)

Operations and Maintenance

Proper O&M practices are essential for acquiring accurate solar resource measurements. As addressed in this subsection, there are several elements in the chain that forms a quality system. Collectively, these elements produce accurate and reliable solar resource data: station location, measurement system design, equipment installation, data acquisition, and O&M practices. Proper O&M requires long-term consistency, attention to detail, and a thorough appreciation for the importance of preventative and corrective maintenance of sensitive equipment.

Radiometer Calibrations

To obtain valid solar measurements, the relationship between the radiometer response to solar irradiance and its output signal must be periodically determined. This relationship is defined by the radiometer's Rs ($\mu V/Wm^{-2}$) as determined by calibration with a measurement reference. A calibration provides an Rs or combination of factors that relate sensor response to the solar irradiance. The calibration factor is applied to radiometer output signal to provide a measure of the solar irradiance in the desired engineering units. The calibration is accompanied by an estimate of the measurement uncertainty, either from the calibration process or from the manufacturer, to help determine measurement performance. The regular calibration of pyrheliometers and pyranometers is an important element of measurement station O&M.

As described in section 2 and previously in this section, the calibration of broadband radiometers should be traceable to the WRR, the international measurement reference for solar irradiance. The user must determine a calibration interval based on either the **manufacturer's recommendations** or from instrument history based on stability of periodic calibrations or records indicating a calibration drift with time or exposure. Consideration should also be given to the possibility of instrument error due to factors other than sensor drift. Physical changes or damage can result in marginal changes to radiometer Rs that may still produce seemingly reasonable, but incorrect, measurements. Thus, periodic calibrations are a prudent approach to a defensible measurement protocol. Annual calibrations are common practice for radiometers.

There are two standards for the calibration of pyrheliometers used to measure DNI (ASTM 1997; ISO 1990). Consistent with these standards (and as described in section 2), is the need to include the additional measurement uncertainty associated with each calibration transfer beginning with the use of reference radiometers directly traceable to the World Standard Group (WSG) that is used to define the WRR (Figure 2-11). The lowest measurement uncertainty for the calibration of a field pyrheliometer is generally achieved by direct comparison with an absolute cavity radiometer, with traceability to the WRR, for at least one clear sky daylight interval. A typical estimated measurement uncertainty assigned to the calibration of a field pyrheliometer is ± 1.0% (see section 2 for details). Because of additional sources of error, the uncertainty of the field measurements from a well-calibrated pyrheliometer will be at least twice the calibration uncertainty. Pyrheliometer calibrations are available from the radiometer manufacturer and other providers. (See the Appendix and www.nrel.gov/solar_radiation.)

Instrument Maintenance

Calibrations are performed with clean instrument optics and a carefully aligned detector. To properly apply the calibration factor, the instrument should be kept in the same condition during field measurements. To maintain the calibration relationship between irradiance and radiometer output, proper cleaning and other routine maintenance are necessary. The maintenance process includes:

- *Checking the alignment of the detector.* Pyrheliometers must be accurately aligned with the solar disk for accurate DNI measurements. Pyranometer detectors must be horizontal for GHI and DHI measurements and accurately aligned with a flat plate collector for POA measurements. The radiometer orientation should be checked periodically using the features described in section 3. (In some cases, a carefully leveled pyranometer may produce GHI readings that are not symmetrical around solar noon under clear skies. If this cannot be attributed to any change in atmospheric composition (aerosols or water vapor), or optical asymmetries can be verified under strict laboratory conditions, the optical axis of the detector is probably not exactly vertical. This is a manufacturing defect.

- *Cleaning the instrument optics.* To properly measure the solar intensity, no contaminant should block or reduce the amount of sunshine falling on the detector. The outdoor environment provides many sources of such contamination, such as dust, precipitation, dew, plant matter, insects, and bird droppings. The sensors should be cleaned regularly to minimize the effect of contaminants on the measurements. Depending on the local conditions, this can require daily maintenance of unventilated or otherwise protected radiometers.

- *Documenting the condition of the radiometer.* For analysts to understand limitations of the data, conditions that affect the measurement must be documented. This includes substandard measurement conditions, but it is just as important to document proper operations to add credibility to the dataset. Observations and notes provide a critical record of conditions that positively and negatively affect data quality.

- *Documenting the environment.* As a consistency check, note the sky and weather conditions at the time of maintenance when interpreting data from the radiometer, including measurements with unusual values.

- *Documenting the infrastructure.* The measurement station as a whole should be examined for general robustness. Any defects should be noted and corrected.

Maintenance frequency depends on prevailing conditions that soil the instruments. This includes dust, rain, snow, birds, and insects. It is also depends on instrument type. Radiometer designs based on optical diffusers (such as LI-COR LI-200) are less susceptible to dust contamination than are instruments with clear optics (Myers et al. 2002). This may be due in part to the area subject to soiling (e.g., a larger dome versus a smaller diffuser). Also, fine dust on the surface of a diffuser can become an integral part of the diffuser, and may lessen the impact of the dust on the diffuser transmittance compared to that on a precision-ground optical dome. Soiling of the windowed or domed radiometers can quickly affect the measurement and increase by many-fold the measurement uncertainty. As described earlier, a pyranometer in a ventilator can reduce this risk of contamination. Thus, the frequency and cost of maintenance should be considerations in instrument specification. If a remote site will be difficult to maintain for extended periods, a higher class windowed instrument might not be optimal, despite its potential for better measurements. The cost of maintenance for a remote site may dominate the estimated cost of setting up and operating a station. This aspect should be anticipated when planning a measurement campaign.

A conservative maintenance schedule will support the credibility of the measurement dataset and provide the analyst a base of justification when assigning confidence intervals for the data. Daily inspection should be scheduled for instruments with clear optics and twice monthly inspections for diffuser instruments. More frequent spot inspections should be conducted after significant weather events. Radiometer optics may not necessarily soil within a 24-hour period, but the effects of soiling can best be mitigated with frequent inspection.

Radiometers should be carefully cleaned at each inspection, even if soiling appears minimal. Cleaning is generally a very short procedure, and removes the possibility of differing interpretations of the need to clean among different technicians. With such a procedure in place, the analyst can claim with confidence that the instruments were kept clean according to the documented schedule.

Maintenance at remote measurement sites away from institutional or corporate employment centers will require finding a qualified person nearby who can perform the necessary maintenance duties. The qualifications for maintenance are generally nontechnical, but require someone with the interest and disposition to reliably complete the tasks. As a rule, compensating these people for time and vehicle mileage—rather than seeking volunteers— becomes a worthwhile investment in the long run, as it sets up a firm contractual commitment to perform all necessary maintenance duties. Absent that formal relationship, it can become difficult to assert the need for reliable and regular attention.

All O&M should be carefully documented with log sheets or electronic databases that contain enough information to reveal problems and solutions, or that assert that the instruments were in good form when inspected. This information enables an analyst to identify potentially bad data, and provides important documentation to determine and defend the overall quality of the measurements.

Data Quality Control and Data Quality Assessment

The data quality is generally established when the measurement is taken. Little can be done after the fact to improve fundamental quality. For example, a poorly maintained station with dirty optics or misaligned instruments will produce data with presumed (or even apparent) errors, and the *magnitude* of those errors is not likely to be discernable until days or weeks later. There is no way to systematically reduce the uncertainty of such a measurement, and one can only guess at which corrections to make. In this context, data quality control involves a well-defined supervisory process by which station operators are confident that, when a measurement is taken with unattended instruments, the instruments are in a state that produces data of known quality. This process largely encompasses the calibration, inspection, and maintenance procedures discussed earlier, along with log sheets and other items that document the condition of the station. It also includes a critical inspection or assessment of the data to help detect problems not evident from physical inspection of the instruments.

Data quality assessment is a method by which data quality can be judged based on criteria for a particular application.

Data can be compared with certain physical limits that have been determined to be reasonable, with redundant or complementary measurements, or with physical or empirical models, all of which will provide some degree of independent measure for a quality judgment.

One common method for evaluating DNI, GHI, and DHI is a three-component coupling test. As described in secton 2, the measurements of DNI and DHI can be combined mathematically to derive a global measurement as described in Equation 2-3 on page 8.

When all three components are measured, measurement redundancy is apparent, because any one component can be derived from the other two. Thus, in the context of quality assurance (QA), expected values for each component can be calculated from the other two. This method helps quantify the relative error among the three components, although it does not necessarily determine strictly which measurement—or measurements—are in error. However, operational knowledge of the instruments and trackers can provide valuable insight into likely errors.

For example, a misaligned tracker would cause either a low DNI or high diffuse measurement (low DNI from a poorly aligned pyrheliometer or high diffuse from a poorly aligned shading disk).

With this knowledge, and an observation of trends in the magnitude of flagging, a data quality expert can quickly spot common operational errors. The measurement of the three redundant components—rather than just a single measurement or two components of specific interest—is a significant and important tool for data quality analysis, and it should be strongly considered when specifying instrumentation for a station.

For example, the SERI QC software (NREL 1993) produces flags that can be plotted (see Figure 3-14). The left-hand plot indicates more severe flags with a darker shade, plotted here by day of month (y axis) and hour of day (x axis). In this temporal view, areas of expanding errors are seen over several days, indicating a tracker that has not been adjusted for the changing solar declination, resulting in a longer and more severe error condition as the condition is neglected. Further, the other three plots correspond respectively to a normalized GHI, DNI, and DHI measurements, providing the analyst with additional information to pinpoint the measurement causing the error.

In the case shown in Figure 3-14, the three component data (GHI, DNI, and DHI) were submitted to the SERI QC software, which performs the three component coupling test in the realm of the clearness index, or Kt, Kn, and Kd (see section 2). This K-space value normalizes the solar irradiance values to remove the effect of the SZA of incidence. Thus, in K-space

$$Kt = Kn + Kd.$$

Or rearranged, the deviation from this equation of component coupling can be quantified as the residual from

$$\varepsilon = Kt - Kn - Kd.$$

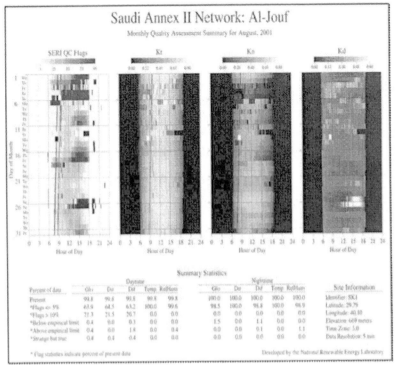

Credit: Steve Wilcox, NREL.

Figure 3-14. Example of SERI quality control data QA reporting.

Perfect component coupling would result in $\varepsilon = 0$, and any nonzero value indicates some disagreement among the instruments. However, this method does not reveal *which* component or components are in error; only that there is some disagreement. Further, instrument errors in opposing directions could result in a false zero value.

Despite these ambiguities, a knowledgeable analyst can confidently detect measurement errors in most typical measurement scenarios. In the case of Figure 3-14, for each minute data record containing the three components, the residual was plotted as a quality flag, with darker flags (leftmost column) indicating a greater deviation or apparent error. The actual Kt, Kn, and Kd values are also plotted in the next three columns, with lighter shades roughly correlating to higher irradiance. In the case of days 8–10, darker flags of growing magnitude are evident each day, which correlate with lower Kn (or DNI). This is most likely due to pyrheliometer tracker misalignment. This condition was corrected on day 11. Likewise for days 14–18, a subsequent tracker alignment error was corrected partway through day 18. Days 25 and 26 show significant flags in the afternoon, which are due to diffuse tracker error where the diffuse pyranometer is not adequately shaded, resulting in high diffuse irradiance. Other error conditions are also evident in the plot, including shading from nearby poles, which appear in the flag plot as double-angled stripes each morning. This occurs when the pole shaded individual instruments at slightly different times of the day, resulting in a significant decoupling of the three components.

In each case, examination of the quality flags resulted in feedback to station operators, who corrected tracker alignments.

Data from an RSR consist of GHI, DNI, and DHI, and are derived from a single pyranometer. To some extent, this limitation can be mitigated by including a secondary unshaded (GHI) pyranoemeter on the RSR to provide some redundant measurements. This enhancement is a relatively low-cost method of adding confidence in the measurements and can be included in a two- or three-component quality assessment test.

The three component methods described here are generally more reliable than a simple clear sky data analysis where some conclusions are drawn based on modeled or other expected values of the clear sky data. Significant day-to-day variations in cloudless, clear sky data can occur because of variations in atmospheric constituents such as aerosols or water vapor. Thus, such variation can make it difficult to draw conclusions about possible instrument error without specific information regarding other critical atmospheric components.

A successful quality control process requires elements of quality assessment and feedback. Figure 3-15 depicts a QA cycle that couples data acquisition with quality assessment and feedback.

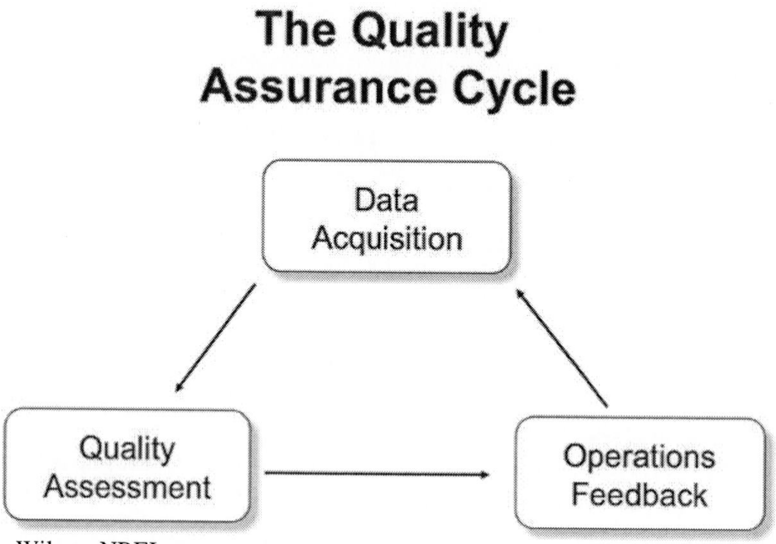

Credit: Steve Wilcox, NREL.

Figure 3-15. Information flow of a QA cycle.

In Figure 3-15, the information flows from the Data Acquisition box to Quality Assessment, where some criteria are used to establish data quality. The results of the quality assessment are analyzed and formed into feedback that goes back to the data acquisition module. The activities in the boxes can take several forms. For example, quality assessment could be the daily site inspection, and the analysis and feedback a simple procedure that corrects equipment malfunctions. Or, the quality assessment could be a weekly summary of data flags, and the analysis provides a determination of specific instrument error that is transmitted back to maintenance personnel with instructions to correct deficiencies or further troubleshoot problems.

The faster the cycle runs, the sooner errors will be detected, and the fewer bad data will collected during failure modes. Conversely, if the site is inspected infrequently, the chances increase that a large portion of the dataset would be contaminated with substandard equipment. More than one QA cycle can—and likely will—run at any time, each with a different period and emphasis as noted above: daily inspection, weekly quality reports, monthly summaries, etc.

One practical aspect of this cycle is the importance of *positive* feedback—a regular report back to site personnel of error conditions and of high-quality operations or datasets exceeding quality thresholds. This positively reinforces a job well done and keeps site operators cognizant that data are being used and that their efforts are an integral part of an ongoing process.

The QA cycle is a deliberate part of the quality control process, *and should be well defined and funded* to maintain a consistency of data quality over time.

Metadata

The interpretation and application of solar resource measurements depend greatly on the efforts to record and include metadata relevant to the observations. This includes site location, local horizon survey, data acquisition system(s), input signal channel assignments, radiometer types, models, serial numbers, calibration histories, installation schemes, and maintenance records. An example of on-line metadata is available from www.nrel.gov/midc/ srrl_bms. Such metadata should be included with the archival of the measured solar resource data.

4. MODELING SOLAR RADIATION - CURRENT PRACTICES

Introduction

High-quality solar resource assessment accelerates technology deployment by making a positive impact on decision making and reducing uncertainty in investment decisions. GHI and DNI are the two quantities of interest for resource assessment and characterization at a particular location. GHI is defined as the total energy from sunlight, both direct and diffuse, that reaches unit area horizontal to the surface of the Earth. DNI is the amount of energy from direct sunlight that reaches unit area normal to the sun. Surface based measurements of DNI and GHI are best measured using well calibrated pyrheliometers and pyranometers, but such measurements can only be made on a sparse network given the costs of operation and maintenance. For example, currently there are only seven National Oceanic and Atmospheric Administration (NOAA) measurement sites under the SURFRAD (Surface Radiation) Network (Augustine et al. 2000). Nevertheless, observations from ground networks have been used in conjunction with models to create maps of surface solar radiation.

Another option is to use information from geostationary satellites to estimate GHI and DNI at the surface (e.g., Perez and Ineichen 2002; Pinker and Laszlo 1992). As geostationary satellite coverage is available at regular intervals on a fixed grid surface, radiation can be available for the entire globe at temporal and spatial resolution representative of the particular satellite.

This section contains a summary of available ground-based techniques, discussions of satellite-based methods, currently operational models that have surface radiation data available for current or recent periods, a summary of two radiative transfer models used in the operational models, and a discussion of uncertainty in solar-based resource assessment.

Surface-Based Methods

The sunshine recorder, in which the direct beam is focused to create burn marks during clear periods, has been used for more than a century to measure solar radiation around the world (Iqbal 1983). The monthly mean global solar radiation is measured using a regression fit to the number of clear hours measured by the burn marks where the regression coefficients are calculated using GHI measurements. Sunshine recorder data are often more widely available than GHI measurements, so the spatial coverage is expanded by using the regression fits. The exact method to calculate GHI using sunshine recorder information is empirical and therefore specific to each geographical area and not standardized. Moreover, the meteorological services of some countries, such as the United States and Canada, have stopped measuring sunshine because of the limited quality and significance of this measurement, which is not standardized and varies from country to country.

In the absence of surface measurements, estimates of surface radiation can also be made using meteorological information such as cloud cover, temperature, and water vapor in a radiative transfer model (Marion and Wilcox 1994). Reliable methods have been developed over the years and have been used to create the NSRDB, for instance (George et al. 2007). Initially created for the period between 1961 and 1990 for 239 stations in the United States, the NSRDB is an hourly dataset created using the meteorological-statistical (METSTAT) radiative transfer model of Maxwell (1998). The METSTAT model uses information about cloud cover, water vapor, ozone, and aerosol optical depth to compute atmospheric transmittance extinction under both clear and cloudy sky conditions. Ideally, surface-based cloud information comes from human-observed cloud cover, which includes total and opaque cloud amounts. More recently, automated cloud observations are derived from vertical ceilometer data, mainly for airport locations, reducing the accuracy of cloud cover observations. The atmospheric transmittance extinction is then used to produce DNI, GHI, and diffuse irradiance at the surface. A modification of the METSTAT model called the Climatological Solar Radiation Model (Maxwell et al. 1998) is used to calculate monthly average daily totals of DNI, GHI, and diffuse irradiance using cloud information derived from the US Air Force Real-Time Nephanalysis data. This cloud information is derived on a 40-km resolution grid from surface observations and satellite estimates (from polar orbiting satellites). The NSRDB was updated to create GHI and DNI for the period between 1991 and 2005 (Wilcox et al. 2007). Although the period between 1991 and 1997 was covered using METSTAT model runs, with cloud observations similar to the original NSRDB, the years 1998 through 2005 were processed in parallel, using hourly satellite-based model outputs.

Satellite Coverage and Satellite-Based Methods

Satellite-based retrievals of GHI have primarily been used for climate studies for three decades (Justus et al. 1986). Their goal is to use observed information about TOA radiances and albedos to calculate GHI and DNI. These methods can primarily be divided into statistical and empirical methods and physical methods (Pinker et al. 1995; Schmetz 1989). The empirical methods are based on developing relationships between satellite- and ground-based observations; the physical methods estimate surface radiation directly from satellite information using retrieval schemes to determine the atmospheric properties important to radiative transfer. Empirical methods generally produce only GHI and require additional models to calculate DNI from GHI.

Global Coverage

Geostationary Satellites

Geostationary satellites near the equator provide continuous global coverage (measurements are usable up to 66 degrees north and south latitudes because of the Earth's curvature) (see Figure 4-1). As an example of satellite coverage the Geostationary Operational Environmental Satellite (GOES) series covers North and South America every 3 hours and the Northern Hemisphere, including the United States, every 30 minutes. Two GOES satellites (GOES-East or GOES-12 and GOES-West or GOES-11) operate concurrently and provide 30-minute coverage for the entire United States. The Imager instrument on the current GOES satellites measures at 5 wavelength bands. The visible channel (0.64 μm) has a nominal 1-km resolution; the infrared channels (3.9 μm, 6.5 μm, 10.7 μm, and 12 μm) have 4-km resolution. The next (future) series of GOES satellites that are expected in 2015 will have a new instrument called the Advance Baseline Imager with 5 minutes coverage at 1-km resolution for 16 channels (6 in the visible and near-infrared). The European Organisation for the Exploitation of Meteorological Satellites Union owned the METEOSAT series of satellites that covered Europe and Africa as well as the Indian Ocean. The Visible and Infrared Imager on the METEOSAT first-generation satellites (up to METEOSAT 7) had 3 channels in the visible, water vapor, and infrared. The visible channel had a 2.5 that produced 8-km nadir resolution; the infrared channel's nadir resolution is 5 km. Repetition frequency is imagery every 30 minutes. The Spin Enhance Visible and Infrared Imager on the MSG satellites (METEOSAT 8 onward) provide satellite imagery every 15 minutes at a nominal 3-km resolution for 11 channels (Schmetz et al. 2002).

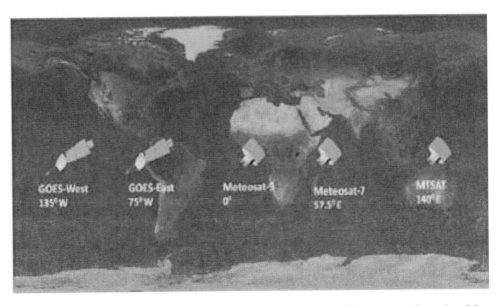

Figure 4-1. The location of the current geostationary satellites that provide coverage about the globe. (Image courtesy NOAA).

The twelfth channel, a high-resolution visible channel, has a nadir resolution of 1 km. The Japanese Multifunctional Transport Satellite covers East Asia and the Western Pacific at 4 km spatial and 30-minute temporal resolution taking measurement in 5 channels. It replaced the GMS series of satellites, which has been in operation since 1977.

Polar-Orbiting Satellites

Polar-orbiting satellites are also used to continuously sense the Earth and retrieve cloud properties and solar radiation at the surface. An example of such instruments is the Advanced Very High Resolution Radiometer on the NOAA series of polar orbiting platforms. Another recent example is the Moderate Resolution Imaging Spectroradiometer instrument on NASA's Aqua and Terra satellites. Although polar orbiters provide global coverage, their temporal coverage is limited because of their orbit where they essentially cover a particular location only once a day at the lower latitudes.

Satellite-Based Empirical Methods

Solar radiation reflects to space and is well correlated to radiation reaching the surface of the Earth. The empirical methods create regression relationships between what is simultaneously observed by a satellite and ground-based instruments (e.g., Cano et al. 1986; Hay et al. 1978; Paris and Tarpley 1986; Tarpley 1979). Hay et al. created a regression model that relates atmospheric transmittance to the ratio of incoming to outgoing radiation at TOA. The transmittance is then used to compute GHI. In this method, the coefficients of the regression model change significantly based on location and need to be trained with surface observations (Nunez 1990) to produce accurate results. The Tarpley method also used the well known relation between surface radiation, the TOA radiation (both upwelling and downwelling) and atmospheric transmittance to create three separate regression equations. The regression equations were classified based on sky conditions labeled as clear, partly cloudy, and cloudy and used accordingly.

Satellite-Based Physical Models

Physical models generally use radiative transfer theory to directly estimate surface radiation. These can be classified as either broadband or spectral, depending on whether the radiative transfer calculations involve a single broadband calculation or multiple calculations in different wavelength bands.

The broadband method of Gautier et al. (1980) used thresholds depending on multiple days of satellite pixel measurements to determine clear and cloudy skies. Separate clear sky and cloudy sky models were then used to compute surface DNI and GHI. The clear sky model initially included water vapor and Rayleigh scatter but progressively added ozone (Diak and Gautier 1983) and aerosols (Gautier and Frouin 1984). Assuming attenuation caused by the atmosphere does not vary from clear to cloudy conditions, Dedieu et al. (1987) created a method that combines the impact of clouds and the atmosphere. This method again uses a time series of images to determine clear sky for computing surface albedo. Darnell et al. (1988) created a parameterized model to calculate surface radiation using a product of the TOA insolation, atmospheric transmittance, and cloud transmittance. Developed with data from polar orbiting satellites, this model used collocated surface and satellite measurements to create relationships between cloud transmittance and planetary albedo.

Möser and Raschke (1983) created a model based on the premise that GHI is related to fractional cloud cover and used it with Meteosat data to estimate solar radiation over Europe (Möser and Raschke 1984). The fractional sky cover is determined to be a function of satellite measurements in the visible channel. This method uses radiative transfer modeling (Kerschegens et al. 1978) to determine the clear and overcast sky boundaries. Stuhlmann et al. (1990) have since enhanced the model to include elevation dependence, and additional constituents as well as multiple reflections in the all sky model. An important spectral model developed by Pinker and Ewing (1985) divided the solar spectrum into 12 intervals and applies the Delta-Eddington radiative transfer (Joseph et al. 1976) to a three-layer atmosphere. The primary input to the model is cloud optical depth that can be provided from various sources. This model was enhanced by Pinker and Laszlo (1992) and used in conjunction with cloud information from the International Satellite Cloud Climatology Project (ISSCP) (Schiffer and Rossow 1983). Another physical method involves the use of satellite information from multiple channels to derive cloud properties (Stowe et al. 1999) and then computing DNI and GHI using the cloud properties in a radiative transfer model. This method, called Clouds (from an advanced very high resolution radiometer), was originally developed for the polar orbiting. It is an advanced, very high-resolution radiometer instrument on NOAA satellites (Stowe et al. 1999) and has been modified and enhanced to obtain cloud properties from the GOES satellites (Heidinger 2003; Pavlonis et al. 2005). The cloud information is then input to the Pinker and Laszlo (1992) model to produce surface radiation.

Empirical and semi-empirical models (discussed in next subsection) have been used to produce good estimates of surface radiation as they are computationally less expensive. Although physical models are computationally more intensive, they can use additional channels from new satellites (such as MSG) to improve cloud property retrieval, and hence, surface radiation.

Semi-Empirical Models

Semi-empirical models are so classified because of their hybrid approach to retrieving surface radiation from satellite observations where normalized satellite-observed reflectance is related to GHI at the surface.

Cloud cover indices that use visible satellite imagery are first created with budget equations between TOA and surface radiation. Those indices are then used to modify clear sky GHI and estimate GHI at the ground consistent with the cloud scene. The Cano model was modified by Diabate et al. (1988) and Moussu et al. (1989), who used METEOSAT data to develop the Heliosat model to create solar resource. These data are available commercially from Ecole des Mines de Paris (see section 5). Models such as those developed by Perez et al. (2002) also evolved from Cano et al. (1986) and are currently being used to estimate GHI and DNI. For the United States, datasets created using the Perez et al. (2002) model, for the period between 1998 and 2005, are available for free from NREL. Beyond 2005 the datasets are commercially available.

Currently Available Operational Models

NASA/GEWEX Surface Radiation Budget

To serve the needs of the World Climate Research Programme (WCRP), Whitlock et al. (1995) developed a global Surface Radiation Budget (SRB) dataset using cloud information from the ISCCP C1 dataset at a 250 km × 250 km (approximately 2.5 degrees × 2.5 degrees) resolution every 3 hours (Schiffer and Rossow 1983; Zhang et al. 2004). Information from the ISCCP-C1 dataset is used as input into the Pinker and Laszlo (1992) model and the Darnell et al. (1988) model.

The currently available version is the NASA/GEWEX SRB Release-3.0 datasets that contain global 3-hourly, daily, monthly/3-hourly, and monthly averages of surface longwave and shortwave radiative parameters on a 1 degree × 1 degree grid (http://eosweb.larc.nasa.gov/PRODOCS/srb/table_srb.html). Primary inputs to the models include:

- Visible and infrared radiances, and cloud and surface properties inferred from ISCCP pixel-level (DX) data
- Temperature and moisture profiles from GEOS-4 reanalysis product obtained from the NASA Global Modeling and Assimilation Office
- Column ozone amounts constituted from Total Ozone Mapping Spectrometer and TIROS Operational Vertical Sounder archives, and Stratospheric Monitoring-group's Ozone Blended Analysis, an assimilation product from NOAA's Climate Prediction Center.

The SRB dataset are also available from the Surface Meteorology and Solar Energy Web site (http://eosweb.larc.nasa.gov/sse/) in a version that is more applicable to renewable energy. SRB datasets are also available from the Clouds and the Earth's Radiant Energy System project (http://eosweb.larc.nasa.gov/PRODOCS/ceres/table_ceres.html). Additionally, the Fast Longwave and Shortwave Radiative Fluxes (FLASHFlux) project makes real-time SRB data available from http://eosweb.larc.nasa.gov/PRODOCS/ flashflux/ table_ flashflux.html.

Both projects use global observations from Clouds and the Earth's Radiant Energy System and moderate-resolution imaging spectroradiometer instruments. Table 4-1 shows the estimated bias and root-mean-square (RMS) error between measured WMO Baseline Surface Radiation Network (BSRN) monthly averages of the three solar radiation components. The NASA SSE accuracy and methodology are documented on the SSE Web site.

Table 4-1. Regression Analysis of NASA SSE Versus BSRN Bias and RMS Error for Monthly Averaged Values for July 1983 Through June 2006

Parameter	Region	Bias (%)	RMS (%)
	Global	–.01	10.25
GHI	60° Poleward	–1.18	34.37
	60° Equatorward	0.29	8.71
	Global	7.49	29.34
DHI	60° Poleward	11.29	54.14
	60° Equatorward	6.86	22.78
	Global	–4.06	22.73
DNI	60° Poleward	–15.66	33.12
	60° Equatorward	2.40	20.93

DLR-ISIS Model

Similar to the NASA SSE datasets discussed in section 5, the DLR-ISIS dataset (available at www.pa.op.dlr.de/ISIS/) is a 21-year DNI and GHI dataset (280 km × 280 km every 3 hours) based on the ISCCP cloud product covering the period between July 1983 through December 2004. The cloud products are used in a 2-stream radiative transfer model (Kylling et al. 1995) to compute DNI and GHI. The correlated-k method of Kato et al. (1999) is used to compute atmospheric absorption in the solar spectrum. Scattering and absorption in water clouds are analyzed using the parameterization of Hu and Stamnes (1993); ice cloud properties are obtained from Yang et al. (2000) and Key et al. (2002). Fixed effective radii of 10 μm and 30 μm are used for water and ice clouds, respectively. The radiative transfer algorithm and parameterizations are included in the radiative transfer library libRadtran (Mayer and Kylling 2005, available at www.libradtran.org/doku.php). The complete method for creating the DLRISIS dataset using the ISCCP cloud products and the libRadtran library is outlined in Lohmann et al. (2006). The cloud data used for the derivation of the DLR-ISIS dataset are taken from the ISCCP FD input dataset (Zhang et al. 2004), which is based on ISCCP D1 cloud data (see ISCCP homepage at http://isccp.giss.nasa.gov for more information about cloud datasets). It provides 3-hourly cloud observations on a 280 km × 280 km equal area grid. The whole dataset consists of 6,596 grid boxes on 72 latitude steps of 2.5 degrees. This grid is maintained for the DLR-ISIS dataset.

ISCCP differentiates between 15 cloud types. The classification includes three intervals of optical thickness in three cloud levels: low, middle and high clouds. Low and middle cloud types are further divided into water and ice clouds; high clouds are always ice clouds.

For DLR-ISIS, optical thickness, cloud top pressure, and cloud phase given in the ISCCP dataset are processed to generate clouds for the radiative transfer calculations. One radiative transfer calculation is carried out for each occurring cloud type assuming 100% cloud coverage, plus one calculation for clear sky. For the final result, irradiances are weighted with the cloud amount for each cloud type and for clear sky, respectively.

HelioClim

The Heliosat method based on Cano et al. (1986) is used to produce the HelioClim database (Rigollier et al. 2004) that uses METEOSAT data (www.soda-is.com/eng/help/helioclim_eng. html). HelioClim covers Europe, Africa, the Mediterranean Basin, the Atlantic Ocean, and part of the Indian Ocean. Mines Paristech - Armines produces that can be accessed through the SoDa Service (www.soda-is.com/eng/index.html). Mines ParisTech produced the method Heliosat-2 in November 2002, partly with the support of the European Commission; Heliosat-4 is being developed by Mines Paris Tech and the German Aerospace Agency DLR. Table 4-2 shows representative differences in comparisons of HelioClim modeled data and ground measurements in Europe and Africa between 1994 and 1997 (Lefe`vre 2007).

Solar Energy Mining

Solar Energy Mining (SOLEMI) is a service provided by DLR (Deutsches Zentrum für Luft- und Raumfahrt) German Aerospace Center that provides irradiance data commercially. The data are derived from Meteosat satellite images. GHI and DNI datasets are available every hour at 2.5-km resolution and cover Europe and Africa (1991 to 2005) and Asia (1999 to 2006). SOLEMI uses the Heliosat method of Cano et al. (1986), modified by Beyer et al. (1996) at http://wdc.dlr.de/.

Table 4-2. HelioClim Versus Ground Bias and RMS Error for Monthly Averaged Values for 1994–1997

Parameter	Region	Bias (%)	RMS (%)
GHI	Europe	−9% to −1%	25%
	Africa	−3% to +4%	18%

Perez/Clean Power Research

The Perez et al. (2002) method (herein referred to as the Perez State University of New York [Perez SUNY] model) for computing GHI and DNI is based on the concept that atmospheric transmittance is directly proportional to the TOA planetary albedo (Schmetz 1989). This method is being applied to the GOES satellites and is currently available from Clean Power Research (www.cleanpower.com). The concept of using satellite-based measurements of radiance assumes the visible imagery demonstrates cloud cover for high levels of brightness and lower levels for more clear sky conditions (e.g., dark ground cover). The method is outlined below and readers are referred to Perez et al. (2002) for additional details. The method:

- Normalizes the satellite measurement with the SZA to remove effects of solar geometry.
- Creates a dynamic range of satellite measurements using time series information for each pixel.
- Calculates cloud index for every pixel in an image by scaling with the dynamic range for the corresponding pixel that was created in Step 3.
- Uses the SOLIS model (Mueller et al. 2004) to create a GHI map for clear sky (GHIclr).
- Calculates GHI by scaling GHIclr with the cloud index.
- Calculates clear sky DNI (DNIclr) and DNI from GHIclr and GHI, respectively, using the DIRINT model (Perez et al. 1992).
- Calculates clear sky DNI from the Bird Model (DNIclr, Bird) using water vapor, ozone, and aerosol optical depths as inputs (DNIclr, Bird is estimated to be more accurate than DNIclr).
- Scales DNIclr, Bird with ratio of DNI and DNIclr from Step 6 to calculate the DNI.

The above steps are used to calculate DNI and GHI from satellite visible imagery. Some additional corrections and ancillary data are used to make the product more accurate. These include:

- Using snow cover information from the National Snow and Ice Data Center to reset the lower bound of the dynamic range
- Using surface elevation from the US Geological Survey's digital elevation models (DEMs) to adjust for atmospheric optical depth based on elevation
- Adjusting the lower bound of the dynamic range for high AM effects

- Adjusting for specular reflection caused by the angle between the sun and satellite
- Adjusting the cloud index to a clearness index using a nonlinear conversion process and applying the clearness index to GHI calculations.

3-TIER Solar Dataset

A new dataset, the 3-TIER dataset, has become available. It follows the method of Perez et al. (2002). Datasets for the Western Hemisphere are available at 3-km resolution from 1997 (White paper 2009a). Also available are data for India (White paper 2009b) at the same resolution from 1999. Data for Australia are available (White paper 2009c) from 1998 at 3-km resolution.

SolarGIS

A new model for high-performance calculation of global and direct irradiances has been implemented for the region covered by the MSG, the satellite covering Europe, Africa, and the Middle East.

The model philosophy is based on the principles of Heliosat-2 calculation scheme (Hammer et al. 2003) and the model by Perez et al. (2002), and it is implemented to operationally process MSG data at full spatial and temporal resolution.

The model was developed by GeoModel (Cebecauer et al. 2010). The enhancements include:

- Multispectral satellite information to improve classification of snow/land/cloud signals
- A new algorithm to find lower bound values preserving diurnal variability Implementation of backscatter correction
- Variable upper bound for dynamic range and cloud index calculations
- Simplified SOLIS clear sky model
- Downscaling with high-resolution DEM to include local variability of solar irradiance. In particular, the following algorithms are implemented:
- Clear sky model: broadband simplified Solis (Ineichen 2008)
- Satellite model: modified version of Heliosat by Perez et al. (2002), adapted for multispectral MSG data, with improvements of snow classification and cloud index determination
- Snow detection: Dürr and Zelenka (2009)
- DHI: Perez model, Perez et al. (1987)
- DNI: DirIndex, Perez et al. (1992, 2002)
- Terrain disaggregation: Ruiz-Arias et al. (2010).

NOAA Global Surface Insolation Project

NOAA is currently running a physical model (www.osdpd.noaa.gov/ml/land/gsip/index.html) that produces GHI at approximately 12-km resolution for the northern hemisphere. Its output is called the *GOES Surface Insolation Product.* The GOES Surface Isolation Product algorithm follows a 2-step process:

1. Uses multichannel GOES satellite information and ancillary datasets, including snow cover, surface albedo, and digital elevation to retrieve cloud properties (Heidinger 2003).
2. Uses the cloud properties from Step 1 to produce GHI (Lazslo and Pinker 1992; Laszlo et al. 2008).

Although the GOES Surface Isolation Product was primarily developed to estimate sea surface temperature for coral bleaching and numerical weather prediction applications, it can be tailored to CSP needs as DNI is currently produced, but not saved, in the official product (Istvan Laszlo, personal communication).

Clear Sky Models Used in Operation Models

Bird Clear Sky Model
The Bird Clear Sky Model (Bird and Hulstrom 1981) is a broadband algorithm that produces estimates of clear sky direct beam, hemispherical diffuse, and total hemispherical solar radiation on a horizontal surface. The model is based on parameterization built using radiative transfer computations and is composed of simple algebraic expressions. Model results are expected to agree within ± 10% with radiative transfer models. The model computes hourly average solar radiation for every hour of the year, based on the 10-user input parameters; however, variable atmospheric parameters such as aerosol optical depth, ozone, and water vapor, are fixed for the entire year. The Bird Clear Sky Model also forms the basis of the clear sky part of METSTAT, with only minor modifications. The performance of these two models has been assessed rigorously and compared to other algorithms (Gueymard 1993, 2003a, 2003b; Gueymard and Myers 2008).

European Solar Radiation Atlas Model
The European Solar Radiation Atlas (ESRA) model is another example of a clear sky model. Used in the Heliosat-2 model that retrieves GHI from satellites, this model computes DNI, GHI, and DHI using Rayleigh optical depth, elevation, and the Linke Turbidy factor as its inputs.

SOLIS Model
The SOLIS model (Mueller et al. 2004) is a simple clear sky model that can calculate DNI, GHI, and diffuse radiation based on an approximation to the Lambert-Beer relation for computing DNI:

$$I = I0e^{(-T)}$$

where

τ is the atmospheric optical depth,
I0 is the TOA direct radiation, and
I is the DNI at the surface for a monochromatic wavelength.

This equation is modified to account for slant paths and adapted for GHI and diffuse. The modified Lambert-Beer relation (Mueller et al. 2004) is

$$I(SZA) = I0exp\ (-T0\ /\ Cosa\ (SZA)$$

where

I(θz) is the irradiance associated with the empirical factor, a, used to compute the DNI, DHI, or GHI (a = 1 for DNI),
τ0 is the vertical broadband optical depth of the atmosphere, and SZA is the solar zenith angle.

The Beer-Lambert equation is a simple relationship as it accounts for monochromatic DNI and is impacted only by atmospheric attenuation. On the other hand, DHI and GHI are broadband values that contain energy that is scattered by the atmosphere. The empirical factor a is used as an adjustment factor to compute GHI and DHI, as explained in Mueller et al. (2004).

Model Uncertainty and Validation

It is important to understand the accuracy of satellite measurements compared to surface data. A satellite pixel provides an estimate of surface radiation based on cloud and aerosol information spread over a certain area; the surface observations are based on an instrument viewing the sky from a point. If the satellite pixel size is small enough, parallax errors enter into the comparison. Terrain effects may also influence a comparison where cloudiness may vary within a short distance. According to Perez et al. (1987), satellite-based retrievals are accurate to 10%–12%. According to Renné et al. (1999) and Zelenka et al. (1999), the target-specific comparison with ground-based observations will have a root mean square error (RMSE) of at least 20%; the time specific pixel wide accuracy is 10%–12% on an hourly basis. The various empirical and theoretical methods discussed above have been tested for accuracy. Although there is no standardized method for accuracy assessment, the authors have mostly reported root mean square deviation (RMSD) and bias error either as a percent or in energy units. As an example, the physical model of Darnell et al. (1988) was used to compute surface radiation using cloud information from the ISCCP-C1 data. The results were then compared to surface observations collected by the WRDC by Darnell and Staylor (1992).
The RMSD from this comparison was found to be about 16 W/m^2 and the mean bias was about 4 W/m^2 (See Tables 4-3 through 4-6). It should also be noted that interpretation of reported errors is dependent on the spatial and temporal resolution of the data being compared.
A rigorous method that is currently gaining acceptance for benchmarking satellite-retrieved GHI and DNI with ground-based observations is the Kolmogorov-Smirnov test (Massey Jr. 1951).
This test has the advantage of being nonparametric and is therefore not distribution dependent.
It compares the distributions of GHI and DNI obtained from the two sources.

Table 4-3. Summary of Applications and Validation Results of Satellite Models—Empirical/Statistical Models (after Renné et al. 1999)

References	Objective	Satellite Data/ Study Period	Location/Resolution	Methodology	Accuracy
Nullet 1987	GHI over tropical Pacific	ESSA 1,3,5,7; ITOS I, NOAA 1,2/Feb 1965– Jan 1973	Tropical Pacific/ monthly, 2.5 km x 2.5 km	Cloud cover by Sadler et al. 1976; 2 irradiance models	Three islands (annual)–0.5% to +4.4%
Shaltout and Hassen 1990	Seasonal maps of daily GHI and DHI	METEOSAT 1100 LST cloud cover images	Egypt, one observation/day, 2.5 km x 2.5 km (visible) and 5 km x 5 km (infrared)	Linear regression with 24 ground stations	GHI ± 7.0% DHI ± 12.5%
Delorme et al. 1992	Real-time daily images	METEOSTAT visible Mar 15 – Jun 30, 1990	Southern France/daily 367 km x 725 km	"Gistel" model applied to WEFAX images	Generally high inaccuracies
Ben Djemaa and Delorme 1992	Comparison with 7 ground stations	METEOSAT B2/Oct 1985– Sept 1986	Tunisia/daily 30 km x 30 km	"Gistel" model applied to B2 data for daily values	0%–10% (51% of data) –10% to 0% (38% of data)

Table 4-4. Summary of Applications and Validation Results of Satellite Models—Empirical/Physical Models (after Renné et al. 1999)

References	Objective	Satellite Data/ Study Period	Location/ Resolution	Methodology	Accuracy
Nunez 1990	Solar energy for Australian cities	GMS/1986– 1988	8 Australian cities/daily 219 km x 177 km	Simple physical model by author	< 10% (6 cities) > 10% (2 cities)
Tarpley 1979	GHI from GOES	Summer 1997	USA Great Plains/ daily totals from hourly images 50 km x 50 km	Empirical relation with ground stations coupled with physical models	RMSE < 10% (daily) RMSE < 20% (1 image/day)
Klink and Dollhopf 1986	Resource assessment for Ohio	GOES 1982	8 stations in Ohio/50 km x 50 km	Tarpley 1979	10%–12% RMSE (snow-free) –3.5% MBE
Czeplak et al. 1991	Comparisons of Tarpley method	METEOSATvisible/Nov 1986	Western Germany/8 km x 8 km	Tarpley 1979	21% RMSE (daily) 11% RMSE (monthly)
Frulla et al. 1988	Solar radiation Over Argentina	GOES-E/1982– 1983	Northern Argentina/daily 1 km x 1 km	Tarpley 1979	RMSE 10%– 15% (daily) RMSE 25% (hourly)
Diabate et al. 1989	Establish a HELIOSAT station	METEOSAT1983–1985	European and eastern Mediterranean/ hourly	HELIOSAT (Cano et al. 1986; Moussu et al. 1989)	RMSE 0.06 kWh/m^2

A detailed analysis of uncertainty is beyond the scope of this handbook; however, it is important to indicate possible sources of these uncertainties. One important issue to DNI and GHI assessments is the aerosol optical depth of the atmosphere. Depending on its composition, an aerosol can scatter, absorb, or scatter and absorb the DNI. This interaction is called *atmospheric extinction*. The proportion of absorption and scattering is determined by the aerosol type.

As an example, mineral dust is a mostly scattering aerosol; black carbon is highly absorbing. To calculate the DNI, we need only the aerosol extinction, but GHI calculations are more accurate if the scattering and absorption components are available. Aerosol optical depths vary over the wavelength range and the use of a single broadband aerosol optical depth results in additional uncertainties.

Climatological aerosol optical depths can be used for resource assessment but sometimes lead to large DNI errors. This happens in areas of biomass burning, urban air pollution, and dust storms where the use of climatology results smoothes out episodic events, ultimately leading to an underestimation of DNI.

It is difficult to discriminate between clouds and snow cover on the ground by using the satellite visible imagery. As snow results in elevated reflection of sunlight, the satellite image may be interpreted as cloud covered.

This results in underestimation of GHI and DNI. The use of multiple satellite channels in the visible and infrared can solve this issue.

Specular reflection, especially from sandy desert surface during certain times of the day, may result in the satellite image being interpreted as cloudy and result in underestimation of GHI and DNI. This issue can be resolved by theoretically estimating the probability of specular reflection and factoring that into the calculation of surface radiation.

Table 4-5. Summary of Applications and Validation Results of Satellite Models — Broadband Theoretical Models (after Renné et al. 1999)

References	Objective	Satellite Data/ Study Period	Location/ Resolution	Methodology	Accuracy
Frouin et al. 1988	Compare Gautier's method with five empirical models	GMS/1986–1988	8 Australian cities/daily 219 km × 177 km	Gautier et al. 1980, with refinements	RMSE 12.0 Wm2 (daily) MBE –4.9 Wm2
Gautier 1988	GHI over oceanic regions	Summer 1997	USA Great Plains/daily totals from hourly images 50 km × 50 km	Gautier et al. 1980, with refinements	RMSE 12 Wm2 or 5% (daily) MBE –6 Wm2
Darnell et al. 1988	GHI estimates using sun-synchronoussatellites	GOES 1982	8 stations in Ohio/ 50 km × 50 km	GHI technique from sun-synchronous satellites	RMSE 19.2% (daily) 2.7% (monthly)
Dedieu et al. 1987	Calculate GHI and albedo from METEOSAT	METEOSATvisible/Nov 1986	Western Germany/8 km × 8 km	Physical relationship between computed TOA and satellite values	RMSE 19.5% (hourly, noon) RMSE 6.7% (monthly)

Table 4-6. Summary of Applications and Validation Results of Satellite Models—Spectral Theoretical Models (after Renné et al. 1999)

References	Objective	Satellite Data/Study Period	Location/ Resolution	Methodology	Accuracy
Möser and Raschke 1984	Solar radiation over Europe	METEOSAT-I-II Jun 1979 and Apr 1982	Europe/daily(3–6 images/ day) 25 km × 25 km	Normalized reflected radiance; 2-stream radiative transfer model	RMSE 5% – 6% (monthly) RMSE 10% – 14% (daily) Daily RE < 20% (no snow) > 20% (snow)
Stuhlmann et al. 1990	Improve IGMK model of Möser and Raschke 1983 (cloud transmittance)	METEOSAT ISCCP B2	Europe, Africa, Western South Africa 30–50 km	Explicitly account for multiple reflections between surface and atmospheric layers; improved clear sky algorithm	Monthly means generally within ± 10% (better over Europe)
Pereira et al. 1996	Surface GHI	METEOSAT-II 1985–1986	Brazil monthly	IGMK model (Sthuhlman et al. 1990)	RMSE 13% MBE –7%
Raschke et al. 1991	Solar radiation atlas for Africa	METEOSAT ISSCP B2 1985–1986	Africa: 30–50 km (IGMK), 2.5 km (HELIOSAT) monthly (derived from 3-hourly values)	IGMK (HELIOSAT for selected areas over western Africa)	RMSE–8% to 16% (monthly) MBE – 2% to 8% (monthly)
Pinker and Laszlo 1992	Global SRB estimates	ISCCP C1 (based on ISSCP B3) July 1983	Global 2.5 degrees latitude × 2.5 degrees longitude	Pinker and Ewing 1985	High level of consistency on global scale

5. HISTORICAL SOLAR RESOURCE DATA

Introduction

Understanding the long-term spatial and temporal variabilities of available solar resources is fundamental to any assessment of CSP potential. Information derived from historical solar resource data can be used to make energy policy decisions, select optimum energy conversion technologies, design systems for specific locations, and operate and maintain installed solar energy conversion systems. Historical solar resource data can be the result of in-situ measurement programs, satellite-remote sensing methods, or meteorological model outputs. As described in the previous sections, each type of data has different information content and applicability.

This section summarizes historical solar resource data available for the United States and selected international locations. It is an inventory of representative sources of solar radiation data and provides a summary of important data characteristics associated with each data source (e.g., period of record, temporal and spatial resolutions, available data elements, and estimated uncertainties).

NREL and other agencies have made every effort to make data products that are as useful, robust, and as representative as possible; however, the responsibility for applying the data correctly resides with the user. A thorough understanding of the data sources, how they are created, and their limitations is vital to proper application of the resource data to analyses and subsequent decision-making. Discussion and examples of the use of several of these datasets for CSP applications are presented here. Users are encouraged to read the pertinent sections of this section before applying solar resource and meteorological data.

Measured solar irradiance data can provide detailed temporal information for a specific site. Because solar radiation measurement stations are challenging to operate and the data collected are not used for routine weather forecasts, they are few in number and have limited data collection records. The largest national measurement network for obtaining hourly solar resource data in the United States was the 39-station NOAA Network, which operated from 1977 through 1980 (see section on the NOAA network, page 69). Currently, measured solar irradiance of some form is available from more than 3,000 sites in the United States that are operated by various interests producing data with a wide range of data quality (see section on the PVGIS, page 73).

Satellite-based observations and mesoscale meteorological models address the needs for understanding the spatial variability of solar radiation resources over a range of distances. Present state-of-the-art models provide estimates for GHI and DNI at spatial resolutions of 10 km or less for the United States. The rapidly growing needs for more accurate solar resource information over shorter temporal and smaller spatial scales require the user to fully appreciate the characteristics of all available data, especially those from historical sources.

Solar Resource Data Characteristics

Characterizing the available solar resources for CSP applications is important for all aspects of realizing the full potential of this utility-scale energy source. Energy policy decisions, engineering designs, and system deployment considerations require an accurate understanding of the relevant historical solar resource data, the ability to assess the accuracy of current solar measurement and modeling techniques, and to forecast the levels of solar irradiance for various temporal and spatial scales.

Solar resource data can be the result of in-situ measurement programs, remote sensing instruments, or meteorological modeling outputs. Each type of data product has different information content and applicability.

Measured solar irradiance data can provide information about the temporal variability at a specific site. Practical radiometer designs were developed in the early 1900s to determine the sun's energy output based on high-altitude measurements of DNI made with pyrheliometers (Hulstrom 1989). To address the needs of agriculture for monitoring such quantities as evapotranspiration, the US Weather Bureau deployed a national radiometer network in the 1950s to collect GHI. Since then, radiometer design and data acquisition system performance have seen many advancements. The earliest records of solar flux measurements were based on thermopile-type pyranometer signals stored on analog strip chart recordings to determine daily amounts of solar flux on a horizontal surface. Today, 1-minute (or shorter) digital recordings are available from fast-response silicon photodiodes and improved thermopile-type pyranometers and pyrheliometers that are deployed in regional measurement networks to provide solar energy resource data for a variety of applications.

Historically, there have been four radiometer calibration reference scales: Ångström Scale (ÅS 1905), Smithsonian Scale (SS 1913), International Pyrheliometric Scale (IPS 1956), and the WRR (1979). The relative differences among these scales can introduce a data bias on the order of 2%. The user should be aware of this potential bias in data measured before 1979.[3]

Modeled solar resource data derived from available surface meteorological observations and satellite measurements provide estimates of solar resource potential for locations lacking actual measurements. These modeling methods address the needs for improved spatial resolution of the resource data. The first national effort to model solar resources in the 1970s advanced our understanding of solar radiation distributions based on the then available historical measurements at 26 locations to an additional 222 meteorological observing stations with detailed records of hourly cloud amounts and other relevant data (see SOLMET/ ERSATZ section, page 58). Today, satellite-based observations of clouds are used to model hourly surface solar fluxes with 10-km spatial resolution (see 1991–2005 NSRDB, page 80).

Long-Term and Typical Meteorological Year Datasets

Understanding the timeframe, or period of record, associated with solar resource and other meteorological data is important for conducting useful analyses. These weather-driven data have fluctuations that can range from seconds to years and longer. Long-term data can be representative of the climate if the period of record is at least 30 years. By convention, the 30-year interval has been deemed sufficient to reflect longer term climatic trends and filter the short-term interannual fluctuations and anomalies.[4] Climate normals are recomputed each decade to address temperature, pressure, precipitation, and other surface meteorological variables. The most recent climatic normals are based on data from 1971 to 2000.

A TMY dataset provides designers and other users with a reasonably sized annual dataset that holds 8,760 hourly meteorological values that typify conditions at a specific location over a longer period, such as the 30-year climatic normal. The TMY dataset is composed of 12 TMMs selected on the basis of their similarity of individual cumulative frequency distributions for selected data elements. The longer term distributions are determined for that month using data from the full period of record. The TMMs are then concatenated, essentially without modification, to form a single year with a serially complete data record. The resulting TMY dataset contains measured and modeled time-series solar radiation and surface meteorological data, although some hourly records may contain filled or interpolated data for periods when original observations are missing from the data archive.

TMY datasets are widely used by building designers and others for modeling renewable energy conversion systems. Although not designed to provide meteorological extremes, TMY data have natural diurnal and seasonal variations and represent a year of typical climatic conditions for a location. The TMY should not be used to predict weather or solar resources for a particular period of time, nor is it an appropriate basis for evaluating real-time energy production. Rather, a TMY represents conditions judged to be typical over a long period, such as 30 years. Because they represent typical rather than extreme conditions, they are not suited for designing systems and their components to meet the worst-case weather conditions that could occur at a location.

The next section describes the three versions of TMY data for the United States. In 1978, Sandia National Laboratories produced the first TMY for 248 locations using long-term weather and solar data from the 1952–1975 Solar Meteorological (SOLMET)/ERSATZ database (Hall et al. 1978). In 1994, NREL developed the TMY2 using data from the 1961–1990 NSRDB (Marion and Urban 1995). In 2007, NREL released a 15-year updated NSRDB for 1991–2005 (Wilcox 2007) that formed the basis of the TMY3 dataset.

Solar Resource Data

An inventory of solar resource data sources is presented in chronological order, based on the first data record.

The attributes of each data source are presented using the list of key considerations (see sidebar). DNI data are available from these sources or can be estimated by using available models and the data elements present in each dataset.

NCEP/NCAR Global Reanalysis Products

Products from National Center for Environmental Prediction/National Center for Atmospheric Research (NCEP/NCAR) Reanalysis Project are archived in the dataset called ds090.0. The resolution of the global Reanalysis Model is 209 km with 28 vertical levels. Results are available at 6-hour intervals. Although the initial plan was to reanalyze the data for a 40-year period (1957–1996), production has gone back to 1948 and is going forward continuously. Plans call for rerunning the entire period as next generation models are ready (Kalnay et al. 1996; Kistler et al. 2001).

There are more than 80 variables, including incoming solar radiation (GHI), temperature, relative humidity, and wind components, in several coordinate systems. They are organized as different subgroups in the archive. Some special periods are analyzed more than once to provide data for special research studies.

The Research Data Archive is maintained by the Computational and Information Systems Laboratory at NCAR. NCAR is sponsored by the National Science Foundation. The original data are available from the Research Data Archive (http://dss.ucar.edu) in dataset number ds090.0.

Period of record: 1948–2009.

Temporal resolution: 6 hours (W/m^2).

Spatial coverage: Global.

Spatial resolution: 2.5 degrees (nominal).

Data elements and sources: GHI and more than 80 variables, including geopotential height, temperature, relative humidity, and U and V wind components, in several coordinate systems, such as a 17 pressure level stack on 2.5 × 2.5 degree grids, 28 sigma level stacks on 192 × 94 Gaussian grids, and 11 isentropic level stacks on a 2.5 × 2.5 degree grid.

Data quality control and assessment: No information.

Estimated uncertainties: None stated.

Availability: University Center for Atmospheric Research, Computational and Information Systems Laboratory Research Data Archive, http://dss.ucar.edu/datasets/ds 090.0.

Updates: Monthly.

Key Considerations

Applying solar and meteorological data from different sources requires attention to these key considerations:

- Period of record. Influenced by many factors, solar resource data vary from year to year, seasonally, monthly, weekly, daily, and on timescales down to a few seconds. Thus, climate normals are based on 30 years of meteorological data. Another popular approach is to determine a TMY dataset from a statistical analysis of multiyear data to derive a single year of data that are representative of a longer term record. Comparative analyses must account for any natural differences that result from the periods when the data were acquired.
- Temporal resolution. Solar resource data can range from annually averaged daily-integrated power (kWh/m2/day) typically used for mapping resource distributions to 1-s samples of irradiance (W/m2) for operational time-series analyses.

Other considerations depend on the data type:

- *Spatial coverage.* The area represented by the data can range from a single station to a sample geographic region to a global perspective.
- *Spatial resolution.* Ground-based measurements are site specific. Current satellite-remote sensing estimates can be representative of 10-km × 10-km or smaller areas.
- *Data elements and sources of the data.* The usefulness of solar resource data may depend on the available data elements (e.g., DNI) and whether the data were measured, modeled, or produced in combination.
- *Data quality control and quality assessments.* Descriptions of the measurement operations, model validation methods, and data adjustments or corrections are key metadata elements.
- *Estimated uncertainties.* Stated uncertainties should include a description of the methodology used to provide this information.
- *Availability.* Data are distributed in the public domain, for purchase, or license.
- *Updates.* The need to include the most recent data and other revisions can require regular database updates.

SOLMET/ERSATZ

In response to the energy crisis in the mid-1970s, NOAA and the Energy Research and Development Administration (later the US Department of Energy [DOE]) funded the "rehabilitation" of surface meteorological and solar measurement data to create the SOLMET hourly dataset. SOLMET data were derived from the best available solar radiation measurements from 26 stations operated by the National Weather Service (NWS) (NCDC 1978, 1979).

Additional ERSATZ data, literally "inferior substitute," were modeled from available hourly and 3-hourly cloud and other surface meteorological observations to expand the data coverage by an additional 222 NWS stations. The SOLMET/ERSATZ database was created to address the needs of the solar energy R&D community.

The database provided:

- A single source of merged suitable solar measurements and meteorological data
- Data consistent with SI
- Time-series data so users can access the information in true solar and standard time
- Time-series data so users will be aware of the selected meteorological observation that is closest to the time of the solar observation (e.g., selected to be the observation nearest to the midpoint of the solar hour)
- Data recorded in local standard time for conversion to solar time
- A data format with additional solar radiation parameters (direct and tilted, normal incidence, diffuse, and net), as well as additional measurements (ultraviolet and other spectral regions) to be available from stations in the future
- Historical solar radiation data (including the ETR field) converted to the same international scale based on a solar constant value of $1,377$ W/m^2
- Eliminated undesirable format features that were inherent in the past data sources such as over punches and blanks
- Missing observations and observations that were estimated via models (e.g., bright sunshine duration and cloud regression models)
- Solar GHI data as they were originally observed and provided the user with data corrected for all known scale, instrument, and calibration problems in addition to a dataset corrected via a model.

This database provides some of the earliest measurements of solar irradiance from a national network.

Period of record: December 1951 through December 1976.

Temporal resolution: Hourly (hour ending in local solar time).

Spatial coverage: United States and territories (Figure 5-1).

Spatial resolution: 26 measurement stations and 222 modeled stations.

Data elements and sources: ETR, GHI (observed-SOLMET or modeled-ERSATZ, engineering corrected, standard year corrected), direct normal radiation (estimated from global), minutes of sunshine, clouds (ceiling height, total and opaque cloud fractions, and information for up to four cloud layers), and surface meteorological conditions (temperature, wind speed, pressure, snow cover, horizontal visibility, sky condition, and current weather).

Estimated uncertainties: Based on comparisons with subsequent NOAA Network measurements from 1977 to 1980, the monthly mean daily total SOLMET GHI and DNI accuracies are $\pm$ 7.5% and $\pm$ 10% respectively. Similarly, the monthly mean daily total ERSATZ GHI and DNI accuracies are $\pm$ 10% and $\pm$ 20%. The modeling method eliminated any evidence for long-term trends in atmospheric opacity resulting from volcanic eruption, urbanization, or other causes. The uncertainty of individual hourly values is higher than the monthly mean daily statistics.

Availability: National Climatic Data Center (NCDC), NESDIS, NOAA, US Department of Commerce, www.ncdc.noaa.gov/.

Updates: Released in 1978, the SOLMET/ERSATZ database was replaced in 1992 by the 1961–1990 NSRDB.

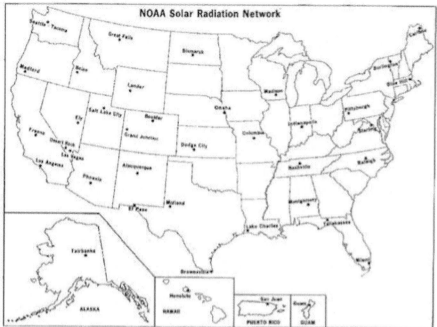

Credit: NREL.

Figure 5-1. SOLDAY and SOLMET measurement stations (26 each).

SOLDAY

SOLDAY is the second of two data rehabilitation projects completed for NOAA and the Energy Research and Development Administration (now DOE) to produce a solar resource dataset with merged suitable solar measurements and meteorological data consistent with SI (NCDC 1979b). The daily GHI data were reformatted by removing all known procedural and instrumental errors and included all available meteorological elements. Rehabilitated hourly solar measurement stations used in SOLMET were not selected for the SOLDAY format to eliminate data redundancy. Daily GHI data were based on recorded solar radiation on strip charts and daily amounts obtained for a part of the time by summing hand-computed hourly values. For the remainder of the time, daily sums were obtained from a mechanical integrator. This dataset provides some of the earliest measurements of solar radiation and complements the geographic distribution of the SOLMET measurement stations.

Period of record: January 1952 through December 1976. *Temporal resolution*: Daily.

Spatial coverage: Continental United States (Figure 5-1). *Spatial resolution*: 26 measurement stations.

Data elements and sources: Computed times of daily sunrise and sunset, ETR (based on solar constant = 1,377 W/m^2), measured GHI from mechanical integrators and strip charts and daily amounts calculated by summing hand-computed hourly values, minutes, and percent of possible sunshine, temperature (maximum, minimum, mean), precipitation, snowfall, snow depth, weather codes, and sky cover from hourly observations. None of the 26 SOLDAY measurement stations are in the hourly SOLMET dataset.

Data quality control and assessment: Individual station histories note pertinent information, making it possible to properly interpret the data. If more than 60 days elapsed between clear solar noon irradiance values, no sky cover/sunshine model was used to fill the irradiance data gaps.

Estimated uncertainties: Based on the known measurement characteristics of the Eppley Laboratory, Inc., Model 50 and Model PSP pyranometers used to measure GHI at SOLDAY stations, the estimated daily total irradiances are expected to be within ± 10%. Measured data from Model PSP radiometers were not corrected for thermal offsets that were discovered much later.

Availability: NCDC, NESDIS, NOAA, US Department of Commerce, www.ncdc.noaa.gov/.

Updates: Released in 1979, the SOLDAY database was replaced in 1992 by the 1961–1990 NSRDB.

Typical Meteorological Year

A TMY dataset provides a single year of hourly data for solar radiation and other meteorological elements that permit performance comparisons of system types and configurations for one or more locations. A TMY is not necessarily a good indicator of conditions over the next year, or even the next 5 years. Rather, it represents conditions judged to be typical over a long period, such as 30 years. Because they represent typical rather than extreme conditions, TMYs are not suited for designing systems and their components to meet the worst-case weather conditions that could occur at a location.

The first TMY dataset[5] is a subset of the hourly SOLMET measurement and ERSATZ model estimates for 248 locations in the United States and territorial possessions. The TMY data consists of typical months concatenated to form a complete year of 8,760 hourly records. The TMMs were selected in part by comparing weighted cumulative distribution functions of nine data elements as shown in Table 5-1 with the long-term distributions. Examining the weighted sum of the 13 Finkelstein-Schafer statistics for each year and persistence characterized by frequency and run length above and below fixed long-term percentiles resulted in 5 "candidate years" for the month in question. The final selection of a TMM was somewhat subjective; years with small weighted sum statistics, small deviations, and "typical" run structures were chosen.

TMY data provide hourly GHI and DNI solar data and other surface meteorological elements.

Table 5-1. Weighting Factors Applied to Cumulative Distributions

Version	Temperature						Wind Velocity		Solar Radiation	
	Dry Bulb			Dew Point						
	Max.	Min.	Mean	Max.	Min.	Mean	Max.	Mean	GHI	DNI
TMY	1/24	1/24	2/24	1/24	1/24	2/24	2/24	2/24	12/24	N/A
TMY2-3	1/20	1/20	2/20	1/20	1/20	2/20	1/20	1/20	5/20	5/20

Period of record: One year representative of the SOLMET/ERSATZ data period 1952–1976. *Temporal resolution*: Hourly.

Spatial coverage: United States and territories (Figure 5-1).

Spatial resolution: 26 measurement stations and 222 modeled stations.

Data elements and sources: ETR, GHI (observed-SOLMET or modeled-ERSATZ, engineering corrected, standard year corrected), direct normal radiation (estimated from global), minutes of sunshine, clouds (ceiling height, total and opaque cloud fractions, and information for up to four cloud layers), and surface meteorological conditions (temperature, wind speed, pressure, snow cover, horizontal visibility, sky condition, and current weather).

Data quality control and assessment: Measured hourly GHI determined from strip chart recordings and labeled as "observed" data. Known instrument corrections for temperature response were applied to observed GHI and labeled as "engineering corrected" data. Measured data from single-black thermopile radiometers were not corrected for thermal offsets that were discovered much later. Clear sky model estimates of pyranometer calibration changes were applied to observed GHI and labeled as "standard year irradiance corrected" data. The clear sky model was also used to fill missing GHI observations. Only the standard year irradiance data field is serially complete. All SOLMET DNI data were computed based on a regression relationship between observed hourly global and direct normal irradiance measurements taken at five measurement stations: Livermore, California; Raleigh, North Carolina; Maynard, Massachusetts; and Fort Hood, Texas. All ERSATZ GHI and DNI data were estimated from clear sky models and available cloud observations.

Estimated uncertainties: Based on comparisons with subsequent NOAA Network measurements from 1977 to 1980, the monthly mean daily total SOLMET GHI and DNI accuracies are ± 7.5% and ± 10%, respectively. Similarly, the monthly mean daily total ERSATZ GHI and DNI accuracies are ± 10% and ± 20%, respectively. The modeling method destroyed any evidence for long-term trends in atmospheric opacity resulting from volcanic eruption, urbanization, or other causes. The uncertainty of individual hourly values is certainly higher than the monthly mean daily statistics.

Availability: NCDC, NESDIS, NOAA, US Department of Commerce, www.ncdc.noaa.gov/.

Updates: TMY was released in 1978. TMY Version 2 (TMY2) is based on the 1961–1990 NSRDB and was available in 1994. TMY Version 3 (TMY3) is based on input data for 1976–2005 from the 1961–1990 NSRDB, Version 1.1 and the 1991–2005 NSRDB update. TMY3 was available in 2008.

1961–1990 National Solar Radiation Database

NREL completed the 1961–1990 NSRDB in 1992 (NREL 1992). The database consists of serially complete hourly modeled (93%) and measured (7%) solar radiation data for 239 locations in the United States. Data records include associated meteorological measurements such as temperature, humidity, cloud cover, and visibility. Measured solar radiation data are included in the datasets when available for 52 NSRDB primary stations, but among those, no station has more than a few years of measured data. All remaining GHI solar data were modeled using a METSTAT solar radiation model. The METSTAT model was designed to accept hourly cloud information from the then readily available data from trained NWS observers. DNI measurements were available from primary stations; otherwise, these data were modeled from available meteorological data.

The NSRDB contains statistical summaries computed from the hourly data for the entire period of record for all stations. For the solar radiation data, these statistics include the average and standard deviations of the daily total solar energy (DNI, DHI, and GHI) for each station-yearmonth and each station-year. The 30-year averages and the standard deviations of monthly and annual means from 1961 through 1990 are also provided. For the meteorological elements, only monthly, annual, and 30-year averages were computed.

The hourly statistical products include monthly, annual, and 30-year averages and standard deviations for each hour of the day for GHI, DNI, and DHI. The averages can be used to prepare average diurnal profiles of hourly solar energy. The hourly values have also been binned in 24, 50-Wh/m^2 bins from 0 to 1200 Wh/m^2. The mean number of hourly values falling into each bin has been determined for each station-month for the 30-year period of record from 1961 through 1990. These statistics can be used to plot histograms and determine cumulative frequency distributions.

A solar radiation persistence product was created for each station-month by calculating the number of times the daily total solar radiation energy persisted above or below set thresholds for periods from 1 to 15 days. These calculations were performed for the entire 30-year period from 1961 to 1990.

Period of record: 1961–1990.

Temporal resolution: Hourly.

Spatial coverage: United States, Guam, and Puerto Rico (Figure 5-2).

Spatial resolution: 239 stations (56 stations have some measurements).

Data elements and sources: Hourly GHI, DNI, DHI, ETR, direct normal ETR, total sky cover, opaque sky cover, ceiling height, dry-bulb temperature, dew point temperature, relative humidity, atmospheric pressure, horizontal visibility, wind speed, wind direction, present weather, aerosol optical depth, total precipitable water, snow depth, number of days since last snowfall. About 93% of the irradiance data were modeled from cloud observations. Measured DNI are available from primary stations.

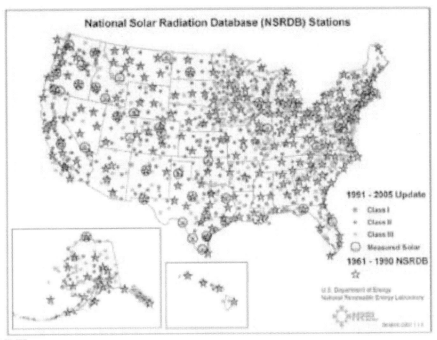

Credit: NREL.

Figure 5-2. Original 239 stations in the 1961–1990 NSRDB released in 1992 and the 1,454 stations in the 1991–2005 NSRDB released in 2007.

Data quality control and assessment: An automated data processing method was developed to apply quality flags to each hourly solar radiation and meteorological element. These flags provide information on the source and uncertainty of a data element, allowing the user to evaluate its usefulness. Because of the difficulties frequently encountered when measuring solar radiation and the resultant unknown quality of some solar radiation data, a major effort was undertaken to develop procedures and software for performing post-measurement quality assessment of these data. Such assessments were needed to ensure that the data selected for model development and other applications were of the highest quality available. The assessments also were needed to calculate the uncertainty of measured solar radiation data.

A quality assessment software package (SERI QC) was developed to address these needs (NREL 1993). SERI QC is based on the establishment of boundaries or limits within which acceptable data are expected to lie. This is similar to previous quality assessment procedures that used extraterrestrial values for the upper limit and zero for the lower limit within which solar radiation data were expected.

SERI QC increased the sophistication of this approach by establishing much more restrictive boundaries specific to each station-month. Measured data from single-black thermopile radiometers were not corrected for thermal offsets that were discovered much later.

Estimated uncertainties: Statistics on the quality of the solar radiation data were determined by calculating the percentage of the hourly values to which each source and uncertainty flag was assigned. These percentages were calculated for each station-year and for the 30-year period of record and are available as a separate product.

Availability: NCDC, NESDIS, NOAA, US Department of Commerce Renewable Energy Data Sources at www.ncdc.noaa.gov/oa/reds/index.html.

Solar data only and documentation are maintained by the NREL Renewable Resource Data Center (RRDC) at http://rredc.nrel.gov/solar/ old_data/nsrdb/1961-1990.

Updates: Released in 1992; updated in 2007 (see 1991–2005 NSRDB, page 80).

Typical Meteorological Year Version 2

TMY provides a single year of hourly data for solar radiation and other meteorological elements that permit performance comparisons of system types and configurations for one or more locations.

A TMY is not necessarily a good indicator of conditions over the next year, or even the next 5 years. Rather, it represents conditions judged to be typical over a long period of time, such as 30 years. Because they represent typical rather than extreme conditions, they are not suited for designing systems and their components to meet the worst-case conditions occurring at a location.

TMY2 was developed from the 1961–1990 NSRDB. Succeeding the older 1952–1975 SOLMET/ ERSATZ database, the NSRDB accounted for any 1975–1990 climate changes and provided more accurate values of solar radiation for several reasons:

- Better model for estimating values (more than 90% of the solar radiation data in both databases are modeled)
- More measured data, some of which are DNI

- Improved instrument calibration methods
- Rigorous procedures for assessing data quality.

A comparison of the older and newer databases provided an incentive for developing the TMY2s. On an annual basis, 40% of the NSRDB and SOLMET/ERSATZ stations were in disagreement for values of GHI by more than 5%; some stations showed disagreement of up to 18% (Marion and Myers 1992). For DNI, 60% of the NSRDB and SOLMET/ERSATZ stations were in disagreement by more than 5%; some showed disagreement of up to 33%. Disagreement between the two databases is even greater when compared on a monthly basis.

An analysis of cloud cover data indicated little or no change for the two periods; consequently, most of the disagreement for NSRDB and SOLMET/ERSATZ data is attributed to differences in reconstructing the instrument calibrations and differences in the solar radiation models (NSRDB Vol. 2 1995). Because of differences in the databases from which they were derived, the old TMYs and the new TMY2s will differ. For some stations the differences may be minor, but others will be significant.

For the TMY2 and the more recent TMY3 data (see Solar Radiation Research Laboratory section, page 71), selection of the months in the typical year included a weighting index for DNI radiation (see Table 5-1). This improves the agreement between annual DNI for the TMY and the 30-year annual average by about a factor of 2 (based on 20 geographically representative NSRDB stations) as follows. When only GHI is used for the solar index, the TMY annual direct radiation values for the 20 stations were within 4% (95% confidence level) of the 30-year annual average. Using both GHI and DNI indices reduced the differences to 2%, with no adverse effect on GHI comparisons.

Because they represent typical rather than extreme conditions, TMYs are not suited for designing systems and their components to meet the worst-case conditions at a location.

Period of record: One year representative of the 1961–1990 NSRDB data period.

Temporal resolution: Hourly.

Spatial coverage: United States and territories (Figure 5-1).

Spatial resolution: 239 stations representing the 1961–1990 NSRDB.

Data elements and sources: Hourly GHI, DNI, DHI, ETR, direct normal ETR, total sky cover, opaque sky cover, ceiling height, dry-bulb temperature, dew point temperature, relative humidity, atmospheric pressure, horizontal visibility, wind speed, wind direction, present weather, aerosol optical depth, total precipitable water, snow depth, number of days since last snowfall. About 93% of the irradiance data were modeled from surface observations of clouds. Measured DNI is available from primary stations. The format of the TMY2 data files is different from the format used for the NSRDB and the original TMY data files.

Data quality control and assessment: The data are serially complete; each hourly record in the file contains values for solar radiation, illuminance, and meteorological elements. A two-character source and uncertainty flag is attached to each data value to indicate whether the data value was measured, modeled, or missing, and to provide an estimate of the uncertainty of the data value. Measured data from single-black thermopile radiometers were not corrected for thermal offsets that were discovered much later.

Estimated uncertainties: The TMY2 data were compared with 30-year NSRDB datasets to show differences in mean values between TMY2 data and long-term data for the same stations. Comparisons were made on a monthly and an annual basis for GHI, DNI, and south-facing latitude tilt radiation; and for heating and cooling degree-days. These comparisons give general insight into how well, with respect to long-term conditions, the TMY2s portray the mean solar resource and the dry-bulb temperature environment for simulations of solar energy conversion systems and building systems. On an annual basis, the TMY2s compare closely to the 30-year datasets. The monthly comparisons are less favorable than the annual comparisons (Table 5-2).

Table 5-2. Comparisons of TMY2 Data With 30 Years of NSRDB Data

Data Element	Confidence Interval (kWh/m2 per day)	
	Monthly	Annual
GHI	± 0.20	± 0.06
DNI	± 0.50	± 0.16
Global on tilted surface (tilt angle = site latitude)	± 0.29	± 0.09

Availability: NREL RRDC at http://rredc.nrel.gov/solar/old_data/nsrdb/ 1961-1990/tmy2/.

Updates: TMY2 was released in 1994. TMY3 is based on input data for 1976–2005 from the 1961–1990 NSRDB, Version 1.1 and the 1991–2005 NSRDB update. TMY3 was available in 2008 (see page 82).

World Meteorological Organization World Radiation Data Center

Established in 1962, the WRDC is one of the recognized World Data Centers sponsored by the WMO. Located at the Main Geophysical Observatory in St. Petersburg (formerly Leningrad), Russian Federation, the WRDC has collected, archived, and published solar radiation data from observing stations from around the world in accordance with Resolution 31 of WMO Executive Committee XVIII, which ensures the availability of these data for research by the international scientific community. Daily total GHI measurements comprise most of the data from the more than 1000 sites that have contributed to the archive. Some diffuse, sunshine duration, and radiation balance observations are also submitted. Data are submitted mainly by National Meteorological Services of contributing countries. Some recent hourly measurements are present for a few measurement stations. Dense coverage is available for the western European continent, whereas the South American continent has large unrepresented areas.

Period of record: 1964–present.

Temporal resolution: Daily totals with some hourly measurements at a few sites.

Spatial coverage: Global (Figure 5-3).

Spatial resolution: 1000+ measurement stations.

Data elements and sources: Primarily daily total GHI, radiation balance, and sunshine duration, but some DHI and DNI. Some hourly measurements are available from a few sites.

Data quality control and assessment: In an effort to ameliorate the differing practices among submitting countries, the WRDC has a long-term practice of processing data arrays from many stations. However, the processing of data, and especially quality control, is carried out without knowledge of in-situ weather conditions.

Estimated uncertainties: No information.

Availability: http://wrdc-mgo.nrel.gov and http://wrdc.mgo.rssi.ru.

For more detailed information, contact: Voeikov Main Geophysical Observatory World Radiation Data Centre

7, Karbyshev Str.

194021, St. Petersburg, Russian Federation tel.: (812) 297-43-90

fax: (812) 297-86-61

Please direct any comments or suggestions regarding the Web site to

Dr. Anatoly V. Tsvetkov, Head of WRDC

tel: (812) 295-04-45

e-mail: wrdc@main.mgo.rssi.ru

e-mail: tsvetkov@main.mgo.rssi.ru

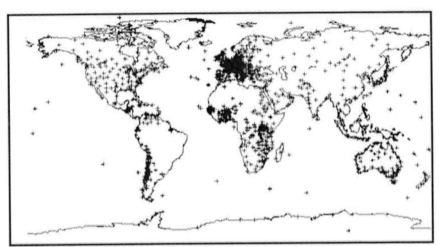

Credit: NREL.

Figure 5-3. WRDC measurement stations.

Western Energy Supply and Transmission Associates Solar Monitoring Network

In the mid-1970s, Southern California Edison submitted a proposal to Western Energy Supply and Transmission Associates to expand the solar monitoring effort outside the Southern California Edison service territory in an effort to establish an accurate solar resource database. The resulting Western Energy Supply and

Transmission Solar Monitoring Network eventually included 52 stations in 6 western states (Arizona, California, Colorado, Nevada, New Mexico, and Wyoming). The network operated for 5 years during 1976–1980 collecting 15-minute GHI, and solar DNI, as well as dry-bulb temperatures. Not all stations were in operation all 5 years, nor did all collect all data parameters. Thirteen stations reported data in the first West Associates Network publication in 1976.

All told, during the approximately 41/2 years of network operation, 52 stations gathered data on GHI and ambient temperature. Twenty-six also reported DNI measurements.

Period of record: 1976–1980.

Temporal resolution: 15 min.

Spatial coverage: Arizona, California, Colorado, Nevada, New Mexico, and Wyoming.

Spatial resolution: 52 measurement stations (Figure 5-4).

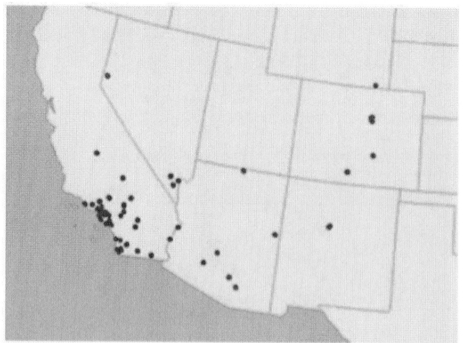

Credit: NREL.

Figure 5-4. Western Energy Supply and Transmission Associates Solar Monitoring Network of 52 measurement stations (1976–1980).

Data elements and sources: GHI, DNI, and dry-bulb temperature measured with pyranometers (Eppley Black and White, Eppley PSP, and the Spectrolab Spectrosun SR75) and pyrheliometers (Eppley NIP) in automatic solar trackers. DNI was measured at 26 of the 52 stations.

Data quality control and assessment: Southern California Edison instituted a rigorous program of radiometer maintenance and calibration for the Western Energy Supply and

Transmission Associates Solar Monitoring Network. Procedures included maintenance to be performed once per week at stations that monitored GHI and dry-bulb temperature. The pyranometer dome was cleaned and the electronics package checked for correct operation. At stations that also monitored DNI, additional procedures called for maintenance to be performed three times per week. During this maintenance, the pyrheliometer was cleaned and the semiautomatic solar tracker was adjusted for changes in declination and azimuth. All network radiometers were calibrated twice per year to the WRR. Measured data from single-black thermopile radiometers were not corrected for thermal offsets that were discovered much later.

Estimated uncertainties: Accounting for the frequency of maintenance and radiometer calibrations, the daily total GHI and DNI are likely accurate to ± 5% and ± 8%. (DNI uncertainty estimate accounts for semiautomatic operation of the solar tracker requiring manual adjustment for changing solar declination.)

Availability: Data and documentation are maintained by the NREL RRDC at http://rredc.nrel. gov/solar/pubs/wa/wajndex.html.

Updates: Released in 1981.

Pacific Northwest Solar Radiation Data Network

The University of Oregon's Pacific Northwest Solar Data Network has the longest continuous record of measured DNI in the United States. Beginning in 1977 with an 11-station network, the goal has remained to provide high-quality scientific data for solar energy resource evaluation and long-term climate studies. The work is made possible by the Bonneville Power Administration, Energy Trust of Oregon, Eugene Water and Electric Board, Emerald People's Utility District, NREL, Northwest Power and Conservation Council, and Oregon BEST. Information about the monitoring stations, solar data, software tools, and educational material is available from the University of Oregon's Solar Radiation Monitoring Laboratory at http://solardat.uoregon. edu/index.html.

Period of record: 1977–present.

Temporal resolution: 5 min.

Spatial coverage: Idaho, Montana, Oregon, Utah, Washington, and Wyoming. Spatial resolution: 39 measurement stations (Figure 5-5).

Data elements and sources: GHI, DNI, DHI, global irradiance on tilted surfaces (various), spectral irradiance (various), and surface meteorological data (temperature, relative humidity, dew-point temperature, barometric pressure, precipitation, cloud cover, snow depth, etc.).

Data quality control and assessment: A two-digit data quality control flag is assigned to each data value to identify the type of data (observed, corrected, interpolated, computed, missing or rejected). Radiometers are calibrated annually with periodic on-site checks with traveling references.

Estimated uncertainties: Based on the instrument selections, installation, O&M practices, the estimated uncertainties for corrected daily total irradiances are: DNI ± 2%, GHI ± 5%, and DHI ± 15% + 5 W/m^2.

Availability: The University of Oregon's Solar Radiation Monitoring Laboratory operates and maintains the measurement network and provides the data online at http://solardat.uoregon. edu/SolarData.html.

Updates: Continuous.

NOAA Network

Coincident with the rehabilitation of historical data from NWS in the 1970s, DOE and NOAA cofunded the reconstruction of the NWS solar measurement network. The new network of 39 stations was instrumented with new Eppley Laboratory, Inc., model PSP pyranometers and model NIP pyrheliometers for measuring GHI and DNI. Seven stations had shaded PSP pyranometers for measuring DHI. New data acquisition systems were installed to digitally sample the radiometer signals at 1-min intervals and provide strip chart records as a backup medium. Radiometers were calibrated annually at NOAA's solar research facility in Boulder, Colorado, using references traceable to the WRR. Network data were processed and disseminated on 9 track magnetic tape reels by NCDC. These data represent the most complete set of solar resource measurements from the largest federally operated measurement network ever fielded in the United States.

Period of record: 1977–1980.

Temporal resolution: Hourly.

Spatial coverage: United States and territories (Figure 5-6).

Spatial resolution: 39 NWS measurement stations.

Figure 5-5. Pacific Northwest Solar Radiation Data Network operated by the University of Oregon.

Data elements and sources: GHI, DNI, DHI (7 stations), air temperature, relative humidity, cloud amounts, barometric pressure, wind speed and direction at 10 meters, precipitation, snow cover, weather codes measured according to standard NWS operating procedures. Radiation measurements digitally recorded from 1-min instantaneous samples with redundant strip chart recordings.

Data quality control and assessment: Data processing performed at the NCDC using standard procedures that included visual inspection of strip chart records. Radiometers were calibrated annually in Boulder, Colorado, with reference radiometers traceable to the WRR. Monthly data reports and digital data files were produced by the NCDC. Measured data from single-black thermopile radiometers were not corrected for thermal offsets that were discovered much later.

Estimated uncertainties: Based on the instrument selections, installation, and O&M practices, the estimated uncertainties for corrected daily total irradiances are: DNI ± 2%, GHI ± 5%, and DHI ± 15% + 5 W/m^2.

Availability: NCDC; National Environmental, Satellite, Data, and Information Service; NOAA; US Department of Commerce at www.ncdc. noaa.gov/.

Updates: Final release of TD-9736 occurred in 1983.

Solar Energy and Meteorological Research Training Sites

Recognizing the need to provide an educated workforce and advance the knowledge of solar radiation and meteorological measurements, DOE and the Solar Energy Research Institute (now NREL) solicited responses from US universities and colleges to participate in what became the Solar Energy and Meteorological Research Training Sites (SEMRTS) Program. Central to the multiyear effort was the requirement to produce a minimum of 12 months of solar resource data from precision instruments with measurements collected at 1-min maintains the data from four of the original six participants as part of its RRDC (data from Davis, California, and Honolulu, Hawaii, were never made available).

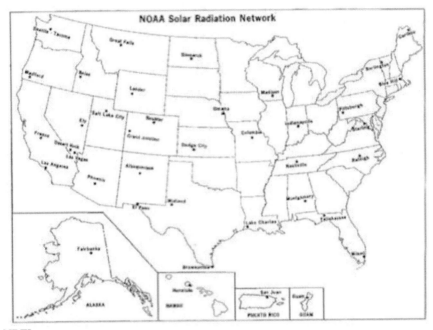

Credit: NREL.

Figure 5-6. NOAA Solar Monitoring Network of 39 stations (1977–1980).

Period of record: 1979–1983. Temporal resolution: 1-min.

Spatial coverage: Fairbanks, Alaska; Atlanta, Georgia; Albany, New York; San Antonio, Texas (see Figure 5-7).

Spatial resolution: Four measurement stations.

Data elements and sources: GHI, DNI, and DHI; global irradiance on tilted surfaces (varies), infrared irradiances, ultraviolet and other spectral irradiance (varies), and surface meteorological conditions (temperature, relative humidity, pressure, visibility, wind speed and direction at 10 meters, precipitation, etc.).

Data quality control and assessment: Research-quality data from proper instrument selection, installation, and maintenance. Data were used to develop automated quality assessment methods. Measured data from single-black thermopile radiometers were not corrected for thermal offsets that were discovered much later.

Estimated uncertainties: Based on radiometer types, installation, and O&M practices, the data uncertainties for daily irradiances were GHI ± 7%, DNI ± 3%, DHI ± 15% + 5 W/m^2.

Availability: Data and documentation are maintained by NREL's RRDC at http://rredc.nrel. gov/solar/old_data/semrts/.

Updates: Released in 1985.

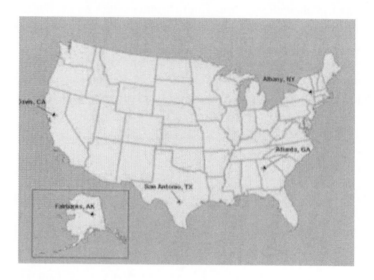

Credit: NREL.

Figure 5-7. SEMRTS provided the first 1-min measurements of multiple solar resource parameters for the United States.

DAYMET

DAYMET generates daily surfaces of temperature, precipitation, humidity, and GHI over large regions of complex terrain. The model was developed at the University of Montana, Numerical Terradynamic Simulation Group, to meet the needs for high-resolution, daily meteorological and climatological data necessary for plant growth model inputs (Thornton et al. 2000; Thornton and Running 1999). A DEM and daily observations of minimum and maximum temperatures and precipitation from ground-based meteorological stations were used to produce an 18-year daily dataset (1980–1997) as a continuous surface at 1-km resolution. A wide range of summary and point daily data over the conterminous United States is available.

Period of record: 1980–1997. Temporal resolution: Daily.

Spatial coverage: Continental United States.

Spatial resolution: 1 km.

Data elements and sources: GHI, air temperature (minimum and maximum), relative humidity, and precipitation.

Data quality control and assessment: No information. Estimated uncertainties: No information. Availability: www.daymet.org.

Solar Radiation Research Laboratory

The SRRL was established at the Solar Energy Research Institute (now NREL) in 1981 to provide continuous measurements of the solar resources, outdoor calibrations of pyranometers and pyrheliometers, and to characterize commercially available instrumentation. The SRRL is an outdoor laboratory located on South Table Mountain, a mesa providing excellent solar access throughout the year, overlooking Denver. Beginning with the basic measurements of DNI, GHI, and DHI at 5-minute intervals, the SRRL Baseline Measurement System now produces more than 130 data elements at 1-min intervals that are available from the Measurement & Instrumentation Data Center Web site (www.nrel.gov/midc/srrl_bms).

Period of record: 1981–present.

Temporal resolution: 5 min (beginning 15 July 1981), 1 min (beginning 13 January 1999).

Spatial coverage: Golden, Colorado (Figure 5-8).

Spatial resolution: Research measurement station.

Data elements and sources: GHI, DNI, DHI (from shadowband and tracking disk), global on tilted surfaces, reflected solar irradiance, ultraviolet, infrared (upwelling and downwelling), photometric and spectral radiometers, sky imagery, and surface meteorological conditions (temperature, relative humidity, barometric pressure, precipitation, snow cover, wind speed and direction at multiple levels).

Data quality control and assessment: Daily instrument maintenance (M–F) with automated data quality control based on real-time examinations of redundant instrumentation and internal consistency checks using the SERI-QC methodology (NREL 1993). Operators are notified of equipment problems by automatic e-mail messages generated by the data acquisition and processing system. Radiometers are recalibrated at least annually with reference instruments traceable to the WRR. An instrument characterization study is available (Wilcox and Myers 2008). Beginning in 2000, measured data from single-black thermopile radiometers are corrected for thermal offsets that were discovered at that time.

Estimated uncertainties: Based on the instrument selections, installation, and O&M practices, the estimated uncertainties for corrected daily total irradiances are: DNI ± 2%, GHI ± 5 %, and DHI ± 15% + 5 W/m^2 (GHI data from thermopile-based detectors under clear sky conditions can exhibit a bias of up to –2.5% if not corrected for thermal offsets).

Availability: NREL Measurement & Instrumentation Data Center at www.nrel.gov/midc/ srrl_bms.

Updates: Data are updated at least hourly.

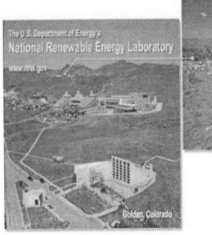

NREL/PIX 10222.

Figure 5-8. The SRRL on South Table Mountain.

European Solar Radiation Atlas

This atlas is a software package offering solar resources for Europe in a broad sense, from Ural to Azores and from Northern Africa to Polar Circle. It is a powerful tool for architects, engineers, meteorologists, agronomists, local authorities, tourism professionals, researchers, and students. It covers the period 1981 through 1990. The volume containing the CD-ROM database offers spatial (every 10 km approximately) and temporal knowledge for different time scales (from climatologically means—more than 700 stations—to hourly values—7 stations) on the solar resources: irradiation (global and its components), sunshine duration, as well as air temperatures, precipitation, water vapor pressure, and air pressure in a number of stations.

The software uses the database in either a map or a station mode at user choice. More than 50 maps provide information about the global irradiation, direct and diffuse components, and clearness index. Once a station is selected, the program looks for all the data available for this station. The software includes algorithms covering solar geometry, optical properties of the atmosphere, estimation of hourly slope irradiation under cloudless skies, estimation of solar irradiation values (from daily to hourly values, conversion from horizontal to titled surfaces), spectral irradiance, illuminance, and daily mean profiles of temperature and other statistical quantities (central moments, extremes, probability, cumulative probability, and utilization curves). Graphics can be displayed in 2 or 3 dimensions.

Period of record: 1981–1990.

Temporal resolution: Monthly and annual average daily totals (kWh/m^2/day).

Spatial coverage: Europe.

Spatial resolution: 10 km.

Data elements and sources: GHI, DNI, and DHI, sunshine duration, air temperatures, precipitation, water vapor pressure, air pressure in a number of stations.

Data quality control and assessment: No information.

Estimated uncertainties: No information.

Availability: Les Presses Mines Paris Tech.: http://www.ensmp.fr/ Presses/?livreplus=54--col3#54. Also see: www.soda-is.com/eng/index.html.

Updates: No information.

Photovoltaic Geographical Information System

PVGIS provides a map-based inventory of solar energy resource and assessment of the electricity generation from PV systems in Europe, Africa, and southwestern Asia. It is a part of the SOLAREC action that contributes to the implementation of renewable energy in the European Union as a sustainable and long-term energy supply.

As the basis for PVGIS, the Joint Research Council (JRC) European Commission has developed a solar radiation database from climatologic data homogenized for Europe and available in the European Solar Radiation Atlas, using the r.sun model and the interpolation techniques s.vol.rst and s.surf.rst. These GRASS GIS routines are described with references available from http://re.jrc.ec.europa.eu/pvgis/solres/ solresref.htm.

The model algorithm estimates beam, diffuse, and reflected components of the clear sky and real-sky global irradiance/irradiation on horizontal or inclined surfaces.

The total daily irradiation (Wh/m^2) is computed by the integration of the irradiance values (W/m^2) calculated at regular time intervals over the day. For each time-step during the day, the computation accounts for sky obstruction (shadowing) by local terrain features (hills or mountains), calculated from the DEM.

The database consists of raster maps representing 12 monthly averages and 1 annual average of daily sums of global irradiation for horizontal surfaces, as well as those inclined at angles of 15, 25, and 40 degrees. Besides these data, raster maps of clear-sky irradiation, the Linke turbidity,[6] and the ratio DHI/GHI were computed.

Period of record: 1981–1990.

Temporal resolution: Annual average (kWh/m^2).

Spatial coverage: Europe.

Spatial resolution: 1 km aggregated to 5 arc-minutes (~8 km).

Data elements and sources: GHI, DNI, DHI, and POA irradiance based on these inputs for the For the European subcontinent:

- Monthly averages of daily sums of global and diffuse irradiation, measured or calculated for 566 ground meteorological stations distributed over the region. The averages represent the period 1981–1990; the data were collected within the ESRA project.
- Linke turbidity derived from the global database (Remund et al. 2003), available also at the SoDa.
- DEM with a grid resolution 1 x 1 km; derived from the USGS SRTM data.
- CORINE land cover with grid resolution 100 m x 100 m.
- Global land cover 2000 with grid resolution 1-km x 1-km GISCO database (© EuroGeographics Association for the administrative boundaries).
- VMAP0 and ESRI data.

For the Mediterranean Basin, Africa, and southwestern Asia:

- HelioClim-1 database, consisting of daily sums of GHI calculated from Meteosat Prime images over the whole disc. The values represent the period 1985–2004, the original spatial resolution is 15- × 15-arc minute, (about 30 km × 30 km on the equator); the data were processed by the Heliosat-2 method (Rigollier et al. 2000).
- Linke turbidity derived from the global database (Remund et al. 2003), available also at the SoDa.
- DEM with original grid resolution 1 km x 1 km; derived from the USGS SRTM data.
- Global Land Cover 2000 with original grid resolution 1 km x 1 km.
- VMAP0 data.

Data quality control and assessment: A cross-validation was applied to estimate the predictive accuracy of the modeling approach that better explains the distribution of errors further from the locations with known measurements. The cross-validation error shows the maximum possible error that might occur at the given point if it was not taken into consideration in the interpolation. The average yearly mean bias error (MBE) from cross-validation is smaller: 1 Wh/m^2 (0.03%), but the range of monthly averages of MBE is higher – from –3 Wh/m^2 in January to 4 Wh/m^2 in August. The cross-validation RMSE is higher, within the interval of 97 to 299 Wh/m^2/day (4.7% to 11.2%), and the yearly average is 146 Wh/m^2 (4.5%).

Estimated uncertainties: The model accuracy of the PVGIS values in the database was evaluated against the input meteorological data used in the computation. Comparing the yearly averages of the daily GHI, the MBE is 8.9 Wh/m^2 (0.3%) and the RMSE is 118 Wh/m^2 (3.7%). The average RMSE of the PVGIS data is almost the same as for ESRA, the PVGIS approach shows better performance from October to April.

ts advantage is linking the terrain features with changes in radiation fields and considering the shadowing effects. Comparisons of GHI data from 563 measurement stations with PVGIS (version 2) and ESRA raster maps respectively indicate the RMSE of the results to the original measurements of daily global irradiation occur within an interval of 68 to 209 Wh/m^2. In relative terms, it is within the interval of 3.2% to 7.8%; the RMSE values peak in winter months.

The comparison of the ESRA interpolation approach shows that, although the overall accuracy is practically the same (the yearly average of the RSME for ESRA is 113 Wh/m^2, i.e., 3.5%), the PVGIS modeled values are slightly better in period from October to April and poorer in summer months.

Availability: European Commission, JRC, Institute for Energy, Renewable Energy Unit. http://re.jrc.ec.europa.eu/pvgis/download/download.htm.

METEONORM

METEONORM 6.1 (Edition 2009) is a comprehensive meteorological reference, incorporating a catalogue of meteorological data and calculation procedures for solar applications and system design at any desired location in the world. METEONORM addresses the needs of engineers, architects, teachers, planners, and anyone interested in solar energy and climatology by providing access to a unified set of data, models, and software tools.

Database Properties

- Climatological data from more than 8,055 weather stations (1,422 recording GHI)
- Measured parameters: monthly means of global radiation, temperature, humidity, precipitation, days with precipitation, wind speed and direction, and sunshine duration
- Time periods 1961–1990 and 1996–2005 for temperature, humidity, precipitation, and wind speed selectable
- Updated global radiation database for period 1981–2000
- Use of satellite data for areas with low density of weather stations
- Inclusion of climate change projections (Hadley CM3 model).

Models Overview

- Interpolation models to calculate mean values for any site in the world
- One-minute time resolution for radiation parameters
- Calculation of radiation for inclined surfaces with updated models
- Enhanced temperature and humidity generation for building simulation.

Software Functions

- Import of user data (including current data by Internet)
- Effects of high horizon considered in radiation calculation (high horizon calculated automatically for all mountain regions)
- Twenty-eight output formats as well as user-definable output format
- Five languages supported: English, French, German, Italian, and Spanish
- Manual in English, maps and illustrations included on CD-ROM.

Period of record: 1981–2000 (GHI database); current user data also accepted by the software.

Temporal resolution: 1-minute and hourly modeled data.

Spatial coverage: Global.

Spatial resolution: Data from 8,055 meteorological stations are interpolated to establish weather data at any specified point.

Data elements and sources: Measured: monthly means of GHI, temperature, humidity, precipitation, wind speed and direction, and bright sunshine duration. Modeled: 1-minute and hourly typical years radiation parameters (GHI, DNI, DHI, global on a tilted surface, downwelling infrared, luminance, and ultraviolet-A and -B), precipitation, and humidity parameters (dew point, relative humidity, mixing ratio, psychrometric temperature).

Data quality control and assessment: With the Version 6.1 database, solar energy systems can be consistently simulated in all parts of the world. The interpolation errors are within the variations of climate from one year to the next. Extensive testing and validation of the radiation models are documented in the "Handbook Part II: Theory" available from www.meteonorm.com / pages/en/downloads.php.

Estimated uncertainties: Interpolation of GHI – MBE = 0 W/m^2; RSME = 15 W/m^2; for yearly mean GHI – 17 W/m^2 (10%).

Availability: METEOTEST GmgH, Bern, Germany at www.meteonorm. com/pages/en/meteonorm.php.

Updates: Periodic.

NASA Surface Meteorology and Solar Energy

The Prediction of Worldwide Energy Resource (POWER) project was initiated in 2003 to improve subsequent releases of SSE, and to create new datasets applicable to other industries from new satellite observations and the accompanying results from forecast modeling. The POWER Web interface (http://power.larc.nasa.gov) currently encompasses the SSE dataset, tailored for the renewable energy industry, as well as parameters tailored for the sustainable buildings community and the bioenergy/agricultural industries. In general, the underlying data behind the parameters used by each of these industries are the same: solar radiation and meteorology, including surface and air temperatures, moisture, and winds.

The data are on a 1-degree longitude × 1-degree latitude equal-angle grid covering the entire globe (64,800 regions). The data are generated using the NASA GEOS, Version 4 (GEOS 4) Multiyear Assimilation Time Series Data. The GEOS 4 dataset has a spacing of 1.25 degrees of longitude by 1 degree of latitude. Bilinear interpolation is used to produce 1-degree × 1-degree regions.

The solar energy data are generated using the Pinker and Laszlo shortwave algorithm (Pinker and Laszlo 1992). Cloud data are taken from the ISCCP DX dataset. These data are on an equal area grid with an effective 30-km × 30-km pixel size. The output data are generated on a nested grid containing 44,016 regions. The nested grid has a resolution of 1 degree latitude globally, and longitudinal resolution ranging from 1 degree in the tropics and subtropics to 120 degrees at the poles. This in turn is regridded to a 1-degree equal-angle grid (360 longitudes × 180 latitudes). The regridding method is by replication, wherein any grid region that is larger than 1 × 1 degree is subdivided into 1 × 1 degree regions, each with the same value as the original.

SSE estimates were compared with ground site data on a global basis. Radiation parameters were compared with data from the BSRN (NASA 2008). The summary results are presented in Table 5-3.

Table 5-3. Regression Analysis of SSE Versus BSRN Monthly
Averaged Values for July 1983
Through June 2006

Parameter	Region	Bias (%)	RMS (%)
GHI	Global	−.01	10.25
	60 degrees poleward	−1.18	34.37
	60 degrees equatorward	0.29	8.71
DHI	Global	7.49	29.34
	60 degrees poleward	11.29	54.14
	60 degrees equatorward	6.86	22.78
DNI	Global	−4.06	22.73
	60 degrees poleward	−15.66	33.12
	60 degrees equatorward	2.40	20.93

See the NASA SSE Web site at http://eosweb.larc.nasa.gov/sse/. The source data were downloaded from the SSE Web site at Data Retrieval: Meteorology and Solar Energy > Global datasets as text files. The tabular data were then converted to the shapefile format.

Period of record: July 1983–June 2005.
Temporal resolution: Monthly and annual average daily totals (kWh/m^2/day).
Spatial coverage: Global.
Spatial resolution: 1 degree.
Data elements and sources: GHI, DNI, and DHI from a satellite remote sensing model. Also available: Estimates of clear sky GHI, DNI, and DHI and tilted surface irradiance, temperature, pressure, humidity, precipitation, and wind speed.
Estimated uncertainties: Based on comparisons with surface measurements available from the BSRN, the 23-year, monthly mean daily total irradiance uncertainties (Bias%/RMSE%) for mid-latitudes have been determined for GHI (0.29%/8.71%), DHI (6.86%/22.78%), and DNI (2.40%/20.93%).
Availability: NASA SSE Web site at http://eosweb.larc.nasa.gov/sse/.
Updates: Release 6.0 Dataset (January 2008).

DLR ISIS

The Deutsches Zentrum für Luft-und Raumfahrt Irradiance at the Surface derived from ISCCP cloud data (DLR-ISIS) dataset gives an overview of the available total solar irradiance worldwide based on radiative transfer model results using cloud properties and cloud amount data supplied from the ISCCP – http://isccp.giss.nasa.gov. The radiative transfer model also uses atmospheric aerosol optical thickness determined from the NASA-GISS dataset (Lohmann et al. 2006).

With more than 21 years of model estimates, the data can be used to derive stable long-term averages, evaluate the variability of irradiance from year to year, and study the effects of extreme atmospheric conditions on the irradiance at the surface; e.g., after a volcano eruption. The 3-hourly temporal resolution of ISIS enables the study of daily cycles. However, the spatial resolution of 280 km by 280 km is too coarse for site selection (see SOLEMI on page 94).

Period of record: July 1983–December 2004.

Temporal resolution: 3-hourly.

Spatial coverage: Global.

Spatial resolution: 280 km × 280 km.

Data elements and sources: DNI and GHI from radiative transfer model using cloud and aerosol inputs.

Data quality control and assessment: Comparison of monthly mean daily total DLR-ISIS DNI with data from 78 stations shows an average underestimation of 3% for monthly means. For DLR-ISIS GHI, validation with data from 89 stations indicates an overestimation of monthly means by 3%.

Estimated uncertainties: No information.

Availability: http://www.pa.op.dlr.de/ISIS.

Historically Black Colleges and Universities Solar Measurement Network

The Historically Black Colleges and Universities (HBCU) Solar Radiation Monitoring Network operated from July 1985 through December 1996. Funded by DOE, the six-station network provided 5-minute averaged measurements of global and diffuse horizontal solar irradiance.

The data were processed at NREL to improve the assessment of the solar radiation resources in the southeastern United States (Marion 1994).

Three of the stations also measured the DNI with a pyrheliometer mounted in an automatic sun tracker. Historical HBCU data available online include quality assessed 5-min data, monthly reports, and plots.

In January 1997 the HBCU sites became part of the CONFRRM solar monitoring network.

Period of record: 1985–1996.

Temporal resolution: 5 min.

Spatial coverage: Southeastern United States (Daytona Beach, Florida; Savannah, Georgia; Itta Bena, Mississippi; Elizabeth City, North Carolina; Orangeburg, South Carolina; Bluefield, West Virginia).

Spatial resolution: Six measurement stations (Figure 5-9).

Credit: NREL.

Figure 5-9. HBCU Solar Monitoring Network (1985–1996).

Data elements and sources: GHI, DNI (at three stations), DHI (shadowband) from measurements by the Eppley Laboratory, Inc. Model PSP pyranometers and Model NIP pyrheliometers mounted in automatic solar trackers (LI-COR Model 2020). Radiometers were maintained daily and calibrated annually at NREL using the broadband outdoor radiometer calibration process (Myers et al. 2002) with reference standards traceable to the WRR.

Data quality control and assessment: The station operators inspected the instrumentation daily to ensure the radiometers were clean and properly aligned. Data were processed at NREL using SERI-QC software to assign each data value a two-digit quality flag. Measured data from single-black thermopile radiometers were not corrected for thermal offsets that were discovered much later.

Estimated uncertainties: Based on the instrument selections, installation, and O&M practices, the estimated uncertainties for corrected daily total irradiances are: measured DNI ± 2%, computed DNI from measured GHI and DHI ± 8%, GHI ± 5%, and DHI ± 15% + 5 W/m^2.

Availability: NREL RRDC, http://rredc.nrel.gov/solar/old_data/hbcu/ (includes quality assessed monthly data files, monthly summary reports, and monthly irradiance plots).

Updates: Final data released in 1997. Measurements from the Elizabeth City State University station continue to be available from the NREL Measurement & Instrumentation Data Center, www.nrel.gov/midc/ecsu/.

Solar and Wind Energy Resource Assessment

The Solar and Wind Energy Resource Assessment (SWERA) Programme provides easy access to high-quality renewable energy resource information and data to users around the world. Its goal is to help facilitate renewable energy policy and investment by making high-quality information freely available to key user groups. SWERA products include geographic information systems and time series data, along with links to energy optimization tools needed to apply these data.

To view additional information about the available resources or tools, select one of the links in the Resource Information or Analysis Tools section (http://swera.unep.net/index. php?id=7). These products are being offered through a team of international experts and their in-country partners.

Period of record: moderate resolution: 1985–1991 and *high resolution*: 1998–2002.

Temporal resolution: Monthly and annual average daily totals (kWh/m^2/day).

Spatial coverage: Moderate resolution: South America, Central America, Africa, South and East Asia, Caribbean, Mexico, Middle East (Israel, Palestine/Jordan, Lebanon, Syria, Iraq, Yemen, Saudi Arabia [partial], and Kuwait). High resolution: Guatemala, Belize, El Salvador, Honduras, Nicaragua, partial Mexico (Oaxaca), Cuba, Afghanistan, Pakistan, partial Mexico (Chiapas, Vera Cruz, northern Mexico to 24 degree latitude), Dominican Republic, Bhutan, India (NW), Ethiopia, Ghana, Ethiopia, Kenya, Sri Lanka, Nepal, Bangladesh, Western China, United Arab Emirates.

Spatial resolution: Moderate resolution = 40-km high resolution = 10 km.

Data elements and sources: GHI, DNI (DHI), and POA from model estimates based on surface meteorological observations and/or satellite remote sensing input data.

Data quality control and assessment: No information.

Estimated uncertainties: No information.

Availability: SWERA designed and maintained by UNEP/GRID-Sioux Falls:

- httpi/swera.unep.net/index.php?id=ghi_nrel_mod&no_cache=1&dataprovider=8&data type=4,70,79&energycategory=83&resolution=medium
- httpi/swera.unep.net/index.php?id=ghi_suny_high&no_cache=1&dataprovider=10&da tatype=4,70,79&energycategory=83&resolution=high
- httpi/swera.unep.net/index.php?id=metainfo&rowid=109&metaid=226.

Products for Brazil were developed by Brazil's National Institute of Space Research and Laboratory of Solar Energy/Federal University of Santa Catarina. More information about INPE is available at www.inpe.br/ ingles/index.php. Products developed by the Deutsches Zentrum für Luft- und Raumfahrt are available from httpi/swera.unep.net/ index. php?id= metainfo&ro wid=109&metaid=226. Maps of solar power potential in Latin America countries also available from www. temasactuales.com/ tools/ solarmaps.php.

Updates: New datasets are made available on a continuing basis.

HelioClim

HelioClim is a family of databases comprising solar irradiance and irradiation values available at ground level. HelioClim data are modeled from Meteosat imagery covering Europe, Africa, the Mediterranean Basin, the Atlantic Ocean, and part of the Indian Ocean. Three databases on the HelioClim server are presently operated by the Ecole des Mines de Paris/Armines Center for Energy and Processes. The Center Mines Paristech - Armines receives Meteosat data from Eumetsat and processes them in real-time. It produces the databases HelioClim that can be accessed through the SoDa Service.

Period of record: 1985–present.

Temporal resolution: 15 min.

Spatial coverage: Europe and Africa.

Spatial resolution: 5 km.

Data elements and sources: Hourly and daily GHI from satellite remote sensing model.

Data quality control and assessment: Web-based data quality programs compare the data against the extraterrestrial irradiation and data provided by a clear sky model for the day or hour and generate a data quality report. The report explains anomalies in the HelioClim data.

Estimated uncertainties: No information.

Availability: Ecole des Mines de Paris - Armines, Center for Energy and Processes. It is a companion to the SoDa Service. www.helioclim.org /radiation/index.html. Also see: www.soda-is.com/eng/index.html.

Updates: There are presently three databases: HC-1, HC-2, and HC-3. Work continues on the most recent database HC-3. An improved method Heliosat-4 to process Meteosat images is under preparation; it will create the database HC-4.

Solar Data Warehouse

The Solar Data Warehouse accesses climate data from more than 30 measurement networks across the United States, providing hourly and daily data from more than 3000 stations. Measurements from these networks are converted to a uniform format and combined into a consistent dataset.

Period of record: Varies from 5 to 25 years ago to the present.

Temporal resolution: Hourly and daily.

Spatial coverage: Continental United States.

Spatial resolution: 3000+ measurement stations.

Data elements and sources: GHI.

Data quality control and assessment: Most of the radiometers are medium-quality pyranometers. Spatial and temporal comparisons of data among multiple nearby stations are used to identify anomalous data. Continual (weekly) adjustments to quality control routines due to addition, relocation, and discontinuation of measurement stations.

Estimated uncertainties: Data from 13 NSRDB Class 1 measurement stations were compared with 16 Solar Data Warehouse stations separated by less than 40 km for the period 2003– 2005. The average daily error was 9.85% and the RMSE was 19.0 W/m^2.

Availability: http://solardatawarehouse.com.

1991–2005 National Solar Radiation Database

The 1991–2005 NSRDB update contains hourly solar radiation (including GHI, DNI, and GHI) and meteorological data for 1,454 stations. This update builds on the 1961–1990 NSRDB, which contains data for 239 stations (see Figure 5-3). The update includes the conventional time series for NSRDB ground stations as well as a 1/10-degree gridded dataset from SUNY-Albany that contains hourly solar records for 8 years (1998–2005) for the United States (except Alaska above 60 degrees latitude) for about 100,000 pixel locations (at a nominal 10-km × 10-km pixel size). To increase data quantity, developers relaxed the standard of serial completeness mandated by the 1961–1990 NSRDB. In the update, the stations were classified by data quality. The 221 Class I stations have a complete hourly dataset for the 1991–2005 period and were produced with the best available input data. The 637 Class II stations have a complete hourly data record, but they have a higher uncertainty because of lower quality input data (due to NWS automation of weather observations in the mid-1990s). The 596 Class III stations contain gaps in the data period but contain at least 3 years of data that may be useful for some applications.

A significant difference between the 1961–1990 and 1991–2005 NSRDBs involves data storage. In the original database, measured data were merged with modeled data such that a seamless dataset of solar radiation values was produced, i.e., the model essentially filled gaps in the measured data. The updated database includes separate fields for both modeled and measured data, which allows users the flexibility to chose modeled, or, if available, measured data for an application.

The NSRDB user manual is available at www.nrel.gov/docs/fy07osti/ 41364.pdf.

Period of record: 1991–2005.

Temporal resolution: Hourly. Spatial coverage: United States.

Spatial resolution: 1,454 locations and 10-km × 10-km grid (1998–2005) (Figure 5-3).

Data elements and sources: Computed or modeled data: ETR on surfaces horizontal and normal to the sun, GHI, DNI, and DHI. Measured or observed data: total sky cover, opaque sky cover, dry-bulb temperature, dew point temperature, relative humidity, station pressure, wind speed and direction, horizontal visibility, ceiling height, precipitable water, aerosol optical depth, surface albedo, and precipitation.

Data quality control and assessment: Each data element has been assigned flags indicating the source and estimated uncertainty. Thirty-three measurement sites were used for the model evaluation based on their instrumentation, period of record, and proximity to NWS sites (Figure 5-10).

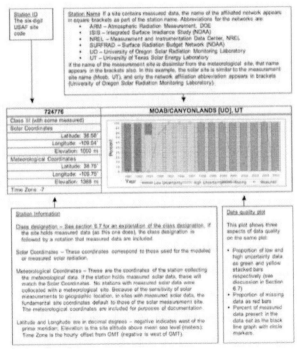

Credit: Steve Wilcox, NREL.

Figure 5-10. Example data quality summary for one of the 239 stations in the 1961–1990 NSRDB.

Estimated uncertainties: Base uncertainty estimates were made for the two models used to generate the database. The base uncertainty of the surface model, METSTAT (Maxwell 1998), was determined from results that used high-quality model input data and compared the model output with measured data. Measured data from single-black thermopile radiometers were not corrected for thermal offsets that were discovered much later. This base uncertainty was then modified for the increased uncertainty of filled meteorological or the Automated Surface Observing System data when such input data were used. Similarly, the base uncertainty of the satellite remote sensing model (Perez et al. 2002) was determined in the model evaluation and then increased for periods of snow cover or high latitude—circumstances known to degrade model performance. Hourly uncertainties for modeled data range from 8% under optimal conditions to more than 25% for less-than-optimal input data. Additional information is available from Zelenka et al. (1999).

Availability: Data are available from the NREL and NCDC as shown in Table 5-4.

Updates: Released in 2007.

Table 5-4. NSRDB Data Access Options

Dataset	Distributor	URL
NSRDB solar and filled meteorological fields	NCDC	ftp://ftp3.ncdc.noaa.gov/pub/data/nsrdb[a]
NSRDB solar and Integrated Surface Database meteorological fields (no data filling)	NCDC	http://cdo.ncdc.noaa.gov and http://gis.ncdc.noaa.gov[a]
NSRDB solar fields (no meteorological data)	NCDC	ftp://ftp.ncdc.noaa.gov/bup/data/nsrdb-solar[b]
SUNY 10-km gridded data	NCDC	ftp://ftp.ncdc.noaa.gov/bup/data/nsrdb-solar[b]
NSRDB statistical summaries	NCDC	ftp://ftp.ncdc.noaa.gov/bup/data/nsrdb-solar[b]
NSRDB research solar fields (no meteorological data)	NREL	http://rredc.nrel.gov/solar/old_data/nsrdb/1991-2005[b]

[a] No-cost access is domain-restricted to .edu, .gov, .k12, and .mil. A fee-access restriction applies to all other domains.

[b] No fee.

Typical Meteorological Year Version 3

The TMY3 data were produced using input data for 1976–2005 from the 1961–1990 NSRDB, Version 1.1 and the 1991–2005 NSRDB update. Because the 1961–1990 NSRDB has 239 sites and the 1991–2005 NSRDB update has more than 1400 sites, production of the TMY3 data was designed to maximize both the number of stations and the number of years from which to characterize the typical conditions (Wilcox and Marion 2008). At sites where data are available for 30 years, the base time period for the TMY algorithm spans 1976–2005. For the remaining sites, the base time period spans 1991–2005.

Except for a few changes to the weighting criteria, which account for the relative importance of the solar radiation and meteorological elements, the TMY2 and TMY3 datasets were created using procedures similar to those developed by Sandia National Laboratories to create the original TMYs from the 1952–1975 SOLMET/ERSATZ data (Table 5-1). Minor changes to the algorithm were made between the TMY2 and TMY3 production runs. A small change to the persistence criteria better accommodates selecting a TMY month for periods of records with fewer years. Also, computer code was removed that prioritized the selection of months with measured solar data because less than one percent of the data records in the 1991–2005 NSRDB update contain measured data. The effects of these changes between the TMY2 and TMY3 algorithm were evaluated as part of the TMY3 production process. In the context of producing datasets with similar characteristics, these effects were small (Wilcox and Meyers 2008). In practice, however, there are differences in the apparent solar resources among the data available as TMY2, TMY3, and the 8-year annual means of the NSRDB/SUNY model. Figure 5-11 illustrates the differences of annual mean daily total DNI for 8 years of NSRDB/ SUNY model estimates and the TMY3 data based on data from 1976 to 2005.

Missing meteorological data have been filled to provide serially complete records as input for modeling the TMY3 solar radiation fields. Filled meteorological data fields (which are flagged in the data file) may also be useful for certain renewable energy applications. However, the filled data are not suitable for climatological studies.

To help guide the development and process validation for the TMY3, a 1961–1990 TMY was created with the updated software using data from the TD3282 NSRDB dataset distributed by the NCDC. This dataset was created solely for algorithm evaluation purposes and no data have been released. Missing meteorological fields were filled according to methods used for the 1991–2005 NSRDB update.

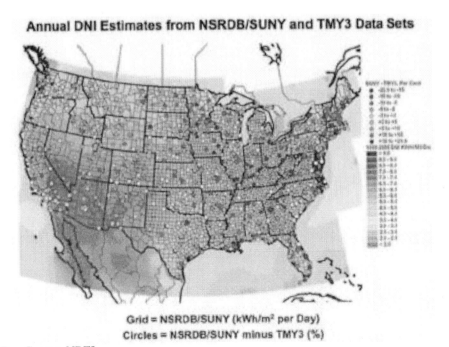

Credit: Ray George, NREL.

Figure 5-11. Annual mean daily total DNI distribution based on NSRDB/SUNY model results for 1998–2005 and the corresponding differences between the model and TMY3 (red circles indicate DNI values from TMY3 < NSRDB/SUNY and blue circles indicate TMY3 > NSRDB/SUNYA).

To evaluate the effects of drawing from differing periods of time for the input dataset, we compared each of the following year-span subgroups using the original 1961–1990 TMY dataset as a benchmark:

- 1961–1990 (30 years for evaluating software algorithm changes)
- 1976–2005 (for evaluating an updated TMY from a 30-year dataset)
- 1991–2005 (for evaluating an updated TMY from a 15-year dataset)
- 1998–2005 (for evaluating an updated TMY from an 8-year dataset).

The TMY software was run on each dataset to create TMYs for the 233 sites common to all subgroups (several sites among the 239 in the TMY2 dataset did not have sufficient data for this analysis). We calculated a mean value for each parameter by site for each subgroup TMY.

Although mean values of any data element are only a minor consideration in the TMY algorithm, they are one characteristic of climate and are a simple method of detecting large shifts or errors in the results.

The ranges of the mean differences (the largest possible mean difference at any one site) in DNI for all stations, except Alaska and Hawaii, between the original 1961 through 1990 TMY2 and TMY3 data interval subgroups) are shown in Table 5-5.

Table 5-5. Ranges of Mean Station Differences for Hourly DNI

Data Interval	Range of Station-Mean DNI Differences* (W/m^2)
1961–1990	± 15
1975–2005	± 25
1991–2005	± 40
1998–2005	± 45

* Differences computed as "new TMY3" minus original TMY2 hourly DNI values at each of the 233 stations. Larger mean differences in DNI, approaching -100 W/m2, were computed for stations in Alaska and Hawaii and require further study.

The mean biases and standard deviations for these comparison datasets are shown in Tables 5-6 and 5-7. The statistics are found by determining the mean of sun-up data for the solar parameters and the mean of all data for meteorological parameters. Biases are determined as the test TMY dataset minus the original 61-90 TMY. This information may give the user some indication of the increased uncertainty in the data (particularly noticeable in Table 5-7) with the smaller source datasets.

The years corresponding to the eruptions of volcanoes El Chichón and Mount Pinatubo (1982–1984 and 1992–1994, respectively) are not represented among the selected years. The TMY algorithm explicitly excluded these years because the effects of increased aerosols on solar radiation for those years are considered atypical.

Table 5-6. Bias Differences (Test Data Minus Original 1961–1990 TMY)

Parameter	1961–1990	1976–2005	1991–2005	1998–2005
Direct normal W/m2	–5.9	–1.1	–7.9	–1.7
Global horizontal W/m2	–4.0	–5.7	–15.2	–11.7
Dry-bulb temperature °C	0.07	0.39	0.77	0.94
Dew point temperature °C	0.08	0.33	0.81	1.08
Wind speed m/s	0.02	–0.1	–0.3	–0.4

Table 5-7. Standard Deviations of Hourly Data

Parameter	1961–1990	1976–2005	1991–2005	1998–2005
Direct normal W/m2	6.7	11.9	21.0	32.5
Global horizontal W/m2	2.8	5.3	10.0	15.1
Dry-bulb temperature °C	0.22	0.37	0.49	0.77
Dew point temperature °C	0.28	0.43	0.57	0.82
Wind speed m/s	0.12	0.20	0.30	0.34

Data quality flags were assigned to each hourly data value to indicate the source and uncertainty, except for the computed values for extraterrestrial horizontal and extraterrestrial direct normal radiation. The source flag indicates whether the data were measured, modeled, or missing, and the uncertainty flag provides an estimate of the uncertainty of the data. Usually, the source and uncertainty flags are the same as those in the NSRDB, from which the TMY files were derived. In the case of the TMY3 data files, the uncertainties are expressed as plus-minus percent rather than the coded uncertainty used in the TMY2 files. Uncertainty values apply to the data with respect to actual values at the time stamp, and not to how typical a particular hour is for a future month and day. The uncertainty values represent the plus or minus interval about the data value that contains the true value 95% of the time.

The uncertainty assigned to modeled solar radiation data includes primarily the model bias error and, to a lesser extent, the random error component, which could be several times larger for partly cloudy skies (Wilcox 2007). For partly cloudy skies, an hour can be composed of large or small amounts of sunshine, depending on whether the sun is mostly free of or occluded by the clouds. Consequently, modeled hourly values may depart significantly from true values for partly cloudy skies. The uncertainty assigned to modeled solar radiation data represents the average uncertainty for a large number of model estimates (such as for a month). When averaging large datasets, random errors tend to cancel, leaving only the bias error.

Period of record: 1991–2005.

Temporal resolution: Hourly.

Spatial coverage: United States and territories.

Spatial resolution: 1020 locations (Figure 5-12).

Data elements and sources: Computed or modeled data: ETR on surfaces horizontal and normal to the sun, GHI and illuminance, DNI and illuminance, DHI and illuminance, zenith luminance. Measured or observed data: total sky cover, opaque sky cover, dry-bulb temperature, dew-point temperature, relative humidity, station pressure, wind speed and direction, horizontal visibility, ceiling height, precipitable water, aerosol optical depth, surface albedo, and precipitation.

Data quality control and assessment: Each data element has been assigned flags indicating the source and estimated uncertainty.

Estimated uncertainties: Base uncertainty estimates were made for the two models used to generate the database. The base uncertainty of the surface model was determined from results that used high-quality model input data and compared the model output with measured hourly data. This base uncertainty was then modified for the increased uncertainty of filled meteorological or the Automated Surface Observing System data when such hourly input data were used. Similarly, the base uncertainty of the satellite remote sensing model was determined in the model evaluation and then increased for periods of snow cover or high latitude— circumstances known to degrade model performance. Hourly uncertainties for modeled data range from 8% under optimal conditions to more than 25% for less-than-optimal input data.

Availability: The NREL RRDC, http://rredc.nrel.gov/solar/old_data/ nsrdb/1991–2005/tmy3.

Updates: Released in 2008 (revision expected in 2010).

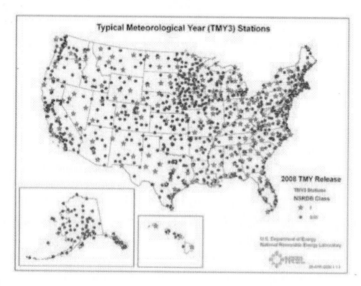

Credit: NREL.

Figure 5-12. TMY3 stations.

Management and Exploitation of Solar Resource Knowledge

The Management and Exploitation of Solar Resource (MESoR) Project started in June 2007 for the purpose of removing the uncertainty and improving the management of solar energy resource knowledge. The results of past and present large-scale initiatives in Europe will be integrated, standardized, and disseminated uniformly to facilitate their effective exploitation by stakeholders. The project will contribute to preparation of the future roadmap for research and development (R&D) and strengthening of the European position in the international field. The project includes activities in user guidance (benchmarking of models and datasets; handbook of best practices), unification of access to information (use of advanced information technologies; offering one-stop-access to several databases), connecting to other initiatives (INSPIRE of the EU, POWER of the NASA, SHC and PVPS of the IEA, GMES/GEO) and to related scientific communities (energy, meteorology, geography, medicine, ecology), and information dissemination (stakeholders involvement, future R&D, communication). MESoR is supported as a Coordination Action by the European Commission.

Period of record: 1991–2005: Europe and Africa; 1999-2006: Asia.

Temporal resolution: Hourly.

Spatial coverage: Europe, Western Asia, Africa, parts of Australia, South America.

Spatial resolution: 2.5 km.

Data elements and sources: GHI, DNI, DHI from ground measurements and modeling results.

Data quality control and assessment: Benchmarking data include ground measurements available from BSRN, International Daylight Measurement Program, Global Atmospheric Watch, and others. Time-series data analyzed for MBE, RMSE, and Kolmogrov-Smirnov Test statistics.

Estimated uncertainties: Sample MBE and RSME results for eight BSRN stations are shown in Table 5-8.

Availability: Deutsches Zentrum für Luft- und Raumfahrt www.mesor. org/.

International Daylight Measurement Program

The International Daylight Measurement Program was initiated in the framework of Technical Committee 3.07 of the CIE (Commission Internationale de l'Eclairage) by Derrick Kendrick of the University of Adelaide, Australia. The year 1991 was designated the International Daylight Measurement Year on the occasion of the CIE quadrennial conference.

Table 5-8. Sample MBE and RSME Results for Eight BSRN Stations

Time Scale	GHI				DNI			
	Mean (Wm^{-2})	MBE (%)	RMSE (%)	R2	Mean (Wm^{-2})	MBE (%)	RMSE (%)	R2
Hour	387.3	1.93%	18.79	0.97	467.8	–0.73	36.83	0.87
Day	n/a	n/a	11.08	0.99	n/a	n/a	23.58	0.95
Month	n/a	n/a	4.95	0.99	n/a	n/a	9.69	0.99
Year	n/a	n/a	3.66	0.99	n/a	n/a	4.92	0.99

Researchers from around the world took this opportunity to start measurement stations based on standard conventions developed by the program. In conjunction with the International Energy Agency Solar Heating and Cooling Program, the International Daylight Measurement Program measurements and modeling of spectral radiation continued through 1994.

Period of record: 1991–1994.

Spatial coverage: Australia, Canada, China, France, Germany, Greece, India, Indonesia, Israel, Japan, Korea, The Netherlands, New Zealand, Portugal, Russia, Singapore, Slovakia, Spain, Sweden, Switzerland, United Kingdom, and the United States.

Spatial resolution: 43 measurement stations.

Data elements and sources: GHI, DNI, DHI, zenith luminance, illuminance (including vertical surfaces), air temperature, relative humidity (or dew point), wind speed and direction, bright sunshine duration, sky imagers, and sky scanners.

Data quality control and assessment: International Daylight Measurement Program guidelines address the use of physical limits (acceptance thresholds), and comparisons of measurements with validated models that account for various sky conditions and solar position. The stand-alone program, AQCCIE, is available from http://idmp.entpe.fr/.

Estimated uncertainties: No information

Availability: Ecole Nationale des Travaux Publics de l'Etat, http://idmp.entpe.fr/.

Baseline Surface Radiation Network

In 1992, the WCRP Radiative Fluxes Working Group initiated a new BSRN to support the research projects of the WCRP and other scientific programs needing high-quality and continuous measurement of the irradiances at the Earth's surface. Some years later the BSRN incorporated into the WCRP Global Energy and Water Cycle Experiment (GEWEX) Radiation Panel.

The objective of the BSRN is to provide, using a high sampling rate, observations of the best possible quality, for short- and long-wave surface radiation fluxes. These readings are taken from a small number of selected stations, in contrasting climatic zones, together with collocated surface and upper air meteorological data and other supporting observations. The uniform and consistent measurements throughout the BSRN network are used to:

- Monitor the background (least influenced by immediate human activities that are regionally concentrated) short-wave and long-wave radiative components and their changes with the best methods currently available.
- Provide data to validate and evaluate satellite-based estimates of the surface radiative fluxes.
- Produce high-quality observational data for comparison with climate model calculations and to develop local and regionally representative radiation climatological analyses.

At present, about 40 BSRN stations are in operation. These stations measure different sets of radiation values. Some carry out only basic measurements according to the BSRN Technical Plan (Hagner et al. 1998). Other stations carry out other measurements in addition to the basic measurements. Some stations also perform synoptic observations, upper air soundings, ozone measurements, and expanded measurements. More stations are being established. Some should be in operation within the current year.

The BSRN database is based on PANGAEA (named after the PANGAEA theory). This Publishing Network for Geoscientific & Environmental Data is an Open Access library aimed at archiving, publishing, and distributing georeferenced data from Earth system research. Data can be found by using the PANGAEA search engine or www.pangaea.de/PHP/BSRN_Status.php. Data descriptions (metadata) of all datasets are visible and include the principal investigator's name and e-mail for contact. The online data access is offered to anybody who accepts the data release guidelines.

In addition to the Web-based PANGAEA access, the original station-to-archive files (without derived quantities and quality flags) can be obtained via the ftp-server: ftp.bsrn.awi.de (contact Gert.Koenig-Langlo@awi.de).

The BSRN data have become widely known for their research quality and used for model development and validation.

Period of record: 1992–present.

Temporal resolution: 1 min.

Spatial coverage: Global.

Spatial resolution: 40 measurement stations (Figure 5-13). A list of stations is available at www.pangaea.de/ddi?request=bsrn/BSRNEvent& format=html&title=BSRN+Stations.

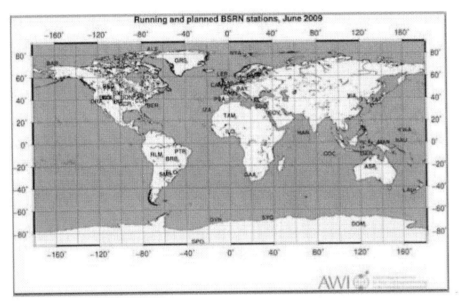

Credit: NREL.

Figure 5-13. Baseline Surface Radiation Network.

Data elements and sources: The number and type of measurements vary with station. Basic radiation measurements include GHI, DNI, DHI, downwelling infrared irradiance, upwelling infrared irradiance, and upwelling (reflected) shortwave irradiance. Measurements are from radiometers of various manufacturers. Synoptic meteorological observations, upper air measurements, and numerous expanded and supporting measurements are available. (Details are available from www.bsrn.awi.de/en/data/measure ments/.)

Data quality control and assessment: Measurement station design and O&M practices must conform to established BSRN requirements. The station scientist is responsible for measurements and data quality. For each month, the station scientist produces a station-to-archive file according to Hegner (1998). (Details are available from www.bsrn.awi.de/en/data/data_input/.)

Estimated uncertainties: The WCRP of the WMO established the standards of measurement for the BSRN. The stated accuracies are 15 W/m^2 for broadband solar measurements and 110 W/m^2 for thermal infrared measurements.

Availability: The WRMC provides Web-based and ftp data access (www.bsrn.awi. de/en/home/).

Updates: The BSRN data archive is maintained by the WRMC and updated regularly (www.bsrn.awi.de/en/home/wrmc/).

Surface Radiation Network

SURFRAD was established in 1993 through the support of NOAA's Office of Global Programs to support climate research with accurate, continuous, long-term measurements of the SRB over the United States.

Currently seven SURFRAD stations operate in climatologically diverse regions: Montana, Colorado, Illinois, Mississippi, Pennsylvania, Nevada, and South Dakota. This represents the first time that a monitoring network in the United States was designed to measure the complete SRB. The site selection process for SURFRAD was a collaborative effort between NOAA, NASA, and university scientists. Locations were chosen with the intent of best representing the diverse climates of the United States. Special consideration was given to places where the landform and vegetation are homogeneous over an extended region so the point measurements would be qualitatively representative of a large area.

Each station is equipped to measure broadband solar and infrared irradiances, including DNI, to compute the net surface fluxes. Measurements of the spectral irradiance are collected to provide the relative amounts of ultraviolet and photosynthetically active radiation. Photometric measurements at selected solar irradiance wavelengths can be used to estimate the aerosol optical depth (important for determining DNI and amounts of forward scattering—circumsolar irradiance), total column ozone, and precipitable water vapor. Surface meteorological measurements, including all-sky digital cameras for measuring cloud cover, complete the instrumentation.

Data are downloaded, quality controlled, and processed into daily files that are distributed in near real-time by anonymous FTP and the Internet. Observations from SURFRAD have been used to evaluate satellite-based estimates of surface radiation, and to validate hydrologic, weather prediction, and climate models. QA built into the design and operation of the network, and good data quality control, ensure continuous high-quality product.

The station at Boulder is an operating SURFRAD station and serves as a calibration facility for network instruments, as well as for spectroradiometers operated by several North American agencies that monitor ultraviolet radiation.

Period of record: 1993–present.

Temporal resolution: Data are reported as 3-min averages of 1-s samples before 1 January 2009, and 1-min averages on and after 1 January 2009.

Spatial coverage: United States.

Spatial resolution: Seven stations: Montana, Colorado, Illinois, Mississippi, Pennsylvania, Nevada, and South Dakota (Figure 5-14).

Data elements and sources: GHI, DNI, DHI, downwelling infrared irradiance, upwelling infrared irradiance, and upwelling (reflected) shortwave irradiance. Photosynthetically active radiation, solar net radiation, infrared net radiation, air temperature, relative humidity, wind speed and direction (10 m AGL), and all-sky images (details available from www.srrb.noaa. gov/ surfrad/).

Data quality control and assessment: The stations are regularly maintained and data are downloaded, quality controlled, and processed into daily files that are distributed in near real-time by anonymous FTP and the World Wide Web (www.srrb.noaa.gov). Radiometers are recalibrated annually and field measurements compared with standards as part of the instrument exchange procedure. Data elements are assigned an individual quality assessment flag. The redundancy of three component solar measurements (global, direct, and diffuse) provides a useful tool for quality control of the SURFRAD data by examining the internal consistency of these measurements at any time interval.

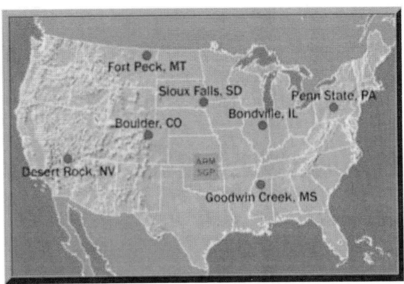

Credit: NREL.

Figure 5-14. The SURFRAD network is operated by the Global Monitoring Division, Earth Systems Research Laboratory, NOAA.

Estimated uncertainties: Based on the instrument selections, installation, and O&M practices, the estimated uncertainties for corrected daily total irradiances are measured DNI ± 2%, computed DNI from measured GHI and DHI ± 8%, computed GHI from measured DNI and DHI ± 5%, measured GHI corrected for unshaded pyranometer thermal offsets ± 5%, and DHI ± 15% + 5 W/m^2. SURFRAD has adopted the standards for measurement set by the BSRN as developed by the WCRP of the WMO. The stated accuracies are 15 W/m^2 for broadband solar measurements and 110 W/m^2 for thermal infrared measurements. To achieve these ambitious goals, the broadband solar instruments are calibrated at NREL against standards traceable to the WWC in Davos, Switzerland.

Availability: NOAA, Earth Systems Research Laboratory, Global Monitoring Division, Boulder, Colorado. ftp://ftp.srrb.noaa.gov/pub/data/ surfrad and www.srrb.noaa.gov.

SURFRAD data are also submitted to the BSRN archives, www.bsrn.awi.de/.

Updates: Continuous data updates accommodate the latest measurements.

Integrated Surface Irradiance Study

The Integrated Surface Irradiance Study (ISIS) is a continuation of earlier NOAA surface-based solar monitoring programs. ISIS addresses questions of spatial distributions and time trends at sites selected to be regionally representative and long-term continuous records of observations. Data from 1995 to 2008 are archived at the NCDC from 10 stations: Albuquerque, New Mexico; Bismarck, North Dakota; Desert Rock, Nevada; Hanford, California; Madison, Wisconsin; Oak Ridge, Tennessee; Seattle, Washington; Salt Lake City, Utah; Sterling, Virginia; and Tallahassee, Florida. Data consist of 15-min-averaged measurements with standard deviations and minimum/maximum values based on 1-s samples of GHI using The Eppley Laboratory, Inc., Model PSP pyranometer, DNI using a Model NIP pyrheliometer, diffuse irradiance using Models PSP or 8-48 pyranometers, ultraviolet-B (UV-B) irradiance using a solar light ultraviolet biometer, GHI using a silicon cell pyranometer, plus its maximum, minimum, photosynthetically active radiation, and GHI using RSRs with photodiode detectors, and SZA.

The network ceased operation in January 2006 because of funding limitations.

Period of record: 1995–2006.

Temporal resolution: 15 min.

Spatial coverage: Continental United States.

Spatial resolution: 9 stations (Figure 5-14).

Data elements and sources: GHI, DNI, DHI, and Global UVB.

Data quality control and assessment: These data are provisional.

The NOAA Solar Radiation Research Branch (SRRB) has attempted to produce the best dataset possible; however, the data quality is constrained by measurement accuracies of the instruments and the quality of the calibrations. Regardless, SRRB attempts to ensure the best quality possible through QA and quality control. The data were subjected to automatic procedures as the daily files were processed. Data were subjected only to this first-level check and a daily eye check before being released.

QA methods were in place to ensure against premature equipment failure in the field and postdeployment data problems. For example, all instruments at each station were exchanged annually for newly calibrated instruments. Calibrations were performed by world-recognized organizations with pyranometers and pyrheliometers calibrated at NREL to the WRR. Calibration factors for the UVB instrument were transferred from three standards maintained by SRRB's National UV Calibration Facility in Boulder. In general, all of the standards collected by SRRB and NREL were traceable to NIST or its equivalent.

Estimated uncertainties: Based on the instrument selections, installation, and O&M practices, the estimated uncertainties for corrected daily total irradiances are: Measured DNI ± 2%, computed DNI from measured GHI and DHI ± 8%, GHI ± 5%, and DHI ± 15% + 5 W/m^2.

Availability: NOAA Earth Systems Research Laboratory, Global Monitoring Division, Boulder, Colorado (see ftp://ftp.srrb.noaa.gov /pub/ data/isis/).

Updates: First released in 1995 and updated through 2005 with subsequent measurements.

Satel-Light

The European database of daylight and solar radiation is based on Meteosat images and a model that uses an estimation of cloud cover to produce a cloud index to produce GHI data. The DNI data are derived from GHI using the Page model (Page 1996). The Satel-Light server provides these data in map form for all of Europe.

Period of record: 1996–2000.

Temporal resolution: 30 min.

Spatial coverage: Europe.

Spatial resolution: ~5 km.

Data elements and sources: DNI, GHI, DHI, POA, horizontal illuminance, tilted illuminance, and sky luminance distribution.

Data quality control and assessment: The satellite-based model results have been compared with measurements from 25 stations. End user products generated from the satellite estimates were also compared to those generated from ground measurements at five stations (Dumortier 1998; Olseth and Skartveit1998).

Estimated uncertainties: Measurements of GHI from 25 sites in Europe were used to evaluate model performance for all sky conditions. The resulting annual mean bias deviation for GHI ranged from –1% to 3% and a RMSD ranged from 20% (south of Europe with a high frequency of sunny skies) to 40% (north of Europe with a high frequency of cloudy skies).

Availability: www.satellight.com/indexgS.htm.

Atmospheric Radiation Measurement

The ARM (Atmospheric Radiation Measurement) Climate Research Facility is a DOE national user facility for the study of global change by the national and international research community. Research at this facility includes the study of alterations in climate, land productivity, oceans or other water resources, atmospheric chemistry, and ecological systems that may alter the capacity of the Earth to sustain life. Measuring solar and infrared irradiances is an important source of data for this research. Continuous measurements of surface radiative flux are made in three geographic areas of the world. Beginning in 1997, ARM began operating 23 solar infrared stations (SIRS) in the southern Great Plains located in parts of Kansas and Oklahoma. GNDRAD and SKYRAD stations are located at three sites in the tropical western Pacific and two sites in the north slope of Alaska. Known for the research quality of these measurements, the data are used for a variety of atmospheric model validations.

Important ancillary data, such as aerosol optical depth, precipitable water vapor, cloud cover and optical depth, surface albedo, spectral irradiance, and atmospheric profiles of temperature, pressure, and water vapor are also available from the ARM facility.

Period of record: 1997–present.

Temporal resolution: 20-s instantaneous samples and 1-min averages of 2-s scans.

Spatial coverage: Southern Great Plains, north slope of Alaska, and tropical western Pacific (Figure 5-15).

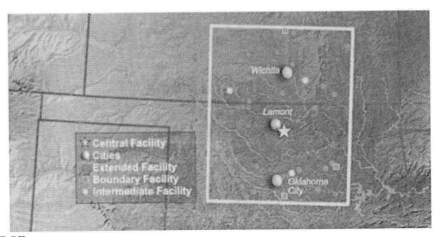

Credit: DOE.

Figure 5-15. DOE has operated the 23 ARM stations in the southern Great Plains since 1997.

Spatial resolution: 23 stations (southern Great Plains), 2 stations (north slope of Alaska), and 2 stations (tropical western Pacific).

Data elements and sources: GHI, DNI, DHI, DIR, UIR, and upwelling (reflected) shortwave irradiance (USI). Measurements from The Eppley Laboratory, Inc., Model PSP (GHI, DHI, and USI), Model 8-48 (DHI after 2000), Model NIP (DNI), and Model PIR (DIR and UIR).

Data quality control and assessment: Measurement stations are inspected daily (north slope Alaska and tropical western Pacific stations) to biweekly (southern Great Plains, except for central facility stations that are maintained daily) for preventative and corrective maintenance. Data are processed using data quality assessment methods based on SERI-QC, checked visually as time-series plots, and compared with relevant ancillary measurements and model outputs (e.g., clear sky solar irradiance model results). The pyranometer data are corrected for known thermal offsets. The ARM Data Quality Office reports on the health and status of the data at hourly and daily intervals. Each measurement is assigned a data quality flag. Radiometers are calibrated annually at the Radiometer Calibration Facility near Lamont, Oklahoma, and control and reference radiometers are compared with standards maintained by NREL. All pyranometers and pyrheliometer calibrations are traceable to the WRR.

*Estimated uncertainties***:** Based on the instrument selections, installation, and O&M practices, the estimated uncertainties for corrected **daily total irradiances are measured** DNI ± 2%, GHI ± 5%, and DHI ± 15% + 5 W/m^2.

*Availability***:** DOE, ARM Climate Research Facility, www.arm.gov. Datasets are labeled SIRS, SKYRAD, and GNDRAD. SIRS data are also submitted to the BSRN archives, www.bsrn.awi.de/.

*Updates***:** Continuous data updates accommodate latest measurements and value-added products are available.

3-TIER Solar Time-Series

The dataset over the Western Hemisphere is based on more than 12 years of half-hourly high-resolution (roughly 1-km) visible satellite imagery from GOES data (GOES East, GOES West, and GOES South) using the broadband visible wavelength channel. The satellite dataset was collected from January 1997 through March 2009) and has been processed to create more than 12 years of hourly values of GHI, DNI, and DIF at a horizontal resolution of roughly 3 km.

3-TIER processes the satellite images based on a combination of in-house research and algorithms published in peer-reviewed scientific literature. These algorithms contain parameters and coefficients that are based on empirical fits to observational data. To develop and validate their model, 3-TIER used observations from the SURFRAD, BSRN, NSRDB, Bureau of Meteorology (Australia), National Institute of Water and Atmospheric Research (New Zealand), Indian Meteorology Department, Linke Turbidity Database from Ecole des Mines de Paris, and snow data from the 24-km dataset developed by the National Snow and Ice Data Center.

The basic processing scheme follows the SUNY model (Perez et al. 2002) with a few key improvements made within the 3-TIER algorithms. These include a higher spatial and temporal resolution, an in-house developed seasonal variability correction factor, an in-house developed empirical fitting of the data to ground station measurements, and the integration of instantaneous irradiance values to determine the hourly value. Each improvement results in a lower RMSE compared to the NREL/NSRDB Update/SUNY dataset (1998–2005).

Period of record: January 1997–March 2009.

Temporal resolution: ~30-min instantaneous and 1-h averages.

Spatial coverage: Western Hemisphere and much of Asia and Oceania.

Spatial resolution: 2 arc-min (~ 3 km).

Data elements and sources: GHI, DNI, and DHI from model estimates based on satellite remote sensing input data.

Data quality control and assessment: The irradiance data are based on the model developed by Perez et al. (2002) with proprietary improvements for increased spatial and temporal resolution, seasonal variability correction factor, empirical fitting of the modeled data to ground station measurements, and integration of instantaneous irradiance values to determine the hourly value. Surface radiation measurements from ground stations operated for the BSRN, SURFRAD, and other regional networks as identified by the NSRDB were used to validate the 3-TIER model.

Estimated uncertainties: Analyses of continental United States based on 36 observing stations for the years 1998 through 2005 indicate the following RSME and Bias values in W/m^2 for each irradiance component: GHI [77/4], DNI [181/4] and DHI[63/4].

Availability: 3-TIER, 2001 Sixth Avenue, Suite 2100, Seattle, Washington 98121 USA. www.3tier.com/products/.

Updates: Released in 2008 (Western Hemisphere) with updates through November 2009 (India, Australia, and Japan).

Clean Power Research – SolarAnywere

SolarAnywhere is a Web-based service that provides hourly estimates of the solar irradiance based on satellite images and atmospheric data using algorithms developed and maintained by Dr. Richard Perez and the State University of New York at Albany (Perez et al. 2002).

Period of record: 1998–present.

Temporal resolution: Hourly.

Spatial coverage: Continental United States and Hawaii.

Spatial resolution: 10 km.

Data elements and sources: GHI, DNI, wind speed, and ambient air temperature.

Data quality control and assessment: The Perez/SUNY model was developed and has been validated using surface irradiance measurements from selected SURFRAD stations.

Estimated uncertainties: Based on comparisons with measured data from 10 stations in the United States (Perez et al. 2002), the annual average hourly RSME and MBE for GHI are 14.0% and 0.8%, respectively, and for DNI, 29.8% and 0.9%, respectively.

Availability: Clean Power Research, www.cleanpower.com/SolarAny where. Updates: Model version control information available.

Solar Energy Mining

SOLEMI is a new service set up by Deutsches Zentrum für Luft- und Raumfahrt (DLR) providing high-quality irradiance data based on Meteosat-data with a nominal spatial resolution of 2.5 km and half-hourly temporal resolution. Solar radiation maps and hourly time series will be available for almost half the Earth's surface.

Period of record: No information.

Temporal resolution: 30 min.

Spatial coverage: Europe, Africa, and Asia.

Spatial resolution: 2.5 km.

Data elements and sources: No information.

Data quality control and assessment: No information.

Estimated uncertainties: No information.

Availability: Deutsches Zentrum für Luft- und Raumfahrt: www.solemi.com/home.html.

Updates: No information.

GeoModel

The GeoModel database is derived from MSG satellite data and atmospheric parameters using in-house algorithms and computing infrastructure.

Period of record: April 2004–present.

Temporal resolution: 15 min.

Spatial coverage: Europe, Africa, and Middle East.

Spatial resolution: ~5 km down scaled to ~80 m using DEM SRTM-3.

Data elements and sources: DNI, GHI, DHI, and air temperature (2 m AGL).

Data quality control and assessment: Model data compared with measurements from 50 stations in Europe and North Africa.

Estimated uncertainties: See Table 5-9 for summary statistics based on comparisons with measurement stations in Europe and North Africa.

Availability: http://geomodel.eu/index.php.

Table 5-9. GeoModel Validation Summary

Component	Number of Stations	MBE	RMSE
GHI	50	−1.4%	20% (hourly) 10.7% (daily) 4.7% (monthly)
DNI	30	−2.5%	38.2% (hourly) 24.4% (daily) 10.7% (monthly)

6. APPLYING SOLAR RESOURCE DATA TO CONCENTRATING SOLAR POWER PROJECTS

This section provides a summary of the tools and techniques for evaluating specific CSP sites based on all available information, as well as guidance on steps to improve the on-site determination of the solar resource relevant to the type of CSP technology that is being considered.

The overall goal is to help the project developer and investor obtain the best estimates of the solar resource and weather information to address four stages of a CSP project evaluation and operation (see Figure 6.1).

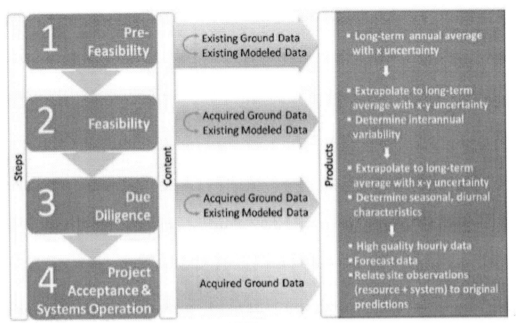

Credit: David Renné and Connie Komomua, NREL.

Figure 6-1. The four stages of a CSP project.

Ideally, a potential CSP site will have several years of high-quality on-site data, using the measurement and metrology procedures described in section 3, in formats directly relevant to the type of technology being considered. However, in the current CSP market, such data are not usually available, and project developers must rely on a number of techniques to provide the most accurate determination of site resource characteristics based on any available information sources. In the United States, these data sources might include some limited on-site measurements of varying quality, access to nearby measurements that may or may not be precisely applicable to the site because of spatial and temporal variability, access to satellite-derived DNI estimates, or access to nearby modeled ground stations, such as found in the NSRDB. In the latter case, both hourly statistics over the entire length of the NSRDB period, and TMY data representing either 15 or 30 years of solar resource data modeled from ground observations, might be available. Most ground stations in the NSRDB provide modeled estimates of the solar resource based on cloud cover and other weather observations obtained at the station, and not on actual solar measurements (see section 5).

We assume that during the site-screening and prefeasibility stages, no high-quality on-site data are available, and that annual energy estimates must be derived from historical datasets such as the Perez SUNY satellite data and the NSRDB. During feasibility assessments, including engineering analysis and due diligence, some periods of high-quality measurements are assumed to be available at the site; however, these relative short-term measurements must be extrapolated to long-term records that capture seasonal trends and the interannual variability of solar resources for the site. During the system acceptance and site operation stages, reliance should be on high-quality ground-based measurements, perhaps supplemented to some extent by ongoing satellite-derived measurements for the region.

The project developer should consult Table 6-1 when evaluating sites through the various stages of project development.

Table 6-1. Site Evaluations

Evaluation Step	Question	Solutions and Insights
Site selection	What proposed site location(s) need to be evaluated?	
	Has a single site been chosen?	If not, is the developer making a choice among two or more sites, or "prospecting" over a wider area? If choosing among multiple sites, the developer will benefit from using maps and graphical techniques to evaluate both the estimated resource and the uncertainty of those resource estimates. See examples below.
Predicted plant output over its project life	How can short-term datas-ets that provide projections over the next few years be extended to long-term (30-year) projections so cash flow projections through the life of the project can be made?	Different locations may have different interannual variability, e.g., locations more subject to a monsoon effect will have higher interannual variability in the summer months. Typically, on-site data cover at most a few years, so we will discuss procedures for extrapolating these datasets to long-term projections using longer term (up to 45 years) modeled DNI data from the NSRDB as well as how to relate the nearest NSRDB stations to site-specific data.
Temporal performance and system operating strategies	How important are seasonal and diurnal patterns for DNI?	Most CSP projects will produce electricity for the public utility grid. If time-of-day pricing has been implemented for the consumer, an understanding of the diurnal patterns and monthly mean values during those months when time-of-day pricing is in place may be more important than the estimate of the annual average. If the CSP project includes thermal storage, the need to analyze when the system will build up storage versus when the system provides power to the grid during daylight hours also emphasizes the importance of understanding the diurnal patterns. Thermal storage greatly mitigates the effect of
		system intermittency, but accurate or realistic daily, hourly, or subhourly solar radiation data may still be needed.
	Are data needed that most closely match actual concur- rent utility load data to con- duct grid-integration studies and system intermittency?	In this case, daily, hourly, or even subhourly data may be needed for a specific time period, which cannot be provided by TMY data.
	What are the temporal and spatial	Example: Measured solar data apply to

Evaluation Step	Question	Solutions and Insights
	characteristics of the data sources available to the developer, and how do these characteristics influence the evaluation of system performance? Satellite data usually represent snapshots in time due to the scanning characteristics of the on-board radiometers and are typically considered to range from nearly instantaneous to about 5-minute averages. For SUNY satellite data used in the NSRDB, individual pixel size is 1 km, and the pixel is at the center of the 10-km grid cell. Newer satellite-based method- ologies now average the 1-km pixel to 3- or 5-km grid cells.	a specific location, and are usually recorded at short time intervals (6 minutes or less), then averaged to the desired time interval (often hourly). Example: Surface modeled data (e.g., NSRDB/METSTAT) are somewhat smoothed, because they are based on cloud cover observations that can be seen from a point location, typically a circle 40 km in radius, averaged over roughly a 30-minute period.

Data Applications for Site Screening and Prefeasibility Assessment

Review of Data Sources for Direct Normal Irradiance Estimation

The following information is for locations in the United States, mostly in the Southwest. The selected data sources are those most likely to be used by a project developer for a CSP plant. These data sources are summarized in Table 6-2. Similar data sources may be available for other locations (see section 3).

The Site Screening Process

In the early stages of project development, a prefeasibility assessment of possible sites is undertaken. A desired outcome at this stage is the estimated annual energy production that could be expected from CSP plants in various proposed locations. Historical solar resource datasets are generally used in this stage, often in the form of maps, such as the NSRDB/SUNY gridded maps (Table 6-2). These datasets use a fairly consistent methodology to reliably identify the regions of highest solar potential. The maps should be used to make a preliminary assessment of solar resource, assuming a fairly large potential for error (about 15%). Thus, if a desirable level of solar resource is 7.0 $kWh/m^2/day$, sites with mapped resource values down to about 6.0 $kWh/m^2/day$ should be considered.

Examples of a "first order" prefeasibility assessment include the analysis of CSP potential in the southwestern United States conducted by NREL's Concentrating Solar Power Program (www.nrel.gov/csp/maps.html; Mehos and Perez 2005).

Using GIS screening techniques, CSP resource maps were developed that highlighted regions potentially suitable for CSP development once various land use constraints, such as protected land areas, sloping terrain, and distance from transmission were taken into consideration (Figures 6-2 and 6-3). The results of these studies show that, even with these constraints, vast areas in the southwestern United States are potentially suitable for CSP development (Mehos and Perez 2005). Maps such as these have been valuable to project developers to highlight specific regions under which various levels of site prospecting and prefeasibility analysis can take place.

Table 6-2. Data Sources for DNI Estimation

Source	Period of Record	Origin	Comments
NSRDB/SUNY Gridded monthly and annual mean DNI values	1998–2005	SUNY model (see section 4)	Monthly and annual mean values available for uniform grid (CONUS and HI) with 0.1-degree spacing. DNI values for about 2100 grid cells in the Southwest have been adjusted upward to correct for satellite model underestimates of DNI in areas of high surface albedo (snow, sand, salt flats).
NSRDB/SUNY Gridded hourly DNI Values	1998–2005	SUNY model (see section 4)	Hourly time series data available from NREL's Solar Prospector and NCDC Web sites in different formats. The mean DNI values have NOT been corrected for the surface albedo issue.
TMY2	1961–1990	1961–1990 NSRDB (see section 4)	The annual and monthly mean DNI for the selected "typical" months may NOT agree with the 30-year monthly means for the same station.
TMY3	1991–2005 1976–2005	1991–2005 NSRDB (see section 4)	Based on 24 years of data for sites near the 1961–1990 NSRDB locations and 12 years of data for remaining sites. Years with large amounts of stratospheric aerosol loading caused by volcanic eruptions are excluded from selection. The mean DNI values may NOT agree with the long-term means for the same location.
DNI measurements	1977–present	Various (see section 4)	Measurement networks in operation 1977–1980 (NOAA network) and 1993-present (SURFRAD)
Surface weather observations	1961–2005	NSRDB	Observations for 15- and 30-year datasets available from NSRDB (usually NWS stations located at airports). Most reliable source.
Modeled weather data	1998–2005	North American Regional Reanalysis	Data from model with 32-m spatial resolution and 3-hour time resolution. Advisable for user to calculate average temperature and dew point for times of interest for comparison with other (best available observations from nearest site).

With the introduction of powerful, easy to use tools such as the Solar Advisor Model (www.nrel.gov/analysis/analysis_tools_tech_sol.html) and the NREL Solar Power Prospector Web site (http://maps.nrel.gov/node/10/), many analysts now expect to use time-dependent modeling of their prospective CSP systems as part of the preliminary analysis. Considerable care must be taken to choose the correct hourly datasets for input to the CSP model. NREL recommends multiple years of hourly input data, rather than data from only one year, or even TMYs, to assess the effects of interannual variability of the solar resource on year-to-year system performance. Each hourly dataset should be evaluated, at least to determine whether the monthly mean values from hourly data match the best estimate of monthly mean DNI at the proposed site (Meyer et al. 2008). Example 1 on page 110 shows an evaluation of the monthly mean values from the 1998–2005 data, and from a TMY3 proposed as a surrogate.

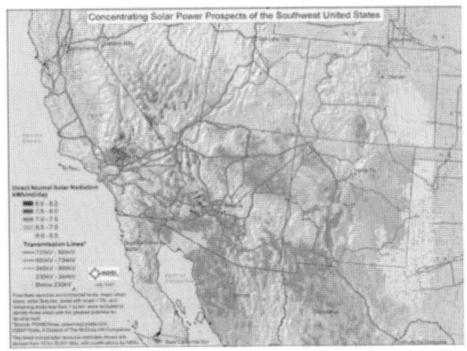

Credit: NREL.

Figure 6-2. GIS analysis for available site selection using DNI resource, land use, and 3% terrain slope.

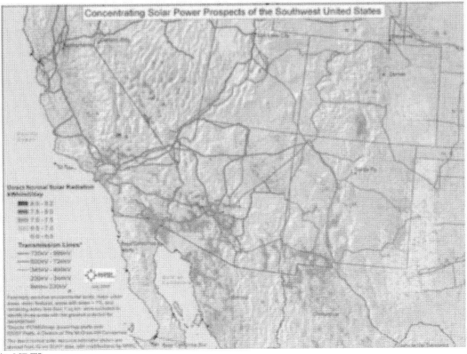

Credit: NREL.

Figure 6-3. GIS analysis for available site selection using DNI resource, land use, and 1% terrain slope.

Clean Air Prospecting

For CSP projects, a key step in site screening is to implement a concept we call *clean air prospecting*. In deserts and other areas with high DNI, most sites have low annual cloud cover. For these locations, the annual average DNI is strongly influenced by the aerosol optical depth (AOD).

Figure 6-4 shows the dependence of the annual DNI on the average AOD for the Daggett, California, area. (Similar dependencies will be found for any location in the southwestern United States.) Knowing the AOD characteristics is vital for assessing the DNI resource and the performance of CSP installations.

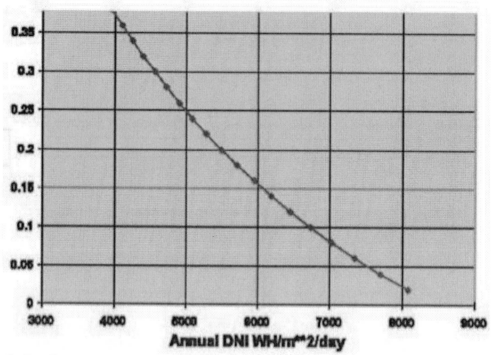

Credit: Ray George, NREL.

Figure 6-4. Annual average DNI (in Wh/m^2/day) as a function of annual average broadband AOD (y-axis). This is based on cloud conditions for the Daggett, California, area.

AOD is a measure of haze and smoke effects in DNI that are not caused by clouds. Sources of AOD include dust and particulates, air pollution, smoke from wildfires and agricultural burning, and sea salt (near coastlines). CSP facilities should, if possible, be sited at locations that are protected from sources of these aerosols. For the NSRDB/SUNY data and the 1991–2005

NSRDB update, NREL provided the average monthly AOD in the southwestern United States and northwest Mexico based on the map in Figure 6-5. For each location in the NSRDB, and the NSRDB/SUNY 10-km grid, the annual value for AOD from this map was adjusted downward based on the local elevation, using an exponential function that reduces AOD by 50% at an elevation of 2000 meters above sea level. This dependence of AOD on elevation is shown in Figure 6-6.

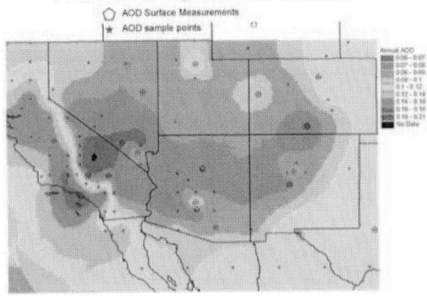

Credit: Ray George, NREL.

Figure 6-5. Annual AOD adjusted to sea level.

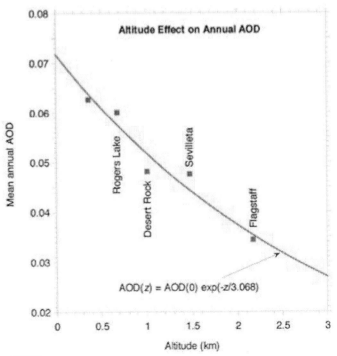

Credit: Ray George, NREL.

Figure 6-6. Dependence of annual average AOD on ground elevation. This relationship is used to create the AOD for all modeled solar data in the NSRDB 1991–2005 Update, for 15-year NSRDB and gridded 8-year NSRDB/SUNY data.

The map in Figure 6-5 assumes that, for most rural areas outside of urban areas or valleys, the AOD is very low; therefore, DNI should be higher than in the urban areas. Several major urban areas, including Salt Lake City, Las Vegas, Phoenix, and Albuquerque, have increased AOD because of air pollution and other factors, so additional artificial data points were added to define the boundaries of the region with enhanced AOD. We refer to these AOD data points as *artificial points*.

For rural areas with low AOD on the map, the DNI averages from the NSRDB/SUNY (gridded) data are more likely to be correct, if we can confirm that the area is indeed protected from sources of aerosols. The analyst should ask the following questions about the site:

- What are sources of potential aerosols?
  - Dust storms
  - Air pollution
  - Fires.
- How close is the site to urban areas?
- Is the site near power plants, mines, etc?
- Does this area have good visibility most of the time?
- Are distant hills or features visible without effects of haze?
  - No visible haze would indicate that the AOD is indeed low and, therefore, the DNI is similar to the NREL map values.
  - If the area is known to have some form of visible haze, there may (or may not) be a problem with the aerosols at the site. Further research or measurements may be necessary.
- How does the US Environmental Protection Agency classify this area?
  - The US Environmental Protection Agency or the utility companies should have projections of future growth, and of possible increases in air pollution or degradation in air quality.
  - If the area is covered by a State Implementation Plan, there should be detailed assessments of future air quality. If changes in the air quality are projected, more research may be needed to quantify the possible changes in solar resource.

If the candidate site is close to an urban area, the (estimated) AOD could also be too large. Figure 6-5 shows urban areas defined by the array of "artificial points" surrounding larger cities (Phoenix, Salt Lake City, Las Vegas, etc.). These are only approximate locations; thus, the areas near these points (on the fringes of the urban areas) are zones of higher uncertainty in AOD.

For example, in the Salt Lake City and Albuquerque areas, a site just beyond the nearby mountains may actually be protected from sources of pollution, but appear on the map as areas of higher AOD. Areas on the fringes of these metropolitan areas may well be good candidates for CSP plants, for economic and infrastructure reasons.

New measured DNI data may be necessary to resolve whether the site is sufficiently protected from urban sources of aerosols.

Future releases of NREL data products such as the NSRDB will incorporate AOD estimates at higher spatial resolution, such as gridded AOD retrievals from space-borne instruments, as well as ground-truth data to correct these satellite observations wherever necessary.

Comparison of Satellite-Derived Direct Normal Irradiation Resource Data Using Geographic Information System Tools

A study conducted by the MESoR project in Europe (Hoyer-Klick et al. 2009) provides insights into the spatial distribution of uncertainty of the estimates of DNI by relative cross-comparison of five data sources: METEONORM, Satel-Light, NASA SSE, SOLEMI, and PVGIS (Šúri et al. 2009).

The map-based comparison is performed as a type of relative benchmarking of solar databases. It does not point to the "best" database, but it gives an indication of the user's uncertainty at any location in the region from comparing data from different sources.

As the spatial products cover different periods of time, this comparison also introduces uncertainty resulting from the interannual variability of solar radiation. The maps of long-term average of DNI yearly sum are cross-compared. The map of standard deviation from the average indicates the combined effect of differences between the databases, and in this study it is used as an indicator of model uncertainty.

As shown on the maps of standard deviation (Figure 6-7), the solar industry in some regions in Europe might expect higher variability in the outputs from the analyzed databases.

These variations are found mainly in complex climatic conditions such as mountainous regions and in some coastal zones, and in areas where solar radiation modeling cannot rely on sufficient density and quality of input data. Significant differences are found in some regions with high DNI potential, such as the Balkan region, Greece, parts of the Iberian Peninsula, and Italy.

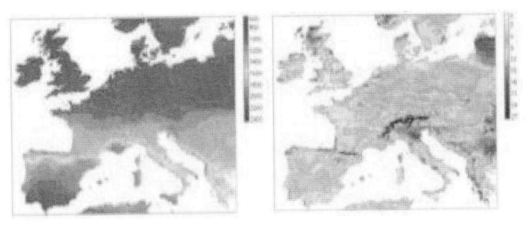

Figure 6-7. Yearly sum of DNI as calculated from five modeled datasets: METEONORM, PVGIS, NASA SSE, Satel-Light, and SOLEMI. Left – average of five databases (kWh/m2); right – relative standard deviation (%).

The MESoR map comparison studies have provided the following results:

- DNI is sensitive to the determination of cloud index that attenuates the solar irradiance reaching the surface. With the older generation satellites (METEOSAT First Generation), effects of snow, ice, and fog interfere with cloud detection. This often leads to underestimation of DNI, mostly in mountainous regions. The current satellite instrument MSG SEVIRI, in orbit since 2004, provides a high-quality calibrated signal with stable and known properties over continents, and with high information potential of 11 multispectral channels. This shows promising improvements in cloud detection.

- DNI is more sensitive than GHI to atmospheric parameters. The quality and spatial detail of satellite-derived databases are determined by input data used in the models, mainly parameters describing the optical state of the atmosphere, such as Linke atmospheric turbidity, or the analytical datasets (ozone, water vapor, and aerosols). The effect of aerosols represented by AOD is, after cloudiness, the most important variable affecting DNI (Gueymard and George 2005).

- Like cloudiness, AOD is highly variable over time and space. Its measurement requires sophisticated instrumentation and complex satellite models. The numerous AOD datasets available to the solar radiation modeling community come from various sources. However, except for the AERONET measurements, they represent only climate (averaged) values for a few years, which do not address high-frequency changes.

There is an inherent difference between in-situ (ground) and satellite observations, and in the methods of processing these data.

Databases relying on the interpolation of ground observations (PVGIS Europe, and partially METEONORM) are sensitive to the quality and completeness of ground measurements (especially those from earlier time periods) and density of the measurement network.

PVGIS and METEONORM include long-term statistical averages, and some geographical regions may show higher uncertainty because of the lower concentration of measurement sites with varying data consistency.

The satellite-derived databases (NASA SSE, SOLEMI, and Satel-Light) offer time series with high time resolution (3-hourly, hourly, and 30-min data, respectively) and provide spatially continuous coverage, but the results may be affected by higher uncertainty of the cloud cover assessment when the ground is covered by snow and ice and for low sun angles. However, these regions are typically not high-value sites for DNI applications.

- Terrain effects (e.g., differences in AM, shadowing by surrounding terrain) play a role in solar radiation modeling in hilly and mountainous regions. The spatial resolution of the input data and the selected DEM have direct impacts on the accuracy of the estimates.
  A coarse resolution DEM results in a smoother spatial pattern of solar irradiance, which also affects the regional mean of the irradiation. However, a high-resolution DEM is presently being used only in METEONORM and PVGIS. Databases with coarser spatial resolution (e.g., NASA SSE) provide global estimates; however, for studies at a local level they may show higher deviations as they smooth out local climate and terrain features.

The studies conducted under the MESoR program provide only a preliminary outline of the state of the art of current knowledge of DNI in Europe.

Such a simple data comparison as provided above does not fully address the needs of the solar energy industry, so further work is needed to improve our knowledge and decrease the uncertainties.

Data Applications for Feasibility, Engineering, and Financial Assessments

Once one or more candidate sites have been selected for engineering feasibility assessment, a common problem facing CSP project developers is how to produce datasets that allow for the most reliable calculation of annual or interannual system performance when only short-term ground measurements, along with other estimated data sources, are available. In the wind energy industry, solutions to this problem are known as measure-correlate-predict (MCP) (Thøgersen et al. 2007).

MCPs are based on various statistical procedures whereby short-term on-site measurements are related to nearby long-term measurements to obtain estimates of the site's long term wind energy potential and interannual variability. The correlation is then used to predict resources for the new site.

The problem tends to be more complex for the wind industry than for the CSP industry because:

- Wind resources are generally much more variable spatially than solar resources.
- Wind characteristics can vary significantly with height above the ground, which complicates the comparison of short-term with long-term measurements if the heights of the two measurement systems are different.
- Wind resources must take speed and direction into account, which complicates the MCP statistical procedures.
- Long-term data, such as those developed from a satellite methodology for solar radiation resources, are generally lacking for wind resources that overlie a proposed site.

For these reasons it is not necessary to employ some of the more complex MCP methods available in the literature for wind energy assessments to CSP analyses. We suggest a simpler approach that should be reasonably viable. Readers interested in learning more about wind-energy related MCP methods will find a good summary of various approaches in Thøgersen et al. (2007).

The degree of accuracy required for system performance and energy yield estimates depends on the stage of project development, as follows:

- *Prefeasibility stage.* Specific sites are evaluated to determine whether they may be suitable for development and thus require more comprehensive evaluation.
- *Feasibility stage.* Sites have been selected for actual project implementation, where system design and energy performance estimates become very important. At this stage, a more comprehensive knowledge of the annual resource, as well as seasonal and diurnal characteristics, with known accuracies, is required.

  After (or concurrent with) this detailed analysis, due diligence on the chosen project site is required, which involves accurate cash flow analysis over the life of the project. In this case, accurate long-term site performance estimates are required, and the variability of the system output from year to year (caused by interannual variability of the resource, again within well-established confidence limits) is required.

Extrapolating Short-Term Measured Datasets

The basic methodology for obtaining an estimate of the annual solar resource suitable for prefeasibility analysis that can be used to make energy yield estimates is to acquire available long-term site estimates, such as satellite-derived estimates or nearby modeled station values (such as those available through the NSRDB or TMYs). These datasets and their uncertainties have already been described in previous sections and sections. When short-term, on-site estimates from new solar radiation measurements are available, they can be used to reduce the uncertainty of the modeled estimates (Gueymard and Wilcox 2009). This process becomes critical in the project feasibility and due diligence stages of project development.

Two methods by which we can combine the short- and long-term data to obtain a more accurate estimate of the long-term solar resource (such as what may be needed for project feasibility studies) are discussed here.

The *ratio method* assumes that at least two independent datasets are available: an on-site measurement dataset (presumed to be relatively short term), and a long-term climatological dataset, such as a satellite-derived database (e.g., the 8-year Perez SUNY data supplied to the NSRDB) or a nearby long-term measurement station or modeled data. The latter is found for many US locations in the NSRDB. Ideally, at least part of the two datasets should be concurrent. If there is no concurrency in the data, the ratio method can still be applied, but the uncertainty of the resulting long-term on-site data profile will likely be much higher than if concurrent data periods are available. This method is described in Gueymard and Wilcox (2009). Basically the method involves calculating the ratios of a selected averaging period of the concurrent datasets, such as hourly or monthly averages, then applying these ratios to the balance of the long-term dataset to produce a long-term estimate for the site.

There are several important considerations to applying this approach, especially if the longterm dataset involves the use of satellite-derived data for the same location as the site data. Although the ratio method removes biases between the short-term and long-term datasets, the biases may in fact vary from year to year, or from season to season. Variations in biases suggest the cross-correlation between the two concurrent measurement sources is less than 1.0, and lower cross-correlation values indicate more uncertainty associated with extrapolating short-term data to long-term means (Gueymard and Wilcox 2009). Consider these possible scenarios:

- In an ideal scenario, there is low month-to-month variability in biases between the reference data and on-site measurements. Under these circumstances, a simple correction factor based on the ratio method should be acceptable for extrapolating the short-term dataset.
- A second scenario is high random variability between the short-term on-site data and the long-term reference data source, indicating a strong random variability (and low cross-correlation) between the two data sources, meaning that an accurate extrapolation to a longer-term value at the site will have high uncertainty.
- A third scenario is a situation where there are strong seasonal trends in the data, which may require additional years of on-site data to better confirm or define the trend. This scenario would ultimately lead to long-term extrapolations with low uncertainty.

A second method is to combine two different datasets by weighting each. They could be weighted equally, or as suggested by Meyer et al. (2008), the weighting can be determined based on the inverse of the uncertainty of each dataset. By assuming that the deviations from truth follow a normal distribution and are statistically independent, the Gaussian law for error propagation can be applied. Meyer et al. (2008) then provides curves showing how the additional datasets do not need to be of the same high quality as the base dataset to add value to the combined datasets (Figure 6-8). Meyer et al. (2008) shows that by using more than two datasets, the resulting quality of the combined dataset can be even further improved. For example, where the base dataset has an uncertainty of 4%, the resulting dataset can be improved by adding two datasets with a moderate 7% quality, rather than 10% (Figure 6-9). However, if the two additional datasets have an uncertainty of 10% or more, the base dataset cannot be improved. Therefore, datasets with such high uncertainties should not be used. If the analyst uses this method, he or she should be prepared to demonstrate that the incorporated datasets are truly independent and there are no correlations (similar instrumentation and measurement protocols, common estimates for model parameters such as aerosols or clouds).

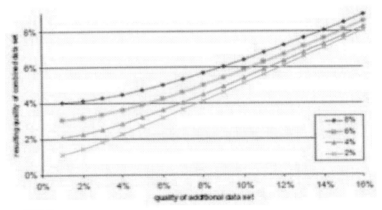

Credit: Ray George, NREL.

Figure 6-8. Resulting uncertainty when combining a base dataset of 2%, 4%, 6%, or 8% overall uncertainty with an additional dataset of varying quality (from Meyer et al. 2008).

σ_{base}=4%	σ_{ad}=1%	2%	3%	4%	5%	6%	7%	8%	9%	10%	11%	12%
σ_{ad2}=1%	1,4%	1,5%	1,7%	1,9%	2,2%	2,4%	2,7%	3,0%	3,3%	3,6%	3,9%	4,2%
2%	1,5%	1,6%	1,8%	2,0%	2,2%	2,5%	2,8%	3,1%	3,3%	3,7%	4,0%	4,3%
3%	1,7%	1,8%	1,9%	2,1%	2,4%	2,6%	2,9%	3,1%	3,4%	3,7%	4,0%	4,3%
4%	1,9%	2,0%	2,1%	2,3%	2,5%	2,7%	3,0%	3,3%	3,5%	3,8%	4,1%	4,4%
5%	2,2%	2,2%	2,4%	2,5%	2,7%	2,9%	3,2%	3,4%	3,7%	4,0%	4,2%	4,5%
6%	2,4%	2,5%	2,6%	2,7%	2,9%	3,1%	3,3%	3,6%	3,8%	4,1%	4,4%	4,7%
7%	2,7%	2,8%	2,9%	3,0%	3,2%	3,3%	3,6%	3,8%	4,0%	4,3%	4,5%	4,8%
8%	3,0%	3,1%	3,1%	3,3%	3,4%	3,6%	3,8%	4,0%	4,2%	4,5%	4,7%	5,0%
9%	3,3%	3,3%	3,4%	3,5%	3,7%	3,8%	4,0%	4,2%	4,4%	4,7%	4,9%	5,2%
10%	3,6%	3,7%	3,7%	3,8%	4,0%	4,1%	4,3%	4,5%	4,7%	4,9%	5,1%	5,4%

Credit: Ray George, NREL.

Figure 6-9. Resulting uncertainty for a case in which the base dataset has an uncertainty of 4% and is combined with two other datasets of varying uncertainties. Good combinations, which should improve the quality of the combined datasets, are highlighted in green, yellow for indifferent situations, and red for combinations that would decrease quality.

This methodology of combining the uncertainties of various input datasets to provide the resulting uncertainty of the "best guess" DNI estimate for a site is elaborated in a more recent paper by Meyer et al. (2009). In this paper, further elaboration on the optimal minimal time period for ground measurements, and exclusion of satellite data from years when abnormal AOD conditions might exist (such as years of major volcanic activity) are also discussed. Studies have also been undertaken to determine how long surface measurements at a proposed site should be taken before the true long-term mean is captured. This is important when no concurrent datasets are available and yet project finance decisions must still be made. Another way to look at the problem is to ask, How representative is a short-term (say, 1-year) measurement to the "true" climatological (nominally, 30 years) mean? In the wind industry, a rule of thumb is that it takes 10 years of on-site wind measurement to obtain a mean annual wind speed that is within ± 10% of the true long-term mean, which is generally required by financial institutions. What about the case with only 1 or 2 years of on-site measurements? These data may be all that are available to a financial institution conducting due diligence on a project.

Gueymard and Wilcox (2009) begin to address this problem through an analysis of the 8-year SUNY dataset used in the updated 1991–2005 NSRDB with coincident measured hourly data at 37 sites from various networks in the conterminous United States. However, only four stations have continuous measurements of 25 years or more, which are needed to determine the climatological average. These stations are Burns, Eugene, and Hermiston, Oregon, and NREL's SRRL station on top of South Table Mountain near Golden, Colorado.

Tomson et al. (2008) show that the mean annual global irradiation in any year is virtually independent of the previous year, which means that 11 years of on-site measurements does not represent the long-term mean. Thus, Gueymard and Wilcox (2008) examined the long-term data from the four stations mentioned to address the questions: How many years of measurements does it take to converge to the long-term mean? Does the variability in annual radiation change significantly from one site to another?

For these stations, Gueymard's and Wilcox's results show that, first, there is much lower interannual variability with GHI than with DNI. GHI is almost always within ± 5% of the true longterm mean after just one year of measurements, regardless of which year these measurements are taken. The situation is quite different for DNI, however. After only one year of measurements, the study shows that the estimate of the average DNI is no better than ± 10% to ± 20% of the true long-term mean. At two of the sites, upwards of 10 years of measurements are required to be within ± 5% of the true long-term mean, which is consistent with the findings of the wind energy industry. Financial institutions prefer to evaluate the risk of uncertainty with solar resource data in terms of exceedance probabilities (e.g., P50 or P90). P50 is the result of achieving an annual energy production based on the long-term median resource value. For this value, the probability of reaching a higher or lower energy value is 50:50. For an exceedance probability of P90, the risk that an annual energy value is not reached is 10% (90% of all values in a distribution exceed the P90 value). Another way of stating this finding is the COV for DNI is generally two to three times higher than the COV for GHI.

Figure 6-10 provides other interesting observations about multiple years of DNI measurements, particularly for Hermiston and Burns, which are in the arid eastern part of Oregon. Even in Golden, Colorado, a cloudier than average year will strongly influence negative anomalies, but these generally converge to zero more quickly than do the positive anomalies. Another factor, especially for clear sites, is that AOD becomes the primary influence on DNI variability; events such as volcanic eruptions or regional forest fires produce significant AOD anomalies that could be the main cause of the asymmetries in Figure 6-10.

These results indicate the importance of having a second, independent quality dataset, such as a satellite-derived dataset, available to reduce the uncertainty of the long-term average DNI estimates for a proposed CSP site to provide reasonable due diligence of a plants estimated performance over the life of the project.

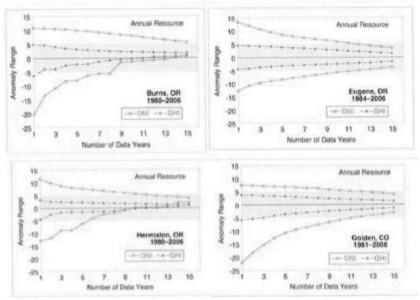

Credit: NREL.

Figure 6-10. Number of years to stabilize DNI and GHI in Burns, Oregon; Eugene, Oregon; Hermiston, Oregon; and Golden, Colorado.

Examples of Mean DNI Estimation and Hourly Data Selection Using NSRDB/SUNY, TMY3, and Measured DNI Data

Example 1 is a proposed trough plant near Harper Lake, California. Harper Lake is actually a dry lake bed with very bright salt deposits on the surface. Our goals for exploring this example are to:

- Determine the best estimate for mean DNI by month and year for a chosen site.
- Procure one or more years of time series DNI (and weather) data for use in time-dependent modeling (CSP plant models or electrical grid models).

To quickly assess the annual and monthly mean DNI, we use the Solar Prospector (http://maps.nrel.gov/node/10/) with satellite ground surface imagery (from Google Maps) as background. Figure 6-11 shows nine NSRDB/SUNY grid cells in the area near Harper Lake in the Mojave Desert. The values of average DNI can be obtained from the Solar Prospector. The upper value is the mean DNI from the hourly data, which is not corrected for specular reflection.

The lower is from the map, which has been corrected for this artifact. Next, we look at the mean DNI values, by month, for the 8 years of data from the 1998–2005 NSRDB. We do this for the desired location and a few nearby locations. If the map value and the hourly averaged values are different by more than 0.2 (kWh/m^2/day), the grid cell map was corrected. In this example, Cells B1 and B2 were corrected. If the candidate site for a CSP plant is located in cell B2, the analyst could select hourly data from another cell that has not been corrected, such as A2 or C2. This procedure will ensure that the hourly simulations (e.g., Solar Advisor Model for CSP www.nrel.gov/analysis/sam/) produce results that are more consistent with the mean value at the proposed site.

In general, cells in need of correction have bright or uneven areas, especially near the center.

Adjacent cells with a darker, more uniform background will have more reliable hourly DNI data. The goal is to select the correct time-series to match the estimate of the mean values. The Google map shows that the time series data from the selected cell should not be used, because the time-series produces different (lower) means. The SUNY team developed corrections to this artifact; in the near future, corrected maps will be available that avoid this problem.

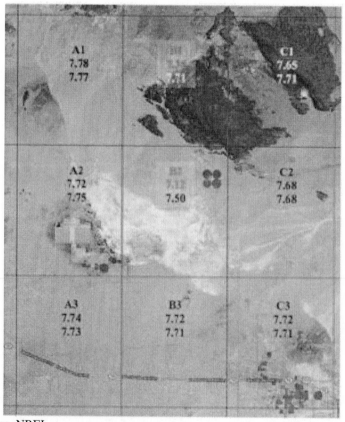

Credit: Ray George, NREL.

Figure 6-11. NSRDB/SUNY 10-km grid cells near Harper Lake, California. Upper value in text box is average from (uncorrected) hourly files. Lower value is average DNI from corrected maps. Values in red show uncorrected time series mean values, substantially lower than the corrected map values.

Although not recommended, the user could choose one of the TMY2 or TMY3 datasets to act as a surrogate for the 8 years of data. If a TMY2 or TMY3 dataset is proposed as a surrogate for this site, the dataset should be carefully evaluated for applicability of the mean values in space and time. Figure 6-12 shows the monthly DNI values for the C2 site and the nearby Daggett, California, TMY3, which is a higher quality, Class I, NSRDB site. In this case, the TMY3 may be a suitable surrogate for the site-specific SUNY data.

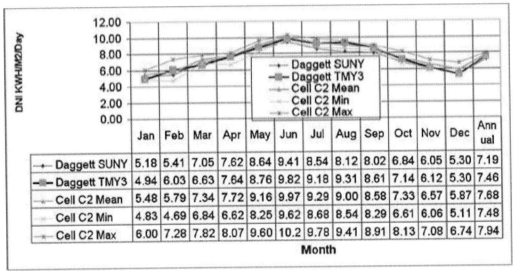

	Jan	Feb	Mar	Apr	May	Jun	Jul	Aug	Sep	Oct	Nov	Dec	Annual
Daggett SUNY	5.18	5.41	7.05	7.62	8.64	9.41	8.54	8.12	8.02	6.84	6.05	5.30	7.19
Daggett TMY3	4.94	6.03	6.63	7.64	8.76	9.82	9.18	9.31	8.61	7.14	6.12	5.30	7.46
Cell C2 Mean	5.48	5.79	7.34	7.72	9.16	9.97	9.29	9.00	8.58	7.33	6.57	5.87	7.68
Cell C2 Min	4.83	4.69	6.84	6.62	8.25	9.62	8.68	8.54	8.29	6.61	6.06	5.11	7.48
Cell C2 Max	6.00	7.28	7.82	8.07	9.60	10.2	9.78	9.41	8.91	8.13	7.08	6.74	7.94

Month

Credit: Ray George, NREL

Figure 6-12. Monthly mean DNI for Harper Lake (Cell C2) and Daggett TMY3. Minimum and maximum values for cell C2 are also shown for each month.

Example 2 is a proposed CSP site near Desert Rock, Nevada. We assume for this example that we have chosen the NSRDB/SUNY data for preliminary analysis, and have now obtained new measured data for the desired site. We show the effects on the annual DNI estimate of including measured and modeled data. Table 6-3 shows the results of using 8 years of modeled NSRDB data with:

- Two years of measured data (2004–2005)
- Year 2004 measured data only
- Year 2005 measured data only

We adjust the average DNI from the 8-year period using the bias error from our observed data, with the simple "ratio method" described above. The bias error using both years is a relatively low value of 1.04%. The bias errors from individual years are higher, and do not show a consistent pattern. The adjusted direct is the new estimate of the long-term mean DNI, and is simply the 8-year mean DNI (7.658) times (1.0 − MBE). The method of Meyer et al. (2008) described on page 107 can also be used advantageously here. If we assume the uncertainty is 3% for measured data and 10% for SUNY data, we can calculate the corrected means for all the months we have both measured and modeled data. If we adopt this value as our best guess for the actual DNI for the years 2004 and 2005, then our new bias error is (SUNY-Meyer)/Meyer, and our bias errors are smaller.

Table 6-3. Annual Mean Values of Global and Direct Radiation for Measured and Modeled Data at Desert Rock, Nevada

Measured Time Period	2004–2005 (kWh/m²/day)	2004 only (kWh/m²/day)	2005 only (kWh/m²/day)	1998–2005 (kWh/m²/day)
Model global	5.615	5.656	5.574	5.622
Model direct	7.642	7.720	7.564	7.658
Measured global	5.703	5.799	5.607	
Measured direct	7.564	7.901	7.227	
MBE global	−1.54%	−2.46%	−0.58%	
MBE direct	1.04%	−2.28%	4.67%	
Adjusted direct 8-year mean	7.579	7.833	7.300	
Meyer corrected mean DNI	7.582	7.859	7.305	
Meyer MBE direct	0.8%	−1.8%	3.6%	
Meyer adjusted 8-year mean	7.597	7.793	7.386	

The Meyer estimate is calculated using the following equation:

$$I_{est} = (I_{me}/U_{me} + I_{mo}/U_{mo})/(1/U_{me} + 1/U_{mo})$$

where

the Meyer estimate	=	I_{est}
I_{me}	=	measured value
I_{mo}	=	modeled value
U_{me}	=	measurement uncertainty (0.03)
U_{mo}	=	modeled uncertainty (0.10)

Monthly mean values of GHI and DNI are shown for the Desert Rock site (see Figure 6-13). For many months, especially during 2005, the bias errors are very small for GHI and large for DNI.

GHI and DNI bias errors are well correlated in 2004, but not in 2005. One interpretation is that the principal source of error during 2004 is the cloud estimation, and the principal source of error in 2005 is in the AOD.

A small error in global radiation along with a large overestimate of the DNI indicates that AOD at the site may have been much higher than the estimated AOD used in the satellite model. A diligent analyst might pursue an explanation for the higher than normal AOD and ask, Could higher levels of AOD be caused by dust storms or forest fires? The average monthly values shown in Figure 6-12 would be helpful in pinpointing the cause of the problem.

These show large shortfalls in the measured DNI in January and April 2005, indicating higher than normal AOD. Once the likely cause has been determined, the analyst should then assess whether that phenomenon might be more prevalent in the future, or is possibly a rare event.

The broadband AOD may be estimated from the new DNI measurements using a clear sky model such as the Bird model, with supplemental data to estimate total column water vapor.

These values can then be used to adjust the modeled DNI estimates. However, AOD is also highly variable from month to month and from year to year, so it would take several years of data to show conclusively that the mean AOD used in the satellite model needs to be adjusted at this site.

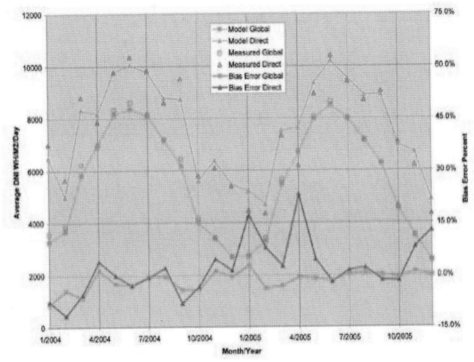

Credit: Ray George, NREL.

Figure 6-13. Desert Rock annual average, GHI and DNI, from satellite and measurements. Mean bias error is defined as (satellite − measured)/measured x 100%.

In this example (see Table 6-3), the new estimate for the 2-year dataset DNI, 7.597 kWh/m^2/day, is less than 1% different from the 8-year model estimate of 7.658. With only 1 year of measurements, the errors are larger, up to 3.6%.

Adjusting Direct Normal Irradiance Data for Concentrating Solar Power System Performance Estimates

The DNI is most often used to characterize the solar resource data for CSP plants. This solar component is the resource available to a two-axis tracking concentrator. If the CSP technology being considered is for trough plants (usually one-axis trackers), the collector-specific average radiation will be less than the average DNI.

In this case a correction factor needs to be applied to the average DNI. Figure 6-14 shows such correction factors for three locations at different latitudes.

The Solar Radiation Data Manual for Flat-Plate and Concentrating Collectors (Marion and Wilcox 1994) is based on data from the 1961–1990 NSRDB and provides statistical tables that include both DNI and single-axis N-S tracker resource data, so monthly correction factors are easily developed from these tables.

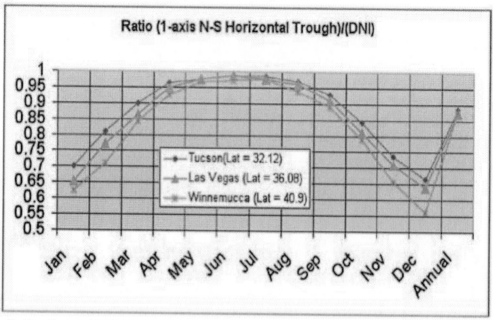

Credit: Ray George, NREL.

Figure 6-14. Ratio of monthly average solar resource available to a trough plant, divided by monthly average DNI. The ratio decreases for locations farther from the equator, especially in winter. These ratios represent correction factors that need to be applied to the DNI solar resource when considering trough plants with an N-S orientation.

Variability of the Solar Resource

The variability of the solar resource is an important consideration in the need to adequately characterize the variability with measurements and for predicting future plant performance. This analysis disregards predictable variability, such as that caused by site latitude and time of day, and concentrates on less predictable behavior caused by climate. The solar variability is closely related to the variability of climate in time and space, because atmospheric forces and constituents have a strong impact on the amount of solar radiation absorbed, reflected, or otherwise prevented from reaching the Earth's surface.

With knowledge of the likelihood of variability from year to year, users are provided some justification for selecting a particular period of time for measurements adequate to characterize the solar resource. Likewise, with knowledge of variability across distance, users can make some statement of the applicability of a measurement to a location some distance away. Knowledge of variability then becomes valuable when deciding how long to make measurements at a particular location and whether the character of the solar resource at that location can be extended to other nearby locations.

NREL has analyzed 8 years of data (1998–2005) from the NSRDB in the realms of temporal and spatial variability. The analysis summarized the values in each 10-km × 10-km cell in the SUNY satellite-derived data in the NSRDB and calculated monthly mean daily totals, annual mean daily totals, and mean daily total for the entire 8-year period.

The values were analyzed by temporal and spatial variability.

Temporal variability. For each cell, the 8 annual values were used to calculate a COV. The 8-year mean irradiance $<E_p>$ and each annual value Ei were used to derive the standard deviation of the dataset. Because there are no missing values, the standard deviation simplifies to

$$\sigma_t = [(<E_p> - Ei)2 / 8]^{1/2}.$$

The temporal COV is $C_t = \sigma_t / <E_p>$.

To understand the variability in a seasonal scope, the process was repeated on a monthly level, e.g. the 8 Januarys, Februarys, etc. The results, expressed in percent, represent the variability in the solar resource year by year at the cell's geographic location. The resulting COV for DNI for all cells plotted as a contour map of the United States is shown in Figure 6-15, providing a quick visual measure of differences in interannual variability. The temporal COV for 48 US states ranges from a low of 0.49% in south central Washington to a high of 15.8% in northwest Washington (an interesting contrast of climate within a single state).

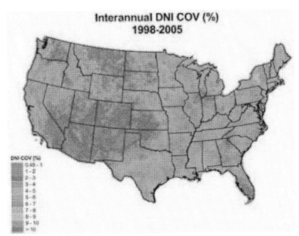

Credit: Ray George, NREL.

Figure 6-15. Interannual DNI variability (COV as percent) for 1998–2005.

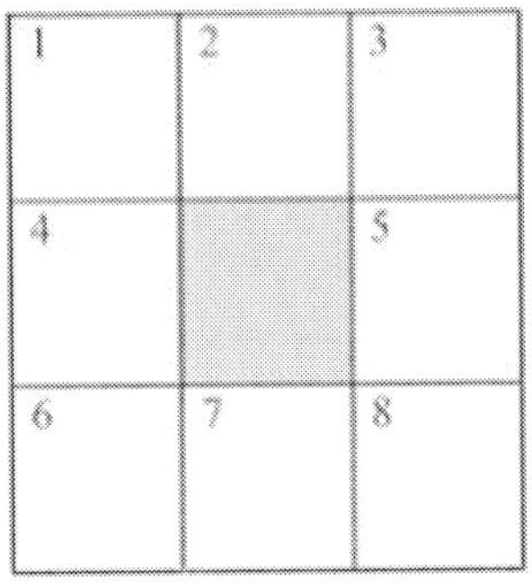

Credit: Ray George, NREL

Figure 6-16. A 3 x 3 grid layout with anchor cell in the center and eight surrounding neighbor cells.

Here the standard deviations of the surrounding cells were calculated as

$$\sigma_s = [\; \Sigma^{i=n} (E_p - E_i)^2 / n\;]_{1/2}.$$

The spatial COV is $c_s = \sigma_s / E_p$.

The same process was applied to the 8-year means on a monthly level, all Januarys, Februarys, etc.

Two matrix sizes were analyzed: a 3×3 (see Figure 6-16) and a 5×5. These represent areas of approximately 30 km × 30 km and 50 km × 50 km, respectively, and likewise roughly represent an area within 15 km and 25 km of a measurement site. The results for DNI, expressed in percents, are mapped in Figure 6-17, which provides a quick visual representation of how the solar resource varies over space. For DNI, the values range from 0.12% in central Missouri to about 11.5% along a corridor between Los Angeles and San Bernardino, California. Variability tends to be higher in coastal areas (particularly the California coast) and in mountainous areas. Greater variability is seen in the 5×5 matrix, which is to be expected because of the effects of terrain. Further, the general pattern of high and low variability remains the same between the two maps, indicating that in locations of significant variability, the magnitude is much a function of distance.

The underlying data for these maps will be available from NREL to provide users with the actual values for each 10-km × 10-km cell both in units of % COV and Wh/m^2. Users should be cautioned that the 8-year period may not be long enough to produce definitive variability values, and the uncertainty of this analysis has not been defined. NREL plans to update this dataset by drawing from a longer period of record; however, the results here are very likely accurate enough to reveal the relative variability of the solar resource throughout the United States.

Credit: Ray George, NREL.

Figure 6-17. DNI spatial coefficient of variability for 3x3 cell matrix (upper) and 5×5 cell matrix (lower) for the average DNI from 1998–2005.

Using these variability statistics, users can better understand the extent of measurements required to best characterize the solar resource for a particular application. In areas with low interannual variability, a shorter measurement period may suffice. In areas with low spatial variability, a measurement station could possibly represent the solar resource at nearby locations, negating the need for additional measurements. An analyst can use this information to better build confidence in a dataset as being sufficient for an analysis and can use these data to understand the consistency of future plant performance and how that relates to the economic viability of a particular location.

Summary of CSP Best Practices for Resource Characterization

Before making site-specific measurements (prefeasibility, feasibility stages)

- Use NSRDB screening maps and other criteria o choose candidate sites.
- Assess monthly/yearly mean DNI values from the NSRDB 8-year dataset. Compare with nearby NSRDB sites that have more years of data. Create a set of best guess target values for the monthly mean DNI.
- Assess the uncertainty of DNI means in your target values. The uncertainty is higher if the site:
- Is close to strong gradients in average DNI.
- Is close to strong gradients in AOD.
- Is subject to possible enhanced aerosols (close to urban areas, mines, power plants, etc.)
- Has bright surface albedo, or highly variable albedo.
- Adjust your expected monthly mean DNI values upward or downward, based on these parameters.
- Choose hourly datasets to match expected mean value; at the same time have diurnal and seasonal patterns close to those of the candidate site.
- If using TMY data, assess the data to see how closely the mean values match your expected patterns.

After new measurements are available (later stages in project development; project qualification phase)

- Realistically assess the quality of the new measured DNI data.
- Use ration method or Meyer method to compare measured and modeled data and create updated estimates of monthly mean DNI.
- Use a comparison of measured and modeled DNI to assess the variability of aerosols. Prepare best possible datasets, multiple year or TMY, based on all available data, for final simulation runs.

---

7. FUTURE WORK

Advancing renewable energy technologies will require improvements to our understanding of solar radiation resources. This section briefly describes the areas of R&D identified by NREL as emerging technology needs.

Forecasting Solar Radiation

Industry representatives and private sector consultants have indicated there will be an increasing need for reliable short-term and day-ahead forecasting as more CSP installations are tied to the nation's electricity grid. Day-ahead forecasting for wind energy applications is already important, because knowledge of the availability of the wind resource influences decisions on implementing power purchase contracts with outside providers to maintain system performance and meet loads. For example, independent system operators need to make system availability forecasts at 15-min increments for traditional power generating equipment; for wind system operations, day-ahead wind energy forecasts are currently viewed as the most practical at this stage of wind farm development.

Industry has also expressed the need to better understand the capability of longer term forecasts (seasonal, annual, and interannual) to assist with system planning. In particular, a better understanding of long-term solar resource trends at a site or in a region would be useful for infrastructure planning and cash flow analyses.

Currently, no operational solar resource forecasts are being implemented in the United States, although several approaches for implementing forecasting procedures have been explored based on cloud observations from satellite (Perez et al. 2007) and using all-sky cameras at the site of interest.

However, in Europe several institutions are developing reliable 1 to 3 day-ahead forecasts and some operational forecasts are being used on a limited basis.

Solar resource forecasting methodologies is a major activity under the International Energy Agency Solar Heating and Cooling Programme's Task 36: Solar Resource Knowledge Management; NREL is the operating agent for the task (see http://re.jrc.cec.ue. int/iea-shc-task36/).

This task provides an excellent opportunity to bring researchers together from around the world to share their approaches and experiences with implementing solar resource forecasts.

High-Resolution Temporal Data

Electrical generation by solar thermal electric power systems is directly proportional to the available DNI. Historical solar resource data are available for hourly time intervals. Subhourly time-series data (15-min or less) with dense spatial coverage (e.g., 5 km or less) are needed to address load-following simulations and related economic considerations. Currently available instrumentation and measurement equipment can acquire solar irradiance data as often as 1-s intervals (Wilcox and Myers 2008).

Research is underway at NREL to deploy solar resource measurement stations that will provide high-resolution data at single locations and within the collector fields.

Site-Specific Resource Data

Characterizing the spatial variability of solar irradiance over distances of 1 km or less is important for improving the siting, design, and performance monitoring of a solar energy conversion system.

The latest NSRDB, along with the 1991–2005 update, provides historical solar irradiance data for specific locations from 1961 through 2005, with a resulting spatial scale of about 100 km.

Additionally, based on satellite remote sensing model estimates, the NSRDB provides solar irradiance data for 10-km grid cells from 1998 through 2005. Methods for increasing the spatial resolution of satellite-based models for estimating solar irradiance at the surface are under development.

Data from large CSP systems that may have high-quality radiometric instrumentation need to be systematically investigated.

Effects of Climate Change on Solar Resource Assessments

How representative will the more recent solar resource data be for estimating the performance of a CSP plant over the system design life (e.g., 25 years) due to changes in atmospheric aerosol loading from natural causes or industrial pollution, changing patterns of precipitation and cloudiness, temperature extremes, and other climatic variables? Research is needed to advance the climate modeling capabilities and merge the output with advanced system performance models.

Need for Cross-Disciplinary Analysis Projects

The use of solar resource and meteorological data to address complex problems such as time-dependent utility load estimations, cloud transient effects on grid stability, and solar generation dispatching, requires close collaboration between analysts, utility planners, and the resource and meteorology communities.

Shared knowledge will advance the identification of resource data needs and the development of methods for improved resource data and information to meet those needs.

ACKNOWLEDGMENTS

This handbook is the collective effort of members of the Electricity, Resources, and Building Systems Integration Center at the National Renewable Energy Laboratory (NREL): Tom Stoffel, Dave Renné, Daryl Myers, Steve Wilcox, Manajit Sengupta, Ray George, and Craig Turchi. The critical reviews by our solar colleagues from industry, academia, and other federal agencies were invaluable to producing what we hope will be a useful reference for the concentrating solar power community.

The coauthors are extremely grateful for the masterful editorial work by Connie Komomua and Stefanie Woodward. The leadership of Mark Mehos, the principal program manager for NREL's Concentrating Solar Power Research Program, is gratefully acknowledged.

The U.S Department of Energy Solar Technology Program supported this work under DOE prime contract number DE-AC36-9-GO10337.

REFERENCES, RESOURCES, AND ANNOTATED BIBLIOGRAPHY

Section 2: Overview of Solar Radiation Resource Concepts

Badescu V. (ed.) (2008). Modeling Solar Radiation at the Earth's Surface. Springer, Berlin.

Barnett, T.P.; Ritchie, J.; Foat, J.; Stokes, G. (1998). "On the Space–Time Scales of the Surface Solar Radiation Field." Journal of Climate 11:88–96.

BIPM. (1995). Guide to the Expression of Uncertainty in Measurement. Comité International des Poids et Mesures. www.bipm.org/utils/common/ documents/jcgm/JCGM_100_2008_E.pdf.

De Toma, G.; White, O.R.; Chapman, G.A.; Walton, S.R. (2004). "Solar Irradiance Variability: Progress in Measurement and Empirical Analysis." Advances in Space Research Vol. 34, pp. 237–242.

Erbs, D.G.; Klein, S.A.; Duffie, J.A. (1982). "Estimation of the Diffuse Radiation Fraction for Hourly, Daily, and Monthly Average Solar Radiation." Solar Energy 28(4):293–304.

Grether, D.; Nelson, J.; Wahlig, M. (1975). "Measurement of Circumsolar Radiation." Proceedings of the Society of Photo-Optical Instrumentation Engineers Vol. 68, Solar Energy Utilization. SPIE, Bellingham, WA.

Gueymard, C. (2009). "Direct and Indirect Uncertainties in the Prediction of Tilted Irradiance for Solar Engineering Applications." Solar Energy, 83:432–444.

Iqbal, M. (1983). An Introduction to Solar Radiation. Academic Press, New York.

Liu, B.Y.H.; Jordan, R.C. (1960). "The Interrelationship and Characteristic Distribution of Direct Diffuse and Total Solar Radiation." Solar Energy, 3:1–19.

Major, G. (1994). "Circumsolar Correction for Pyrheliometers and Diffusometers." WMO-TD 635, World Meteorological Organization, Geneva.

Marion, W.; Riordan, C.; Renné, D. (1992). Shining On: A Primer on Solar Radiation Data. NREL/ TP-463-4856. Golden, CO: National Renewable Energy Laboratory.

Maxwell, E. (1987). A Quasi-Physical Model for Converting Hourly Global Horizontal to Direct Normal Insolation. Golden, CO: Solar Energy Research Institute. www.nrel.gov/rredc.pdfs/3087.pdf.

Mie, G. (1908). "Beitrage zur Optiktrüber Medien Speziell Kolloidaler Metalosungen." Annalen der Physik, Vierte Folge 25(3):377–445.

Orgill, J.F.; Hollands, K.G. (1977). "Correlation Equation for Hourly Diffuse Radiation on a Horizontal Surface." Solar Energy 19(4):357–359.

Perez, R.; Seals, R.; Ineichen, P.; Stewart, R.; Menicucci, D. (1987). "A New Simplified Version of the Perez Diffuse Irradiance Model for Tilted Surfaces." Solar Energy 39(3):221–231.

Perez, R.; Seals, R.; Zelenka, A.; Ineichen, P. (1990). "Climatic Evaluation of Models That Predict Hourly Direct Irradiance From Hourly Global Irradiance: Prospects for Performance Improvements." Solar Energy 44(2):99–108.

Rayleigh, L. (1871). "On the Light From the Sky, Its Polarization and Colour." Philosophical Magazine pp. 107–120, 274–279.

Reda, I.; Stoffel T.; Myers, D. (2003). "A Method To Calibrate a Solar Pyranometer fr Measuring Reference Diffuse Irradiance." Solar Energy 74:103–112.

Spencer, J.W. (1982). "A Comparison of Methods for Estimating Hourly Diffuse Solar Radiation From Global Solar Radiation." Solar Energy 29(1):19–32

Wilcox, S.; Gueymard, C.A. (2010). "Spatial and Temporal Variability of the Solar Resource in the United States." Proceedings of Solar 2010, Phoenix, AZ, May 2010.

Section 3: Measuring Solar Radiation

ASTM, (1997). Standard Test Method for Calibration of Pyrheliometers by Comparison to Reference Pyrheliometers. ASTM E816 – 05. 1997 *Annual Book of ASTM Standards*, Vol. 14. American Society for Testing and Materials, Conshohocken, MA.

Bahm, R.J.; Nakos, J.C. (1979). *The Calibration of Solar Radiation Measuring Instruments, Final Report.* BER-1(79)DOE-684-1. Albuquerque, NM: University of New Mexico College of Engineering.

BIPM; IEC; IFCC; ISO; IUPAC; IUPAP; OIML. (1995). Guide to the Expression of Uncertainty in Measurement. ISO TAG 4, Geneva.

Fröhlich, C. (1991). "History of Solar Radiometry and the World Radiation Reference." *Metrologia* 28:111–115.

ISO. (1990). Specification and Classification of Instruments for Measuring Hemispherical Solar and Direct Solar Radiation. ISO 9060. Geneva. www.iso.org.

Maxwell, E.L; Wilcox, S.M.; Cornwall, C.; Marion, B.; Alawaji, S.H.; Mahfoodh, M.; AL-Amoudi, A. (1999). Progress Report for Annex II – *Assessment of Solar Radiation Resources in Saudi Arabia 1993-1997.* NREL/TP-560-25374. Golden, CO: National Renewable Energy Laboratory.

Micek, L.V. (1981). *Direct Beam Insolation Measurement Errors Caused by Pyrheliometer Misalignment.* M.S. Thesis, Trinity University, San Antonio, TX.

Morrison, R. (1998). *Grounding and Shielding Techniques, Fourth Edition.* John Wiley & Sons. New York.

Myers, D.; Wilcox, S. (2009). *Relative Accuracy of 1-Minute and Daily Total Solar Radiation Data for 12 Global and 4 Direct Beam Solar Radiometers.* NREL/CP-550-45734. Golden, CO: National Renewable Energy Laboratory.

Myers, D.; Wilcox, S.; Marion, W.; Al-Abbadi, N.; Mahfoodh, M.; Al-Otaibi, Z. (2002). *Final Report for Annex II--Assessment of Solar Radiation Resources in Saudi Arabia, 1998-2000.* NREL/TP-50-31546. Golden, CO: National Renewable Energy Laboratory.

Reda, I. (1996). *Calibration of a Solar Absolute Cavity Radiometer with Traceability to the World Radiometric Reference.* NREL/TP-463-20619. Golden, CO: National Renewable Energy Laboratory.

Stoffel, T.L.; Reda, I.; Myers, D.R.; Renné, D.; Wilcox, S.; Treadwell, J. (2000). "Current Issues in Terrestrial Solar Radiation Instrumentation for Energy, Climate, and Space Applications." *Metrologia, Journal of the International Bureau of Weights and Measures* (BIPM) 54.

Taylor, B.N.; Kuyatt, C.E. (1987). Guidelines for Evaluation and Expressing the Uncertainty of NIST Measurement Results. NIST Technical Note 1297, National Institute of Standards and Technology, Gaithersburg, MD.

Vignola, F.; Long, C.N.; Reda, I. (2009). Testing a Model of IR Radiative Losses. NREL/CP-3B0-46411. Presented at the Society of Photo-Optical Instrumentation Engineers (SPIE) 2009 Conference, San Diego, CA.

Wilcox, S.; Myers, D. (2008). *Evaluation of Radiometers in Full-Time Use at the National Renewable Energy Laboratory Solar Radiation Research Laboratory.* NREL/TP-550-44627. Golden, CO: National Renewable Energy Laboratory.

WMO. (2008). *WMO Guide to Meteorological Instruments and Methods of Observation, WMO-No. 8* (Seventh Edition), Geneva. www.wmo.int /pages/prog/www/IMOP/ publications/CIMO-Guide/CIMO_Guide-7th_Edition-2008.html.

Section 4: Modeling Solar Radiation—Current Practices

Augustine, J.A.; Deluisi, J.; Long, C.N. (2000). "SURFRAD-A National Surface Radiation Budget Network for Atmospheric Research." *Bulletin of the American Meteorological Society* 81:2341–2357.

Ben Djemaa, A.; Delorme, C. (1992). "A Comparison Between One Year of Daily Global Irradiation From Ground-Based Measurements Versus METEOSAT Images From Seven Locations in Tunisia." *Solar Energy* 48(5):325–333.

Beyer, H.; Costanzo, C.; Heinemann, D. (1996). "Modifications of the HELIOSAT Procedure for Irradiance Estimates From Satellite Images." *Solar Energy* 56:207–221.

Bird, R.E.; Hulstrom, R.L. (1981). *A Simplified Clear-Sky Model for Direct and Diffuse Insolation On Horizontal Surfaces.* SERI/TR-642-761, Golden, CO: Solar Energy Research Institute.

Cano, D.; Monget, J.M.; Albuisson, M.; Guillard, H.; Regas, N.; Wald, L. (1986). "A Method for the Determination of the Global Solar Radiation From Meteorological Satellite Data." *Solar Energy* 37:31–39.

Cebecauer T.; Suri, M.; Perez, R. (2010). "High Performance MSG Satellite Model for Operational Solar Energy Applications." *Proceedings of the ASES Annual Conference*, Phoenix, AZ.

Czeplak, G.; Noia, M.; Ratto, D.F. (1991). "An Assessment of a Statistical Method To Estimate Solar Irradiance at the Earth's Surface From Geostationary Satellite Data." *Renewable Energy* 1:737–743.

Darnell, W.L.; Staylor (1992). "Seasonal Variation of Surface Radiation Budget Derived From International Satellite Cloud Climatology Project C1 Data." *Journal of Geophysical Research* 97(15):741–760.

Darnell, W.L.; Staylor, W.F.; Gupta, S.K.; Denn, M. (1988). "Estimation of Surface Insolation Using Sun-Synchronous Satellite Data." *Journal of Climate* 1:820–835.

Dedieu, G.; Deschamps, P.Y.; Kerr, Y.H. (1987). "Satellite Estimation of Solar Irradiance at the Surface of the Earth and of Surface Albedo Using a Physical Model Applied to Meteosat Data." *Journal of Climate and Applied Meteorology* 26:79–87.

Delorme, C.; Gallo, A.; Oliveiri, J. (1992). "Quick Use of WEFAX Images From METEOSAT To Determine Daily Solar Radiation in France." *Solar Energy* 49(3):191–197.

Diabate, L.; Demarcq, H.; Michaud-Regas, N.; Wald, L. (1988). "Estimating Incident Solar Radiation at the Surface From Images of the Earth Transmitted by Geostationary Satellites: The Heliosat Project." *International Journal of Solar Energy* 5:261–278.

Diak G.R.; Gautier, C. (1983). "Improvements to a Simple Physical Model for Estimating Insolation From GOES Data." *Journal of Climate and Applied Meteorology* 22:505–508.

Dürr, B.; Zelenka, A. (2009). "Deriving Surface Global Irradiance Over the Alpine Region From METEOSAT Second Generation Data by Supplementing the HELIOSAT Method." *International Journal of Remote Sensing* 30:5821–5841.

Frouin, R.; Gautier, C.; Katsaros, K.B.; Lind, R.J. (1988). "A Comparison of Satellite and Empirical Formula Techniques for Estimating Insolation Over the Oceans." *Journal of Applied Meteorology* 27:1016–1023.

Frulla, L.A.; Gagliardini, D.A.; Grossi Gallegos, H.; Lopardo, R. (1988). "Incident Solar Radiation on Argentina From the Geostationary Satellite GOES: Comparison With Ground Measurements." *Solar Energy* 41(1):61–69.

Gautier, C. (1988). "Surface Solar Irradiance in the Central Pacific During Tropic Heat: Comparisons Between in situ Measurements and Satellite Estimates." *Journal of Climate* 1:600–608.

Gautier, C.; Diak, G.; Masse, S. (1980). "A Simple Physical Model To Estimate Incident Solar Radiation at the Surface From GOES Satellite Data." *Journal of Applied Meteorology* 19:1005–1012.

Gautier, C.; Frouin, R. (1984). "Satellite-Derived Ocean Surface Radiation Fluxes." *Proceeding of the Workshop on Advances in Remote Sensing Retrieval Methods*, Williamsburg, VA.

George, R.; Wilcox, S.; Anderberg, M.; Perez, R. (2007). "National Solar Radiation Database (NSRDB) -- 10 Km Gridded Hourly Solar Database." *Proceedings of the Solar 2007 Conference*, Cleveland, OH (CD-ROM). Boulder, CO: ASES. NREL/CP-581-41599. Golden, CO: National Renewable Energy Laboratory.

Gueymard C.A. (2003a). "Direct Solar Transmittance and Irradiance Predictions With Broadband Models. Part I: Detailed Theoretical Performance Assessment." *Solar Energy* 74:355–379; *Corrigendum* 76:513 (2004).

Gueymard C.A. (2003b). "Direct Solar Transmittance and Irradiance Predictions With Broadband Models. Part II: Validation With High-Quality Measurements." *Solar Energy* 74:381–395; *Corrigendum* 76:515 (2004).

Gueymard C.A. (1993). "Critical Analysis and Performance Assessment of Clear Sky Irradiance Models Using Theoretical and Measured Data." *Solar Energy* 51:121–138.

Gueymard C.A.; Myers D. (2008). "Validation and Ranking Methodologies for Solar Radiation Models" In *Modeling Solar Radiation at the Earth's Surface*. V. Badescu (ed.) and Springer.

Hammer, A.; Heinemann, D.; Hoyer, C.; Kuhlemann, R.; Lorenz, E.; Muller, R.; Beyer, H.G. (2003). "Solar Energy Assessment Using Remote Sensing Technologies," *Remote Sensing of Environment* 8:423–432.

Hay, J.E.; Hanson, K.; Hanson, J. (1978). "A Satellite-Based Methodology for Determining Solar Irradiance at the Ocean Surface During GATE." *Bulletin of the American Meteorological Society* 59:1549.

Heidinger, A.K. (2003). "Rapid Daytime Estimation of Cloud Properties Over a Large Area From Radiance Distributions." *Journal of Atmospheric and Oceanic Technology* 20:1237–1250.

Hu, Y.X.; Stamnes, K. (1993). "An Accurate Parameterization of the Radiative Properties of Water Clouds Suitable for Use in Climate Models." *Journal of Climate* 6:728–742.

Ineichen, P. (2008). "A Broadband Simplified Version of the Solis Clear Sky Model." *Solar Energy* 82:758–762.

Iqbal, M. (1983). *An Introduction to Solar Radiation.* Academic Press, New York.

Joseph, J.H.; Wiscombe, W.J.; Weinman, J.A. (1976). "The Delta-Eddington Approximation for Radiative Transfer." *Journal of Atmospheric Science* 33:2452–2459.

Justus, C.; Paris, M.V.; Tarpley, J.D. (1986). "Satellite-Measured Insolation in the United States, Mexico and South America." *Remote Sensing of Environment* 20:57–83.

Kato, S.; Ackerman, T.P.; Mather, J.H.; Clothiaux, E.E. (1999). "The k-Distribution Method and Correlated-k Approximation for a Shortwave Radiative Transfer Model." *Journal of Quantitative Spectroscopy & Radiative Transfer* 62:109–121.

Kerschegens, M.; Pilz, U.; Raschke, E. (1978). "A Modified Two-Stream Approximation for Computations of the Solar Radiation in a Cloudy Atmosphere." *Tellus* 30:429–435.

Klink, J.C.; Dollhopf, K.J. (1986). An Evaluation of Satellite-Based Insolation Estimates for Ohio. *Journal of Climate and Applied Meteorology* 25:1741–1751.

Kylling, A.; Stamnes, K; Tsay, S.C. (1995). "A Reliable and Efficient Two-Stream Algorithm for Radiative Transfer; Documentation of Accuracy in Realistic Layered Media." *Journal of Atmospheric Chemistry* 21:115–150.

Laszlo, I.; Ciren, P.; Liu, H.; Kondragunta, S.; Tarpley, J.D.; Goldberg. M.D. (2008). "Remote Sensing of Aerosol and Radiation From Geostationary Satellites." *Advances in Space Research* 41:1882–1893.

Lefe'vre, M., Wald, L.; Diabate, L. (2007). "Using Reduced Datasets ISCCP-B2 From the Meteosat Satellites To Assess Surface Solar Irradiance." *Solar Energy* 81:240–253.

Lohmann, S.; Schillings, C.; Mayer, B.; Meyer, R. (2006). "Long-Term Variability of Solar Direct and Global Irradiance Derived From ISCCP Data and comparison With Re-Analysis Data." *Solar Energy* 80:1390–1401.

Marion, W.; Wilcox, S. (1994). *Solar Radiation Data Manual for Flat-Plate and Concentrating Collectors.* NREL/TP-463-5607. Golden, CO: National Renewable Energy Laboratory.

Massey Jr., F.J. (1951). "The Kolmogorov–Smirnov Test for Goodness of Fit." *Journal of the American Statistical Association* 56:68–78.

Maxwell, E.L. (1998). "METSTAT-the Solar Radiation Model Used in the Production of the National Solar Radiation Database (NSRDB)." *Solar Energy* 62:263–279.

Maxwell, E.L.; George, R.L.; Wilcox, S.M. (1998). "A Climatological Radiation Model." Proceedings of the Annual Conference of the American Solar Energy Society, June 14–17, Albuquerque, NM.

Mayer, B.; Kylling, A. (2005). "The libRadtran Software Package for Radiative Transfer Calculations: Description and Examples of Use." *Atmospheric Chemistry and Physics Discussions* 5:1855–1877.

Möser, W.; Raschke, E. (1983). "Mapping of Global Radiation and Cloudiness From METEOSAT Image Data." *Meteorologische Rundschau* 36:33–41.

Möser, W.; Raschke, E. (1984). "Incident Solar Radiation Over Europe Estimated From METEOSAT Data." *Journal of Climate and Applied Meteorology* 23:166–170.

Moussu, G.; Diabaté, L.; Obrecht, D.; Wald, L. (1989). "A Method for the Mapping of the Apparent Ground Brightness Using Visible Images From Geostationary Satellites." *International Journal of Remote Sensing* 10(7):1207–1225.

Mueller, R.W.; Dagestad, K.F.; Ineichen, P.; Schroedter, M.; Cros, S.; Dumortier, D.; Kuhlemann, R.; Olseth, J.A.; Piernavieja, G.; Reise, C.; Wald, L.; Heinnemann, D. (2004). "Rethinking Satellite Based Solar Irradiance Modelling: The SOLIS Clear Sky Module." *Remote Sensing of Environment* 90(2):160–174.

NREL. (1993). *Users Manual for SERI QC Software: Assessing the Quality of Solar Radiation Data.* NREL/TP-463-5608. Golden, CO: National Renewable Energy Laboratory.

Nullett, D. (1987). "A Comparison of Two Methods of Estimating Insolation Over the Tropical Pacific Ocean Using Cloudiness From Satellite Observations." *Solar Energy* 39(3):197–201.

Nunez. M. (1990). Solar Energy Statistics for Australian Capital Regions. *Solar Energy* 44:343–354.

Pavolonis, M.; Heidinger, A.K.; Uttal, T. (2005). "Daytime Global Cloud Typing From AVHRR and VIIRS: Algorithm Description, Validation, and Comparisons." *Journal of Applied Meteorology* 44:804–826.

Pereira, E.B.; Abreu, S.L.; Stuhlmann, R.; Rieland, M.; Colle, S. (1996). "Survey of the Incident Solar Radiation Data in Brazil by Use of METEOSAT Satellite Data." *Solar Energy* 57(2):125–132.

Perez, R.; Ineichen, P. (2002). "A New Operational Model for Satellite-Derived Irradiances: Description and Validation." *Solar Energy* 73:307–317.

Perez, R.; Ineichen, P.; Moore, K.; Kmiecik, M.; Chain, C.; George, R.; Vignola, F. (2002). "A New Operational Satellite-to-Irradiance Model." *Solar Energy* 73(5):307–317.

Perez, R.; Ineichen, P.; Maxwell, E.; Seals, R.; Zelenka, A. (1992). "Dynamic Global-to-Direct Irradiance Conversion Models." *ASHRAE Transactions-Research Series* 354–369.

Perez, R.; Seals, R.; Ineichen, P.; Stewart, P.; Menicucci, D. (1987). "A New Simplified Version of the Perez Diffuse Irradiance Model for Tilted Surfaces. Description Performance Validation." *Solar Energy* 39:221–232.

Pinker, R.T.; Ewing, J.A. (1985). "Modeling Surface Solar Radiation: Model Formulation and Validation." *Journal of Climate and Applied Meteorology* 24:389–401.

Pinker, R.T.; Frouin, R.; Li, Z. (1995). "A Review of Satellite Methods To Derive Surface Shortwave Irradiance." *Remote Sensing of Environment* 51:108–124.

Pinker, R.T.; Laszlo, I. (1992). "Modeling Surface Solar Irradiance for Satellite Applications on a Global Scale." *Journal of Applied Meteorology* 31:194–211.

Pinker, R.T.; Ewing, J.A. (1985). "Modeling Surface Solar Radiation: Model Formulation and Validation." *Journal of Climate and Applied Meteorology* 24:389–401.

Raschke, E.; Stuhlmann, R.; Palz, W.; Steemers, T.C. (1991). *Solar Radiation Atlas of Africa.* A.A. Balakema Publishers, Rotterdam for the Commission of European Communities, p. 155.

Renné, D.S.; Perez, R.; Zelenka, A.; Whitlock, C.; DiPasquale, R. (1999). *Advances in Solar Energy: An Annual Review of Research and Development,* Vol. 13. Goswami, D. Y. and Boer, K.W., eds., American Solar Energy Society, Boulder, CO.

Rigollier, C.; Lefèvre, M.; Wald L. (2004). "The Method Heliosat-2 for Deriving Shortwave Solar Radiation Data From Satellite Images." *Solar Energy* 77:159–169.

Ruiz-Arias, J.A.; Cebecauer, T.; Tovar-Pescador; Šúri, M. (2010). "Spatial Disaggregation of Satellite-Derived Irradiance Using a High-Resolution Digital Elevation Model." *Solar Energy* 84(9):1644–1657.

Sadler, J.C.; Oda, L.; Kilonsky, B.J. (1976). *Pacific Ocean Cloudiness From Satellite Observations.* University of Hawaii Department of Meteorology.

Schiffer, R.A.; Rossow, W.B. (1983). The International Satellite Cloud Climatology Project (ISCCP): The First Project of the World Climate Research Programme. *Bulletin of the American Meteorological Society* 64:779–784.

Schmetz, J. (1989). "Towards a Surface Radiation Climatology: Retrieval of Downward Irradiances From Satellites." *Atmospheric Research* 23:287–321.

Schmetz, J.; Pili, P.; Tjemkes, S.; Just, D.; Kerkmann, J.; Rota, S.; Ratier, A. (2002). "An Introduction to Meteosat Second Generation (MSG)." *Bulletin of the American Meteorological Society* 83:977–992.

Shaltout, M.A.M.; Hassen, A.H. (1990). "Solar Energy Distribution Over Egypt Using METEOSAT Photos." *Solar Energy* 45(6):345–351.

Stowe, L.L.; Davis, P.A.; McClain, E.P. (1999). "Scientific Basis and Initial Evaluation of the CLAVR-1 Global Clear Cloud Classification Algorithm for the Advanced Very High Resolution Radiometer." *Journal of Atmospheric and Oceanic Technology* 16:656–681.

Stuhlmann, R.; Rieland, M.; Raschke, E. (1990). "An Improvement of the IGMK Model To Derive Total and Diffuse Solar Radiation at the Surface From Satellite Data." *Journal of Applied Meteorology* 29:586–603.

Tarpley, J.D. (1979). "Estimating Incident Solar Radiation at the Surface From Geostationary Satellite Data." *Journal of Applied Meteorology* 18:1172–1181.

Thøgersen, M.L.; Motta, M.; Sørensen, T.; Nielsen, P. (2007). "Measure-Correlate-Predict Methods: Case Studies and Software Implementation." European Wind Energy Conference 2007.

White Paper. (2009a). 3-TIER Western Hemisphere Solar Dataset: Methodology and Validation, available at http://c0402442.cdn.cloudfiles. rackspacecloud. com/ static/ttcms/1.0.0.16/us/ documents/ publications/ validations/ solar_ wh_validation.pdf.

White Paper. (2009b). 3-TIER Solar Dataset: India Validation, available at http://c0402442.cdn. cloudfiles.rackspacecloud.com/static/ ttcms /1.0.0. 16/us/ documents/publications/validations/ solar_india_validation.pdf.

White Paper. (2009c). 3-TIER Solar Dataset: Australia Validation, available at http://c0402442.cdn. cloudfiles.rackspacecloud.com/ static/ttcms/ 1.0.0. 16/us/ documents/publications/validations/ solar_ austral lia_validation-final.pdf.

Whitlock, C.H.; Charlock, T.P.; Staylor, W.F.; Pinker, R.T.; Laszlo, I.; Ohmura, A.; Gilgen, H.; Konzelman, T.; DiPasquale, R.C.; Moats, C.D.; LeCroy, S.R.; Ritchey, N.A. (1995). "First Global WRCP Shortwave Surface Radiation Budget Dataset." *Bulletin of the American Meteorological Society* 76:905–922.

Wilcox, S.; Anderberg, M.; Beckman, W.; DeGaetano, A.; George, R.; Gueymard, C.; Lott, N.; Marion, W.; Myers, D.; Perez, R.; Renné, D.; Stackhouse, P.; Vignola, F.; Whitehurst, T. (2007). *National Solar Radiation Database 1991–2005 Update: User's Manual.* NREL/TP-581-41364, Golden, CO: National Renewable Energy Laboratory.

Yang, P.; Liou, K.N.; Wyser, K.; Mitchell, D. (2000). "Parameterization of the Scattering and Absorption Properties of Individual Ice Crystals." *Journal of Geophysical Research* 105:4699–4718.

Zelenka, A.; Perez, R.; Seals R.; Renné, D. (1999). "Effective Accuracy of Satellite-Derived Irradiance." *Theoretical and Applied Climatology* 62:199–207.

Zhang, Y.C.; Rossow, W.B.; Lacis, A.A.; Oinas, V.; Mishchenko, M.I. (2004). "Calculation of Radiative Fluxes From the Surface to Top of Atmosphere Based on ISCCP and Other Global Datasets: Refinements of the Radiative Transfer Model and the Input Data." *Journal of Geophysical Research* 109.

Section 5: Historical Solar Resource Data

Dumortier, D. (1998). Ecole Nationale des Travaux Publics de l'Etat, Vaulx-en-Velin, France. (1998). "Daylight Availability in Freiburg and Nantes, Two Sites Close in Latitude." *Report for the Sixth SATELLIGHT* Meeting in Freiburg, Germany, September 1998.

Hall, I.; Prairie, R.; Anderson, H.; Boes, E. (1978). *Generation of Typical Meteorological Years for 26 SOLMET Stations.* SAND78-1601. Albuquerque, NM: Sandia National Laboratories.

Hegner, H.; Müller, G.; Nespor, V.; Ohmura, A.; Steigrad, R.; Gilgen, H. (1998). *Technical Plan for BSRN Data Management* (WRMC technical report no. 2), WMO/TD-No. 882, WCRP/WMO. Geneva.

Hulstrom, R.L., ed. (1989). *Solar Resources.* The MIT Press, Cambridge, MA.

Kalnay, E.; Kanamitsu, M.; Kistler, R.; Collins, W.; Deaven, D.; Gandin, L.; Iredell, M.; Saha, S.; White, G.; Woollen, J.; Zhu, Y.; Chelliah, M.; Ebisuzaki, W.; Higgins, W.; Janowiak, J.; Mo, K.C.; Ropelewski, C.; Wang, J.; Leetmaa, A.; Reynolds, R.; Jenne, R.; Joseph, D. (1996). "The NCEP/NCAR 40-Year Reanalysis Project." *Bulletin of the American Meteorological Society* 77:437–471.

Kistler, R.; Kalnay, E.; Collins, W.; Saha, S.; White, G.; Woollen, J.; Chelliah, M.; Ebisuzaki, W.; Kanamitsu, M.; Kousky, V.; van den Dool, H.; Jenne, R.; Fiorino, M. (2001). "The NCEP-NCAR 50-Year Reanalysis: Monthly Means CD-ROM and Documentation." *Bulletin of the American Meteorological Society* 82:247–267.

Lohmann, S.; Schillings, C.; Mayer, B.; Meyer, R. (2006). "Long-Term Variability of Solar Direct and Global Irradiance Derived From ISCCP Data and Comparison With Re-Analysis Data." *Solar Energy* 80:1390–1401.

Marion, W. (1994). *Summary Information and Data Sets for the HBCU Solar Measurements Network.* NREL/TP-463-7090. Golden, CO: National Renewable Energy Laboratory.

Marion, W.; Myers, D. (1992). *A Comparison of Data from SOLMET/ERSATZ and the National Solar Radiation Database.* NREL/TP-463-5118. Golden, CO: National Renewable Energy Laboratory.

Marion, W.; Urban, K. (1995). *Users Manual for TMY2s-Typical Meteorological Years Derived From the 1961–1990 National Solar Radiation Database.* NREL/TP-463-7668. Golden, CO: National Renewable Energy Laboratory.

Maxwell, E.L. (1998). "METSTAT – The Solar Radiation Model Used in the Production of the National Solar Radiation Database (NSRDB)." *Solar Energy* 62:263–279.

Mehos, M.; Perez, R. (2005). Mining for Solar Resources: US Southwest Provides Vast Potential. *Imaging Notes* 20(2):12–15; NREL/JA-550-37799. Golden, CO: National Renewable Energy Laboratory.

Meyer, R; Butron, J.T. Marquardt, G.; Schwandt, M.; Geuder, N.; Hoyer-Klick, C.; Lorenz, E.; Hammer, A.; Beyer, H.G. (2008). "Combining Solar Irradiance Measurements and Various Satellite-Derived Products to a Site-Specific Best Estimate." Solar PACES Symposium, Las Vegas, NV, 2008.

Mueller, R.W.; Dagestad, K.F.; Ineichen, P.; Schroedter, M.; Cros, S.; Dumortier, D.; Kuhlemann, R.; Olseth, J.A.; Piernavieja, G.; Reise, C.; Wald, L.; Heinnemann, D. (2004). "Rethinking Satellite Based Solar Irradiance Modelling: The SOLIS Clear Sky Module." *Remote Sensing of Environment* 90 (2):160–174.

Myers, D.R.; Stoffel, T.L.; Reda, I.; Wilcox, S.M.; Andreas. A. (2002). "Recent Progress in Reducing the Uncertainty in and Improving Pyranometer Calibrations." *Transactions of the ASME* 124:44–50.

NASA (2008). http://eosweb.larc.nasa.gov/cgi-bin/sse/print.cgi?accuracy.txt.

NCDC. (1979 a). *Final Report – Hourly Solar Radiation-Surface Meteorological Observations.* TD-9724. Asheville, NC: National Climatic Data Center.

NCDC. (1979 b). *SOLDAY User's Manual (TD9739) Daily Solar Radiation – Surface Meteorological Data.* Asheville, NC: Environmental Data and Information Service.

NCDC (1978). *User's Manual – Hourly Solar Radiation-Surface Meteorological Observations.* TD-9724. Asheville, NC: National Climatic Data Center.

NREL. (1993). *User's Manual for SERI_QC Software – Assessing the Quality of Solar Radiation Data.* NREL/TP-463-5608. Golden, CO: National Renewable Energy Laboratory.

NSRDB. (1992). *User's Manual – National Solar Radiation Database (1961-1990). Version 1.0.* Golden, CO: National Renewable Energy Laboratory and Asheville, NC: National Climatic Data Center.

NSRDB (1995). *Final Technical Report: National Solar Radiation Database* (1961-1990). NREL/TP463-5784. Golden, CO: National Renewable Energy Laboratory.

Olseth J.A.; Skartveit A. (1998). "High Latitude Global and Diffuse Radiation Estimated From METEOSAT Data." *European Conference on Applied Climatology*, ECAC 98, Vienna, Austria, October 19–23, 1998.

Perez, R.; Ineichen, P.; Moore, K.; Kmiecik, M.; Chain, C.; George, R.; Vignola, F. (2002). "A New Operational Satellite-to-Irradiance Model." *Solar Energy* 73(5):307–317.

Pinker, R.T.; I. Laszlo (1992). "Modeling Surface Solar Irradiance for Satellite Applications on a Global Scale." *Journal of Applied Meteorology* 31:194–211.

Remund, J.; Lefèvre, W.L.; Ranchin, M.; Page, T. (2003). "Worldwide Linke Turbidity Information, ISES Solar World Congress." Solar Energy for a Sustainable Future, Göteborg, Sweden.

Rigollier, C.; Bauer, O.; Wald, L. (2000). "On the Clear Sky Model of the 4th European Solar Radiation Atlas With Respect to the Heliosat Method." *Solar Energy* 68(1):33–48. See also Geiger, M.; Diabaté, L.; Ménard L.; Wald, L. (2002). "A Web Service for Controlling the Quality of Global Solar Irradiation." *Solar Energy* 73(6):475–480.

Thornton, P.E.; Running, S.W. (1999). "An Improved Algorithm for Estimating Incident Daily Solar Radiation From Measurements of Temperature, Humidity, and Precipitation." *Agriculture and Forest Meteorology* 93:211–228.

Thornton, P.E.; Hasenauer, H.; White. M.A. (2000). "Simultaneous Estimation of Daily Solar Radiation and Humidity From Observed Temperature and Precipitation: An Application Over Complex Terrain in Austria." *Agricultural and Forest Meteorology* 104:255–271.

Tomson, T.; Russak, V.; Kallis, A. (2008). "Dynamic Behavior of Solar Radiation." In *Modeling Solar Radiation at the Earth's Surface.* V. Badescu, ed., Heidelberg, Berlin: Springer, pp. 257–281.

Wilcox, S. (2007). *National Solar Radiation Database 1991–2005 Update: User's Manual.* NREL/TP581-41364. Golden, CO: National Renewable Energy Laboratory.

Wilcox, S.; Marion, W. (2008). "Development of an Updated Typical Meteorological Year Data Set for the United States." Proceedings of the Solar 2008 Conference.

Wilcox, S.; Marion, W. (2008). *Users Manual for TMY3 Data Sets.* NREL/TP-581-43156, Revised May 2008. Golden, CO: National Renewable Energy Laboratory.

Wilcox, S.; Myers. D. (2008). *Evaluation of Radiometers in Full-Time Use as the National Renewable Energy Laboratory Solar Radiation Research Laboratory.* NREL/TP-550-44627. Golden, CO: National Renewable Energy Laboratory. www.nrel.gov/docs/fy09osti/44627.pdf.

Wilcox, S.; Marion, W. (2008). *Users Manual for TMY3 Data Sets.* NREL/TP-581-43156, revised May 2008. Golden, CO: National Renewable Energy Laboratory.

Zelenka, A.; Perez, R.; Seals, R.; Renné, D. (1999). "Effective Accuracy of Satellite-Derived Irradiance." *Theoretical and Applied Climatology*, 62:199–207.

Section 6: Applying Solar Resource Data to Concentrating Solar Power Projects

George, R.; Wilcox, S.; Anderberg, M.; Perez, R. (2007). National Solar Radiation Database (NSRDB) -- 10 Km Gridded Hourly Solar Database. Campbell-Howe, R., ed. Proceedings of the Solar 2007 Conference, 8-12 July 2007, Cleveland, Ohio (CD-ROM). Boulder, CO: ASES 8 pp.; NREL/ CP-581- 41599. Golden, CO: National Renewable Energy Laboratory.

Gueymard, Christian A. and Stephen M. Wilcox. (2009). Spatial and Temporal Variability in the Solar Resource: Assessing the Value of Short-Term Measurements at Potential Solar Power Plant Sites. Boulder, CO: ASES. Solar 2009 Conference, Buffalo, NY, May 2009.

Marion, W.; Wilcox, S. (1994). *Solar Radiation Data Manual for Flat-Plate and Concentrating Collectors.* NREL/TP-463-5607. Golden, CO: National Renewable Energy Laboratory.

Mehos, M.; Perez, R. (2005). "Mining for Solar Resources: US Southwest Provides Vast Potential." *Imaging Notes* 20(2):12–15; NREL/JA-550-37799. Golden, CO: National Renewable Energy Laboratory.

Meyer, R.; Torres Butron, J.; Marquardt, G; Schwandt, M.; Geuder, N.; Hoyer-Klick, C.; Lorenz, E.; Hammer, A.; Beyer, H.G. (2008). "Combining Solar Irradiance Measurements and Various Satellite-Derived Products to a Site-Specific Best Estimate." Solar PACES Symposium, Las Vegas, NV, 2008.

Thøgersen, M.LL.; Motta, M.; Sørensen, T.; Nielsen, P. (2007). "Measure-Correlate-Predict Methods: Case Studies and Software Implementation." European Wind Energy Conference, 2007.

Tomson, T.; Russak, T.V.; Kallis, V.A. (2008). "Dynamic Behavior of Solar Radiation." *In Modeling Solar Radiation at the Earth's Surface*. Badescu, V., ed., Springer, New York.

Section 7: Future Work

Perez, R., Wilcox, S.; Renné, D.; Moore, K.; Zelenka, A. (2007). "Forecasting Solar Radiation - Preliminary Evaluation of an Approach Based Upon the National Forecast Database." *Solar Energy* 81(6):809–812.

Wilcox, S.M.; Myers, D.R. (2008). *Evaluation of Radiometers in Full-Time Use at the National Renewable Energy Laboratory Solar Radiation Research Laboratory*. NREL/TP-550-44627. Golden, CO: National Renewable Energy Laboratory.

APPENDIX. RADIOMETER MANUFACTURERS AND DISTRIBUTORS

This list is provided for information only. Neither the United States government nor any agency thereof, nor any of their employees, makes any warranty, express or implied, or assumes any legal liability or responsibility for the accuracy, completeness, or usefulness of any information, apparatus, product, or process disclosed, or represents that its use would not infringe privately owned rights. Reference herein to any specific commercial product, process, or service by trade name, trademark, manufacturer, or otherwise does not necessarily constitute or imply its endorsement, recommendation, or favoring by the United States government or any agency thereof.

Analytical Spectral Devices,
Inc. 5335 Sterling Drive, Suite A
Boulder, CO 80301 USA
Telephone: (303) 444-6522
Fax: (303) 444-6852
www.asdi.com
Spectral irradiance measurements

Brusag
Chapfwiesenstrasse 14 CH-8712 Stäfa
Switzerland
Telephone: +41 1 926 74 74 Fax: +41 1 926 73 34
Automatic solar trackers

Campbell Scientific, Inc.
815 West 1800 North
Logan, UT 84321 USA
Telephone: (435) 753.2342 (Info)
Telephone: (435) 750.9681 (Orders)

Fax: (435)750.9540

E-mail: info@campbellsci.com

www.campbellsci.com

Data logger systems, weather stations

Casella London Limited

Regent House Britannia Walk London N1 7ND Telephone: 01-253-8581

Telex: 26 16 41 Radiometers

Davis Instruments Corporation

3465 Diablo Avenue Hayward, CA 94545 USA

Telephone: (510) 732 9229

Fax: (510) 670 0589 www.davisnet.com Weather stations

DAYSTAR

3250 Majestic Ridge

Las Cruces, NM 88011 USA Telephone: (505) 522-4943

www.raydec. com/daystar Radiometers

Delta-T Devices Ltd

130 Low Road, Burwell Cambridge, CB25 0EJ UK

US Distributor:

Gary L. Woods, Sales Manager

garywood s@dynamax.com

www.dynamax.com

Telephone: (800) 896-7108 (toll free)

Telephone: (281) 564-5100

Fax: (281) 564-5200

Radiometers, weather stations, data loggers

EKO Instruments Trading Co., LTD.

21-8

Hatagaya 1-chome

Shibuyaku, Tokyo 151

Japan

Telephone: 81-3-3469-4511

Fax: 81-3-3469-4593

Telex: J25364 EKOTRA

www.eko.co.jp/eko/english/03/a.html

US Distributor:

SC-International, Inc.

346 W. Pine Valley Drive

Phoenix, AZ 85023 USA

Telephone: (602) 993-7877

Fax: (602) 789-6616

Radiometers, trackers, data loggers

The Eppley Laboratory, Inc.
12 Sheffield Avenue
Newport, RI 02840 USA
Telephone: (401) 847-1020 Fax: (401) 847-1031
www.eppleylab.com/
Radiometers, trackers, data loggers

Hukseflux Thermal Sensors B.V.
Elektronicaweg 25
2628 XG Delft
The Netherlands
Telephone: +31-15-2142669
Fax: +31-152574949
Radiometers
Hukseflux US Sales Representative
Robert Dolce
HuksefluxUSA
P.O. Box 850
Manorville, NY 11949 USA
Telephone: (631) 251-6963
E-mail: rdolce@HuksefluxUSA.com

Irradiance. Inc.
41 Laurel Drive
Lincoln, MA 01773 USA
Phone/Fax: (781) 259-1134
www.irradiance.com/rsr.html
Rotating Shadowband Radiometer (RSR)

Kipp & Zonen, Delft BV
P.O. Box 507
2600 AM Delft Holland Mercuriusweg 1
2624 BC Delft Holland
Telephone: 015-561 000
Fax: 015-620351
Telex: 38137
www.kippzonen.com
US Sales Representative
Victor Cassella
Kipp & Zonen
125 Wilbur Place
Bohemia, NY 11716 USA
Telephone: (631) 589-2065 ext 22
Fax: (631) 589-2068
Radiometers, trackers, data loggers

LI-COR, Inc.
4421 Superior Street
Lincoln, NE 68504 USA
Telephone: (800) 447-3576 (toll free)
Telephone: (402) 467-3576
Fax: (402) 467-2819
http://licor.com/
Radiometers, data loggers, weather stations

Matrix, Inc.
537 S. 31st Street
Mesa, AZ 85204 USA
Telephone: (480) 832-1380
Radiometers

Medtherm Corporation
P.O. Box 412
Huntsville, AL 35804 USA Telephone: (256) 837-2000 Fax: (256) 837-2001
www.medtherm.com Cavity radiometers

MicroStrain, Inc.
459 Hurricane Lane, Suite 102 Williston, VT 05495
(800) 449-3878
www.microstrain.com/
Wireless sensors, data loggers

Middleton Solar
Factory 20, 155 Hyde Street Yarraville, Victoria 3013 Australia Telephone: +61-3-9396
1890 Fax: +61-3-9689 2384 (Fax) Radiometers

Ocean Optics, Inc.
830 Douglas Ave.
Dunedin, FL 34698 USA
Telephone: (727) 733.2447
Fax: (727) 733.3962 www.oceanoptics.com
European Sales Office: Geograaf 24
6921 EW DUIVEN
The Netherlands
Telephone: +31 (0) 26 319 0500
Fax: +31 (0) 26 319 05 05

Onset
470 MacArthur Boulevard
Bourne, MA 02532 USA
Telephone: (508) 743-3210
www.onsetcomp.com

HOBO loggers, radiometers, met sensors
PH. Schenk GmbH & Co KG Jedleseer Strasse 59
A-1210 Wien, Austria
Telephone: +43/1 271 51 31-0 E-mail: office@schenk.co.
at www.schenk. co.at/schenk Radiometers

Solar Light Company
721 Oak Lane
Philadelphia, PA 19126 USA Telephone: (215) 927-4206 www. solarlight.com/
Radiometers

Yankee Environmental Systems, Inc.
Montaque Industrial Park
101 Industrial Road
P.O. Box 746
Turners Falls, MA 01376 USA
Telephone: (413) 863-0200 www.yesinc.com/
Radiometers, data systems, sky imagers

In: Concentrating Solar Power
Editors: Burt J. Alexander and Ted F. Richardson

ISBN: 978-1-62081-423-9
© 2012 Nova Science Publishers, Inc.

Chapter 2

CAPACITY VALUE OF CONCENTRATING SOLAR POWER PLANTS[*]

Seyed Hossein Madaeni, Ramteen Sioshansi and Paul Denholm

LIST OF ACRONYMS

APS	Arizona Public Service
CSP	concentrating solar power
EFOR	expected forced outage rate
EIA	U.S. Department of Energy's Energy Information Administration
ELCC	effective load carrying capability
ERCOT	Electric Reliability Council of Texas
FCA	forward capacity auction
FCM	forward capacity market
FERC	Federal Energy Regulatory Commission
GADS	Generating Availability Data System
HTF	heat transfer fluid
ISO	Independent System Operator
LOLE	loss of load expectation
LOLP	loss of load probability
LSE	load-serving entity
MIP	mixed-integer program
MW-e	megawatts of electricity
NERC	North American Electric Reliability Corporation
NP	Nevada Power
PHS	pumped hydroelectric storage
PV	photovoltaic

---

[*] This is an edited, reformatted and augmented version of National Renewable Energy Laboratory Technical Report NREL/TP-6A20-51253 publication, Prepared under Task No. SS10.1410, dated June 2011.

SAM	Solar Advisor Model
SM	solar multiple
TES	thermal energy storage
WECC	Western Electricity Coordinating Council

EXECUTIVE SUMMARY

This study estimates the capacity value of a concentrating solar power (CSP) plant at a variety of locations within the western United States.

This is done by optimizing the operation of the CSP plant and by using the effective load carrying capability (ELCC) metric, which is a standard reliability-based capacity value estimation technique. Although the ELCC metric is the most accurate estimation technique, we show that a simpler capacity-factor-based approximation method can closely estimate the ELCC value.

Without storage, the capacity value of CSP plants varies widely depending on the year and solar multiple.

The average capacity value of plants evaluated ranged from 45%–90% with a solar multiple range of 1.0–1.5. When introducing thermal energy storage (TES), the capacity value of the CSP plant is more difficult to estimate since one must account for energy in storage.

We apply a capacity-factor-based technique under two different market settings: an energy-only market and an energy and capacity market. Our results show that adding TES to a CSP plant can increase its capacity value significantly at all of the locations.

Adding a single hour of TES significantly increases the capacity value above the no-TES case, and with four hours of storage or more, the average capacity value at all locations exceeds 90%.

1 INTRODUCTION

Power system planners are tasked with ensuring adequate supply of electricity to meet demand. In addition, system planners face consumer and political demands to increase the share of renewable energy such as wind and solar in their energy mix. But the variable and uncertain nature of these renewable resources poses some challenges for utilities and system operators. Planners need an accurate estimate of the capacity value of such resources in order to represent renewable resources in reliability models for long-term planning purposes.

Concentrating solar power (CSP) plants are one renewable technology currently being deployed both in the United States and internationally. For planners, CSP has a potential advantage over many other technologies because of its ability to use thermal energy storage (TES). This report details techniques that can be used to estimate the capacity value of CSP plants.

The techniques consist of models, which optimize the commitment and dispatch of the CSP plant, and statistical methods used to estimate the probability of a system outage event. These techniques are compared in terms of their computational cost and accuracy. The report also presents results for case studies conducted at locations throughout the western

United States. We show that adding TES to a CSP plant can significantly increase its capacity value.

Defining Capacity-Related Terms

This document focuses on the capacity value of CSP plants. There are a number of capacity-related terms commonly used with substantially different meanings.

Capacity generally refers to the rated output of the plant when operating at maximum output. Capacity is typically measured in terms of a kilowatt (kW), megawatt (MW), or gigawatt (GW) rating. Rated capacity may also be referred to as "nameplate capacity" or "peak capacity." This may be further distinguished as the "net capacity" of the plant after plant parasitic loads have been considered, which are subtracted from the "gross capacity."

Capacity Factor is a measure of how much energy is produced by a plant compared to its maximum output.

It is measured as a percentage, generally by dividing the total energy produced in a year by the amount of energy it would have produced if it ran at full output over that year. It may also be expressed as the ratio of average output to maximum output over a year.

Capacity Value is the focus of this report and refers to the contribution of a power plant to reliably meeting demand.

Capacity value is the contribution that a plant makes toward the planning reserve margin, with a more comprehensive technical definition provided in Section 2. The capacity value (or capacity credit) is measured either in terms of physical capacity (kW, MW, GW) or the fraction of its nameplate capacity (%). Thus a plant with a nameplate capacity of 150 MW could have a capacity value of 75 MW or 50%.

Capacity Payment is a monetary payment to a generator based on its capacity value. The capacity payment is generally in terms of $/MW where the MW is the generator's capacity value.

---

2. METHODS FOR ESTIMATING CAPACITY VALUE

A number of different methods have been used to calculate the capacity value of renewable and conventional generators [1]-[3]. These methods differ in terms of computational time, complexity, and data requirements. A majority of the methods utilize power system reliability evaluation techniques [4], which are based on two standard reliability indices—loss of load probability (LOLP) and loss of load expectation (LOLE). LOLP is defined as the probability of a loss of load event, in which the system load is greater than available generating capacity during a given time period. LOLP is typically computed in one-hour increments. The LOLE is the sum of the LOLPs during a planning period, typically one year. LOLE gives the expected number of time periods in which a loss of load event occurs. Power system planners typically aim to maintain an LOLE value of 0.1 days/year (based on the target of one outage-day every 10 years) [5]. This value is used as the target LOLE value throughout this report. The capacity value of a plant represents the ability of the plant to reduce the probability or severity of a loss of load event. Thus, a generator's capacity value is measured based on how adding it to the system changes the system's LOLP and LOLE.

Generator outages may leave the system with insufficient capacity to meet load. Conventional generator outages are typically modeled using an expected forced outage rate (EFOR), which is the probability that a particular generator can experience a failure at any given time. When renewables are added to a system, the LOLP and LOLE must also capture the variability of these resources. To do this, renewable generator outages are modeled using an EFOR, and resource variability is estimated using historical data or by simulating such data.

The following sections examine common techniques for estimating capacity value of renewable and conventional generators.

2.1. Effective Load Carrying Capability

One of the most robust and widely accepted techniques for estimating capacity value is determining the effective load carrying capability (ELCC) of a generator [6]-[10]. The ELCC of a generator can be defined in a number of ways, which will yield very similar results [11]. One definition is the amount by which the system's load can increase (when the generator is added to the system), while maintaining the same system reliability (as measured by the LOLP and LOLE) [12]. An alternative definition is the amount of a different generating technology that can be replaced by the new generator without making the system less reliable [5]-[12].[1] In the context of a renewable generator, the latter definition is more attractive because it allows the capacity value of a renewable generator to be measured in terms of a conventional dispatchable generator. The ELCC of a renewable generator equals the power capacity of the conventional generator that yields to the same LOLE as the system with the renewable resource. For example, a 100 MW wind generator may have a capacity value that is equivalent to a 30 MW natural-gas-fired combustion turbine.

The steps used to calculate the ELCC of a CSP generator[2] are as follows:

1. For a given set of conventional generators, the LOLE of the system without the CSP plant is calculated using the following formula:

$$LOLE = \sum_{i=1}^{T} P(G_i < L_i)$$

(1)

where T is the total number of hours of study, G_i represents the available conventional capacity in hour i, and L_i is the amount of load. $P(G_i < L_i)$ indicates the probability of available generating capacity being less than demand, which is the LOLP in each hour. Adding these LOLPs together gives the LOLE.

2. The CSP plant is added to the system and the LOLE is recalculated. This is shown in (2) as LOLECSP, where Ci is the output of the CSP plant in hour i. Since the CSP

plant has been added to the system, LOLECSP will be lower than LOLE (indicating a more reliable system with lower LOLPs).

$$LOLE_{CSP} = \sum_{i=1}^{r} P(G_i + C_i < L_i)$$

(2)

3. The CSP plant is "removed" from the system and a conventional generator is added. The LOLE of the new system, which is denoted as LOLEGen is computed as:

$$LOLE_{Gen} = \sum_{i=1}^{r} P(G_i + X_i < L_i)$$

(3)

where X_i is the available generating capacity in hour i from the added conventional generator. This added conventional generator is assumed to have a fixed EFOR, but the nameplate capacity of the plant is adjusted until the LOLE of the system with the CSP plant and the conventional generator are equal; i.e., until $LOLE_{CSP} = LOLE_{Gen}$. Once the two LOLEs are made equal to one another, we can say that the capacity value of the CSP plant is equivalent to the capacity value of the conventional generator.

An important difference between renewable resources, such as CSP plants, and conventional generators is the cause of unavailability. While CSP plants will experience mechanical failures, they are unavailable mostly due to a lack of solar resource. The ELCC method requires detailed system data, including EFORs of all of the generators in the system, generator capacities, and loads.

Moreover, due to seasonal and annual weather pattern changes, one will typically need several years' worth of data to accurately estimate the capacity value of a CSP plant. Finally, the ELCC method can be computationally expensive, due to the complexity of computing the hourly LOLPs.

2.2. Approximation Methods

Calculating capacity value using the ELCC can be a cumbersome process since the capacity of the added conventional generator must be adjusted iteratively to achieve equality between the two LOLEs. These complications have led to the development of simpler approximation techniques. These approximation methods reduce the computational burden by focusing on the hours in which the system faces a high risk of not meeting load—typically hours with high loads or LOLPs.

Several studies have compared the accuracy of approximation methods and reliability-based approaches, such as the ELCC method, for calculating capacity value of wind and photovoltaic (PV) solar systems. For example, Bernow et al. [14] and El-Sayed [15] estimate the capacity value of a wind plant by considering only the peak-load hours. They use the average capacity factor of wind during peak-load hours, defined as the actual output of the plant during those hours divided by its nameplate capacity, as a proxy for the capacity value. Such comparisons have not, however, been carried out for CSP.

Milligan and Parsons [16] calculate the capacity value of wind by considering a set of "risky" hours, as opposed to only peak-load hours. They introduce three different approximation methods, which differ based on the set of hours examined. One technique uses the average capacity factor during the peak-load hours, whereas another uses the capacity factor during the peak-LOLP hours. A third technique uses the highest-load hours but normalizes the capacity factors by the LOLPs. This technique places higher weight on the capacity factor of the wind plant during hours with high LOLPs. Milligan and Parsons have applied these techniques to the top 1% to 30% of hours and have shown that the approximation can approach the ELCC metric if a suitable number of hours are considered. Their results suggest that using the top 10% of hours is typically sufficient.

Milligan and Porter [17] survey capacity valuation methods applied to wind by different utilities and regional transmission organizations. They note that many entities use time-based, as opposed to reliability-based, approximation techniques for capacity valuations. The PJM Interconnection,[3] for instance, uses the capacity factor of a wind plant between the hours 3 p.m. and 7 p.m. from June 1 through August 30 to calculate the plant's capacity credit. This approach does not require any reliability modeling and is therefore very computationally simple. The New York Independent System Operator (ISO) calculates the summer and winter capacity value of its existing wind plants separately. The capacity factor of a wind plant between 2 p.m. and 6 p.m. in June, July, and August of the previous year determines its summer capacity value. The capacity factor between 4 p.m. and 8 p.m. in December, January, and February of the previous year determines its winter capacity values. Another example is the Electric Reliability Council of Texas (ERCOT), which uses the average output of a wind plant between 4 p.m. and 6 p.m. in July and August [17].

The following sections describe some of these approximation techniques in further detail.

2.2.1. Highest-Load Hours Approximation Method

The highest-load hours approximation method is the simplest approach that can be used to obtain an estimate of a generator's capacity value. This approach uses the average capacity factor of the CSP plant during the highest-load hours as an approximation for the capacity value. The number of hours considered is important since the capacity factor can be highly sensitive to this parameter. This study compares three cases in which the top 10, top 100, and top 10% (or top 876) of load hours are used. Our results indicate that considering only the top 10 load hours results in an approximation that is closest to the ELCC metric. It is worth contrasting this with capacity-factor-based approximations of the capacity value of wind. Milligan and Parsons [16] show that the top 10% load hours give an approximation that is closest to the ELCC.

2.2.2. Highest Loss of Load Probability Hours Approximation Method

The highest-LOLP hours approximation method is similar to that described in Section 2.2.1, except that it uses the highest-LOLP as opposed to highest-load hours. Since this technique requires the LOLPs of the original system to be computed, this is a more computationally expensive technique than an approximation based on the highest-load hours.

This approximation also requires more system data to compute the LOLPs. This technique is, however, less computationally burdensome than an ELCC calculation since the LOLEs do not need to be iteratively recomputed in order to equate the LOLEs of the system with the CSP and conventional generator added. If the generating capacities and EFORs of the generators are the same across all of the hours of the year, then this technique will yield the same capacity value estimate as an approximation based on the highest-load hours. This is because, in such a case, the highest-LOLP hours will also be the highest-load hours.

2.2.3. Loss-of-Load-Probability-Weighted Highest-Load Hours Approximation Method

The weighted LOLP-based approximation method also uses the capacity factor of the CSP plant during the highest-load hours. The capacity factors are weighted, however, based on the hourly LOLPs. This weighting is done since the capacity provided by the CSP is especially needed during hours with higher LOLPs. The weights are obtained as:

$$w_i = \frac{LOLP_i}{\sum_{j=1}^{T} LOLP_j} \tag{4}$$

where w_i is the weight in hour i, $LOLP_i$ is the LOLP in hour i, and T is the number of hours in the study. These weights are then used to calculate the weighted average capacity factor of the CSP plant in the highest-load hours as:

$$CV = \sum_{i=1}^{T} w_i.CF_i \tag{5}$$

where CV is the approximated capacity value of the CSP plant, CF_i is the capacity factor of the CSP plant in hour i, and T' is the number of hours used in the approximation. Our results show that this method yields capacity value approximations that are closest to the ELCC metric.

3. CONCENTRATING SOLAR POWER MODEL

Unlike wind or solar PV, a CSP plant with TES is a partially dispatchable generation technology. This is because when TES is incorporated into a CSP plant, the plant operator has the option (within the capacity limits of the TES system) of using solar energy to either drive the steam turbine in the powerblock or to store the thermal energy instead. Since stored energy can supplement the output of a CSP plant during a system shortage event, the capacity value of a CSP plant will depend on its dispatch. Capacity value estimations involving conventional generators assume that the plants will always be operated in an "optimal" fashion. Thus, we must model the dispatch decisions made by the CSP operator to capture these effects. We assume that the CSP plant will be operated to maximize revenues, based on wholesale market price signals. As such, we base our model on that developed by Sioshansi and Denholm [19], which assumes that the CSP plant is operated to maximize revenues from energy sales. We also consider a case, which we discuss in Section 6.2, in which the CSP plant participates in an energy and capacity market, and the plant is operated to maximize the sum of energy and capacity payments. It should be noted that these are not the only markets in which a CSP plant could participate. Sioshansi and Denholm [19] study CSP participating in energy and ancillary service markets. Moreover, in some cases, such as if the CSP plant has sold its energy through a forward contract, the plant will not necessarily adjust its output based on spot market price signals. As such, there are other operational scenarios that would yield different dispatch decisions and capacity values from what we derive based on these models.

Figure 1 provides a schematic of a parabolic trough CSP plant including the three main components (solar field, TES, and power block). The modeling of each of the components and the system as a whole is described in more detail in the following paragraphs.

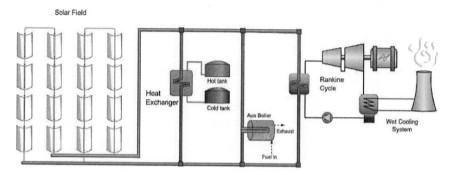

Figure 1. Schematic of a parabolic trough CSP plant with TES.

Our optimization model consists of two main parts. The first part is based on the Solar Advisor Model (SAM), a software program that simulates the dynamics of a CSP plant [20]. SAM takes weather data, including solar radiation and ambient temperature, for each of the locations as an input and is used to determine how much thermal energy is collected by the solar field of the CSP plant in each hour. SAM also accounts for temperature effects on the efficiency of the solar field in collecting solar thermal energy. These data are then used as an input to the mixed-integer program (MIP), which is the second part of our model. The MIP model takes the solar field output as given and determines how much net energy to put into storage and deliver to the powerblock in each hour to maximize revenues.

In order to give the formulation of the general MIP model, which can model both CSP plants with and without TES, we first define the following model parameters:

s: Charging power capacity of TES (MW-t)

d: Discharging power capacity of TES (MW-t)

η: Hours of storage

ρ: Hurly TES energy losses (%)

φ: Roundtrip TES efficiency losses (%)

$Ph\text{-}$ (.): HTF pump parasitic function

τ: Rated thermal capacity of powerblock (MW-t)

τ^{-}, τ^{+}: Minimum and maximum operating level of powerblock, respectively (% of capacity)

SU: Powerblock startup energy (% of capacity)

u: Powerblock minimum up time

f(.): Powerblock heat rate function

P_b(.) Powerblock parasitic function

c: Variable generation cost ($/MWh-e)

SF_t: Energy from solar field in hour (MWh-t)

M^e_t Market-clearing price of energy in hour ($/MWh-e)
We also define the following decision variables of the model:

l_t: Storage level of TES at the end of hour (MWh-t)
st: Energy put into TES in hour (MWh-t)
dt: Energy taken out of TES in hour (MWh-t)
et: Electric energy sold in hour (MWh-e)
τt: Energy put into powerblock in hour (MWh-t)
ut: Binary variable indicating powerblock is up in hour
rt: Binary variable indicating powerblock is started in hour

The formulation of the model is then as follows:

$$max \sum_{t \in T} (M^e_t - c).e_t, \tag{6}$$

$$\text{s.t. } l_t = \rho.l_{t-1} + s_t - d_t, \qquad \forall t \in T \tag{7}$$

$$0 \le l_t \le \eta.\bar{s}, \qquad \forall t \in T \tag{8}$$

$$0 \le s_t \le \bar{s}, \qquad \forall t \in T \tag{9}$$

$$0 \le d_t \le \bar{d}, \qquad \forall t \in T \tag{10}$$

$$s_t - \phi.d_t + \tau_t + SU.\bar{\tau}.r_t \le SF_t \qquad \forall t \in T \tag{11}$$

$$e_t = f(\tau_t) - P_h(d_t) - P_b(f(\tau_t)) \qquad \forall t \in T \tag{12}$$

$$\tau^-.\bar{\tau}.u_t \le \tau_t \le \tau^+.\bar{\tau}.u_t \qquad \forall t \in T \tag{13}$$

$$r_t \ge u_t - u_{t-1} \qquad \forall t \in T \tag{14}$$

$$u_t \ge \sum_{j=t-\bar{u}}^{t} r_j \qquad \forall t \in T \tag{15}$$

$$u_t, r_t \in \{0,1\} \qquad \forall t \in T \tag{16}$$

The objective function (6) maximizes revenues from energy sales. Constraint (7) is a flow-balance constraint that determines the amount of energy in storage at the end of hour t as a function of the amount of energy in storage at the end of hour t-1 and hour t charge and discharge decisions. The term ρ, which multiplies the storage level at the end of hour t-1, captures heat losses that will naturally occur within the TES system. These losses are assumed to be 0.031% based on tests conducted at the Solar Two CSP Plant in California

[21]-[22]. Constraints (8) − (10) set power and energy restrictions on TES charging and discharging. Note that by setting the parameter η, which represents the number of hours of storage in the TES system, at zero, this model can simulate a CSP plant without TES. Constraint (11) requires total thermal energy used by the CSP plant in any hour to be no greater than the energy collected by the solar field. Total thermal energy used by the CSP plant consists of the sum of net energy charged into storage and energy delivered to the powerblock. The term φ in this constraint captures first-law roundtrip efficiency losses when energy is put through the storage cycle. These losses, which we assume to be 1.5% [19], account for energy losses in an indirect TES system due to temperature differences of the heat-transfer fluid (HTF) going into and out of TES. Constraint (12) defines the amount of electric energy produced by the CSP plant in terms of the efficiency of the powerblock and parasitic loads of various CSP plant components. The heat rate function $f(\cdot)$ in constraint (12) **represents the powerblock's efficiency in converting thermal energy to electricity.** The functions $P_h(\cdot)$ and $P_b(\cdot)$ represent HTF pump and powerblock parasitics, respectively. We assume in this analysis that the powerblock is wet-cooled, which implies that temperature will have a negligible effect on the efficiency of the plant. A dry-cooled powerblock could be modeled by multiplying $f(\cdot)$ by a temperature-based correction factor [19]. All of these functions are approximated as being piecewise-linear, which guarantee the linearity of the MIP. Constraint (13) sets power capacity restrictions when the CSP plant is online. Constraint (14) defines the powerblock startup variable in terms of the online variables, while constraint (15) ensures that the minimum up-time requirement is met. Constraint (16) is imposed to ensure the integrality of commitment and startup variables.

Although different CSP technologies, including parabolic troughs, power towers, and Stirling dish systems exist, our analysis focuses on parabolic troughs. Nevertheless, this model is sufficiently general to simulate other CSP technologies. Parabolic trough CSP systems consist of three separate but interrelated parts: the solar field, the powerblock, and the TES system. As such, these three components can be sized differently, each of which can affect the operation and capacity value of the plant. The size of the solar field is typically measured either based on the area that the field covers or by using the concept of the solar multiple (SM). The SM reflects the relative size of the solar field. A plant with an SM of 1 is sized to provide sufficient thermal energy to operate the powerblock at its rated capacity under reference conditions. We measure the size of the solar field using the SM and consider a range of solar field sizes. The size of the TES is measured based on its power and energy capacity. We assume that the power capacity of the TES system is such that the powerblock can operate at its rated capacity using energy from TES only. The energy capacity of TES is typically measured by the number of megawatt-hours of thermal energy (MWh-t) that the system can store or by the number of hours of storage. We use the latter convention and define hours of storage as the number of hours that storage can be charged at its power capacity, which is also reflected in constraint (8) of the model. Defining hours of storage in terms of charging or discharging hours will be nearly identical because of the high roundtrip efficiency of the TES system. The size of the powerblock is typically measured based on its rated output, measured in megawatts of electricity (MW-e). Since the solar field and TES are sized relative to the powerblock size, we hold the capacity of the powerblock fixed at 110 MW-e. Moreover, we base the operating characteristics of the CSP plant on the baseline CSP system modeled in SAM version 2.0. This system assumes that the powerblock can be operated at up to 115% of its design capacity, which yields a maximum output of about 120 MW-e net of parasitic loads.

We also assume that the powerblock has a 6% EFOR, based on the system modeled in SAM.

Although our analysis assumes a parabolic trough CSP plant, our results can provide bounds on the capacity value of other CSP technologies. One technology currently under development is a salt tower CSP plant with direct TES. Such a plant would put all of the thermal energy collected by the solar field into a storage tank first, from which energy can then be fed into the powerblock. Such a design completely decouples solar energy collection from electricity generation, which makes the technology potentially more flexible than parabolic trough systems. The added flexibility from direct storage implies that salt tower plants should have better performance and capacity values than our estimates assuming a parabolic trough system with indirect TES. Parabolic trough developers are considering salt-HTF systems, which will also benefit from the added flexibility and improved performance of direct storage.

In order to simplify the analysis, we assume that the CSP operator knows future weather and price patterns with perfect foresight in optimizing the dispatch of the plant. We further assume that the operation of the CSP plant is optimized 24 hours at a time, using a 48-hour optimization horizon.

This 48-hour horizon is used to ensure that energy is kept in storage at the end of each day if it would provide value on the following day. The operation and profits of CSP plants have been shown to be relatively insensitive to these two assumptions [19].

4. DATA REQUIREMENTS

This study focuses on the sites in the western United States listed in Table 1. Although the sites are not "optimized" for particular market conditions, they have relatively good solar resources and cover several states in the Southwest.

Table 1. Location of CSP Plants

CSP Site	Coordinates
California – Death Valley	36.03o N, 117.45o W
California – Imperial Valley	33.65o N, 116.05o W
Arizona	32.57o N, 112.45o W
Nevada	36.55o N, 116.45o W
New Mexico	34.35o N, 107.35o W

The ELCC metric and approximation techniques described in Section 2.2 are used to estimate the capacity value of a CSP plant with and without TES during the years 1998–2005. These capacity value estimates will be highly sensitive to the coincidence between loads and solar resource, so accurate system data is vital for these calculations. Data requirements and sources used for this analysis are listed below.

1.   Conventional generator data

This analysis uses the rated capacity and EFOR of each generator in the Western Electricity Coordinating Council (WECC) region.[4]

The rated capacities are obtained from Form 860 (Annual Electric Generator Report) data filed with the U.S. Department of Energy's Energy Information Administration (EIA) [24]. The EIA data specifies a winter and summer capacity, which capture the effect of ambient temperature on the maximum operating point of thermal generators.

The EIA data also specify the prime mover and generating fuel of each generator. These data are combined with the North American Electric Reliability Corporation's (NERC's) Generating Availability Data System (GADS) to estimate the EFOR of each generator [25]. The GADS data give historical average EFORs for generators based on generating capacity and technology.

The conventional generator used as the benchmark unit in the ELCC calculation is a natural-gas-fired combustion turbine with an EFOR of 7%, which is based on the EFOR reported in GADS.

2.   Hourly load data

Hourly historical WECC load data for the years 1998–2005 are obtained from Form 714 filings with the Federal Energy Regulatory Commission (FERC) [26].

The FERC data includes load reports for nearly all of the load-serving entities (LSEs) and utilities in the WECC, although some smaller municipalities and cooperatives are not reflected in the data.

One issue with these load data is that LSEs do not always properly account for daylight savings time in their reports. As such, we also conduct a sensitivity analysis, which is described in Section 5.2, in which we shift all loads forward and backward one hour to bound the potential effect of misreported load data.

3.   CSP generation profile

In order to provide the most robust capacity value estimates, multiple years of CSP generation data is needed. Since no CSP plants are operating at the exact study locations,[5] we model the operation of a CSP plant using the optimization model developed by Sioshansi and Denholm [19].

Data requirements for the model include hourly weather and historical energy price data for each location. Hourly weather data are obtained from the National Solar Radiation Data Base.[6]

For the two CSP plants in California, the California ISO market-clearing price of energy for the SP15 zone is used for the energy price in the optimization model (both of the plants studied are located in southern California, which the SP15 zone covers).

For CSP plants in Arizona, Nevada, and New Mexico, load lambda data for Arizona Public Service (APS), Nevada Power (NP), and PNM (the largest utility in New Mexico) are used, respectively. The load lambda data are obtained from Form 714 filing with FERC [26]. Since load lambda data for APS in the year 1999 is not available, capacity values for the Arizona site are not calculated for this year.

5. CAPACITY VALUE OF A CONCENTRATING SOLAR POWER PLANT WITHOUT THERMAL ENERGY STORAGE

We begin by first computing capacity values of CSP plants without TES. These calculations use CSP generation patterns, which are optimized using the model described in equations (6) – (16) in the ELCC and capacity factor calculations. Since we hold the size of the powerblock fixed, the SM is the only size parameter that is adjusted in the plants that we simulate. Figure 2 summarizes the average (over the eight years studied) annual capacity values obtained based on the ELCC method. The capacity values are all normalized by the maximum net output of the CSP plant, which is 120 MW-e.[7]

Figure 2 shows that the SM has a direct impact on the capacity value of the CSP plant. This is because a CSP plant with a small solar field will often operate below its rated capacity, reducing its capacity value. As the solar field size increases, more thermal energy will be available during such hours, increasing the capacity value. On the other hand, a large solar field will lead to greater capital costs and if the CSP plant does not have TES, excess thermal energy that would exceed the powerblock rating will be wasted [19]. Sioshansi and Denholm [19] provide estimates of the amount of solar thermal energy wasted by a CSP plant without TES, as a function of solar field size. While the range of SMs shown is 1.0–3.0, the typical range of SMs for plants with storage is closer to 1.3–1.5. The optimal solar field size for a CSP plant without TES will depend on the relative capital cost of the components and the incremental value of the added energy and capacity value. If the CSP plant is coupled with TES, on the other hand, excess energy that would exceed the powerblock rating could be stored and used in later hours. This can make investments in larger solar fields reasonable and also increase the capacity and energy value of the plant.

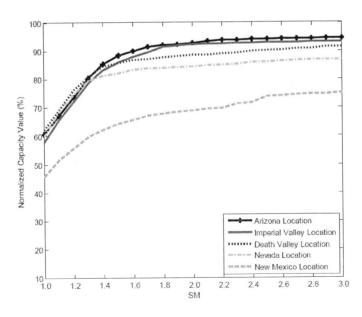

Figure 2. Average annual capacity value of a CSP plant with no TES in different locations.

Selecting an appropriate or optimal solar field size requires an in-depth economic analysis. Figure 2 also shows that the rank ordering of the locations, in terms of capacity value, can vary as a function of solar field size. This is because adjusting the solar field size will change the operation of the CSP plants. In some cases, increasing the SM will allow the powerblock to start up during a high-LOLP hour when it would otherwise not be able to with a smaller solar field due to minimum-load constraints on the powerblock. For instance, with an SM of 1.4 or less, the Death Valley location has the highest capacity value, whereas the Arizona location has the highest capacity value with an SM of 1.5 or greater.

Figure 2 represents average annual capacity values over the eight years of study. Capacity values can, however, vary significantly from year to year. This is also true for conventional generators, since a forced outage during a high-LOLP hour would yield a low capacity value in the year in which it occurs. Figure 3 shows capacity values for a CSP plant at the New Mexico location over the eight individual years. The differences in annual capacity values reinforce the fact that several years of generation data are required to provide a robust capacity value estimate for CSP.

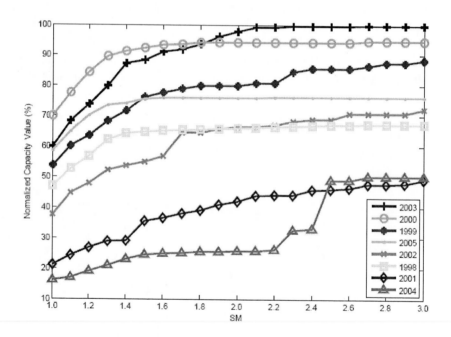

Figure 3. Annual capacity value of a CSP plant with no TES at the New Mexico location.

Figure 3 shows that with an SM of 1.0, the capacity value of the CSP plant in the year 2000 is more than four times greater than that in the year 2004. In order to better understand the reason behind this, the operations of the CSP plant during the highest-LOLP hours in those two years need to be compared. In the year 2000, the highest-LOLP hours occur on August 1. Figure 4 shows the hourly output of the CSP plant and LOLPs on this day and shows that the plant has an average output of about 85 MW-e during the highest-LOLP hours. Since the output of the CSP is correlated with the LOLPs, a high capacity value for the plant can be expected. Figure 5 shows the amount of thermal solar energy collected by the solar field, which reflects the amount of solar irradiance, and load data. As can be seen in Figure 5, load data is strongly correlated with solar energy. This correlation is reasonable during a summer day due to the fact that summer loads are driven by cooling needs, which will be correlated with solar availability.

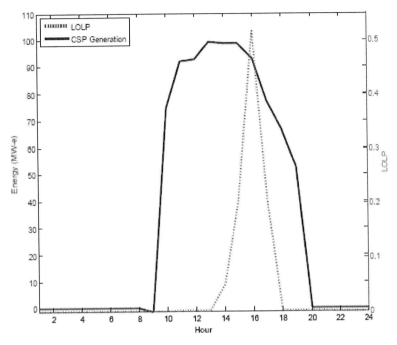

Figure 4. Hourly LOLPs and dispatch of a CSP plant with no TES at the New Mexico location with an SM of 1.0 on August 1, 2000.

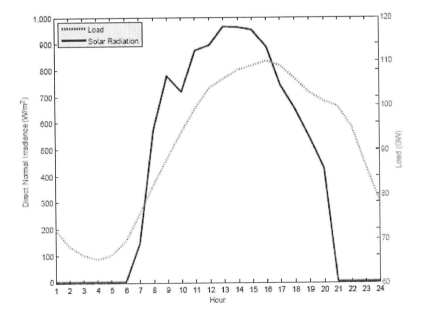

Figure 5. Hourly loads and solar radiation at the New Mexico location on August 1, 2000.

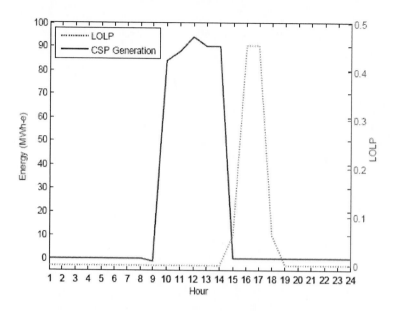

Figure 6. Hourly LOLPs and dispatch of a CSP plan with no TES at the New Mexico location with an SM of 1.0 on August 10, 2004.

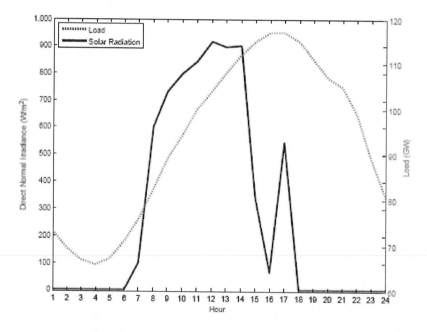

Figure 7. Hourly loads and solar radiation at the New Mexico location on August 10, 2004.

Figure 6 shows the operations of the CSP plant on August 10, 2004, which is the day with the highest LOLPs of that year. The figure shows that CSP generation is not correlated with LOLPs in this case. Hence, the capacity value of the CSP plant is relatively lower in 2004 compared to 2000. Figure 7 shows the amount of thermal solar energy collected by the solar field and load data for the day. Unlike the case shown in Figure 5, electricity demand is less correlated with solar energy, which causes lower capacity value in 2004.

Due to computational complexity and data requirements of the ELCC method, using an approximation method to estimate the capacity value of a CSP plant may be preferred. Doing so can significantly reduce the computational time of the estimation but may affect the accuracy of the results. We compare the ELCC calculations to three approximation techniques that are based on the capacity factor of the plant. The first two use the highest-load and highest-LOLP hours of the year, whereas the third uses the highest-load hours but weighs the capacity factors by the hourly LOLPs. These three techniques are referred to as the "Top Loads," "Top LOLP," and "Top Weighted" techniques, hereafter.

Figures 8 through 10 show the average annual capacity values of a CSP plant at the Imperial Valley location, based on the three approximation techniques. The figures show the capacity value estimates when considering the top 10, top 100, and top 10% of hours of each year, respectively.

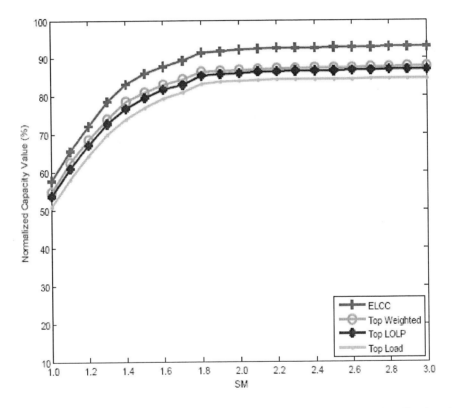

Figure 8. Annual average capacity value of a CSP plant with no TES at the Imperial Valley location using the ELCC metric and approximation techniques that select the top 10 hours.

Comparing Figures 8 through 10 shows that using an approximation method that considers only the top 10 hours of each year yields a capacity value estimate that is closest to the ELCC metric. The figures also show that the "Top Weighted" approximation tends to have greater accuracy. Similar results are obtained for the other sites. This is demonstrated in Figures 11 through 14, which compare the three approximation techniques when considering only the top 10 hours of each year to the ELCC calculation for the other locations.

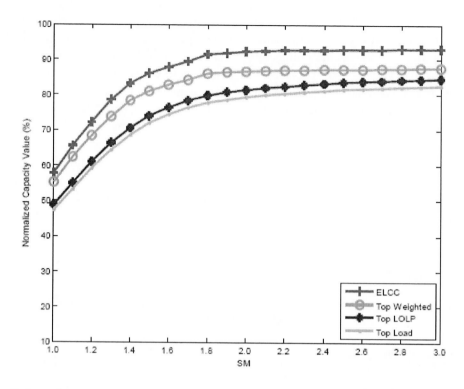

Figure 9. Annual average capacity value of a CSP plant with no TES at the Imperial Valley location.

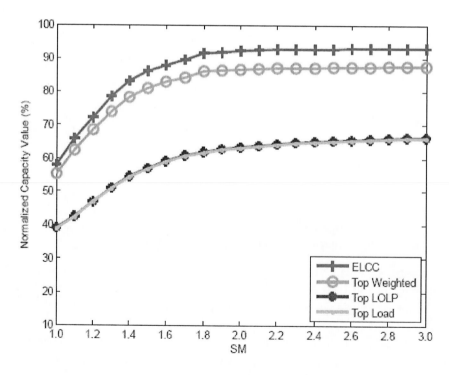

Figure 10. Annual average capacity value of a CSP plant with no TES at the Imperial Valley location using the ELCC metric and approximation techniques that select the top 10% of hours.

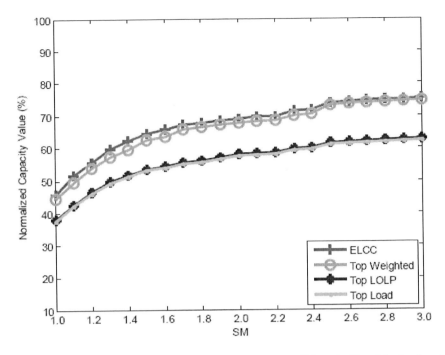

Figure 11. Annual average capacity value of a CSP plant with no TES at the New Mexico location using the ELCC metric and approximation techniques that select the top 10 hours.

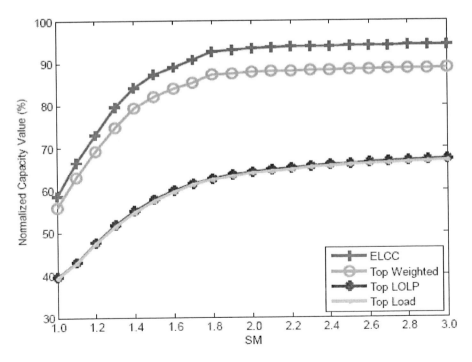

Figure 12. Annual average capacity value of a CSP plant with no TES at the Death Valley location.

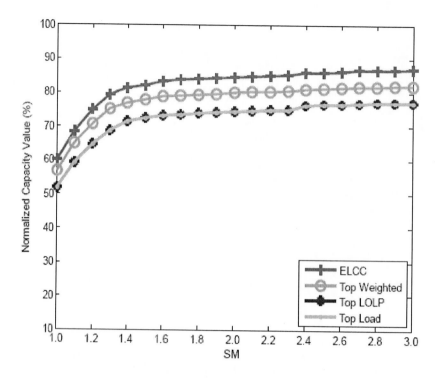

Figure 13. Annual average capacity value of a CSP plant with no TES at the Nevada location using the ELCC metric and approximation techniques that select the top 10 hours.

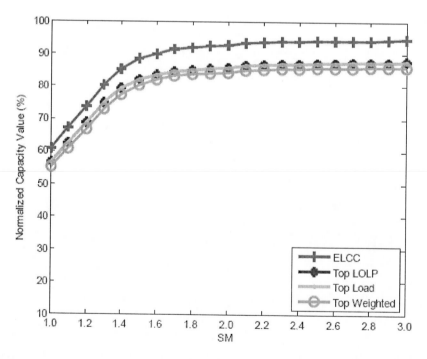

Figure 14. Annual average capacity value of a CSP plant with no TES at the Arizona location using the ELCC metric and approximation techniques that select the top 10 hours.

5.1. Effect of Expected Forced Outage Rates on Concentrating Solar Power Capacity Value

Our analysis thus far is based on modeling a system in which the conventional generator set varies from year to year. This is because we only model conventional generators that were in operation in each year, and this generator set changes from year to year as a result of generator construction and retirements. Moreover, the EFORs that are reported in the NERC GADS database are annual values, which will also vary from year to year depending on how many outages actually occurred. We use these annual EFORs to capture the fact that outage rates can vary from year to year. These differences in the conventional generator mix and EFORs can contribute to the differences in the annual capacity values of the CSP plants, which are shown in Figure 3.

Figure 15 compares the average annual ELCC of a CSP plant at the Imperial Valley location in cases in which these parameters vary to a case in which these parameters are held constant. In the cases in which the parameters are held constant, we use the conventional generator mix that was installed in 2005 and EFORs that are averaged over the eight study years.

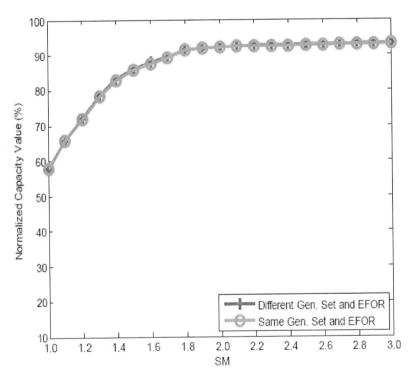

Figure 15. Average annual capacity value of a CSP plant with no TES at the Imperial Valley location based on ELCC metric with constant and varying conventional generator characteristics.

Figure 15 shows that the ELCC values are nearly identical, with very little differences for smaller-sized CSP plants. The other locations have very similar results. As such, we can conclude that variations in the mix and reliability of other generators will have a negligible impact on the capacity value of a CSP plant.

5.2. Effect of Load Errors on Concentrating Solar Power Capacity Value

As noted before, another issue with our capacity value estimates is that some utilities do not properly account for daylight savings time in reporting their hourly loads in FERC Form 714 filings. As such, it is possible that the simulated output of the CSP plant could be offset from the system loads and LOLPs. Since the capacity value of CSP is highly dependent on the correlation between solar resource availability and load, this potential mismatch in the data can lead to different capacity values than what we have estimated thus far. In order to bound the effect of misreported load data, we conduct the same ELCC calculations but shift the loads forward and backward one hour. Figure 16 shows average annual ELCC values for a CSP plant at the Imperial Valley location when the system loads are shifted in this way, and it compares them to the base case in which the reported loads are used without shifting. The figure shows that this shifting in the loads can reduce the estimated capacity value of a CSP plant by up to 5%; the other locations have similar results. The ELCC is reduced regardless of whether the load is shifted forward or backward, which suggests that most of the loads reported in the Form 714 data are correct. This is because solar resource and CSP generation will have some correlation with system loads, and this correlation is maximized when the loads are not shifted.

5.3. Effect of Sub-Hourly Variability on Concentrating Solar Power Capacity Value

Our analysis thus far is based on using hourly solar data and modeled CSP generation to calculate ELCCs and capacity factors. Solar radiation can have noticeable sub-hourly variation due to passing cloud cover. Sub-hourly variation may impact the capacity value and integration costs of many renewable resources, such as wind and solar PV. CSP may not suffer from this issue as much, however, since the HTF of a CSP plant will have some thermal inertia, which can maintain output during a brief reduction in solar radiation. Indeed, a CSP plant with direct TES will not suffer from short-term transients at all since the powerblock is fed by the TES system and not directly from the solar field.

In order to determine the effect of sub-hourly variability on the capacity value of CSP, we compare our ELCC calculations when CSP output is modeled using one-minute and hourly data. We use one-minute solar data for a CSP plant located around the Nevada One site in Boulder City, Nevada. The coordinates of the modeled location are 35.80° N, 114.97° W. We use one-minute weather data from the year 2007 and compare a case in which the CSP plant is modeled using the one-minute data to a case in which hourly averages of the one-minute data are used instead. SAM and the CSP dispatch model are both adapted to model one-minute operations by appropriate scaling of the model variables and parameters.

The same hourly conventional generator and load data are used in both cases; thus, any differences in the ELCC estimates are solely due to the one-minute weather data as opposed to hourly averages. Since the loads are assumed constant during each hour, these ELCC estimates will not capture sub-hourly load variations and potential correlation between these and solar radiation patterns.

Figure 17 shows the ELCC estimates for the CSP plant as a function of the solar field size, using the one-minute and hourly average data. The results show that the hourly average data will provide a close approximation of the ELCC if one-minute data is used. The maximum difference in the ELCC between the one-minute and hourly average data is 5.8%. For most plant configurations, the hourly average data tends to overestimate the ELCC. This is because with one-minute data, subhourly variations in solar radiation can keep the powerblock from running above its minimum operating point. These variations are not fully captured when the one-minute data is averaged.

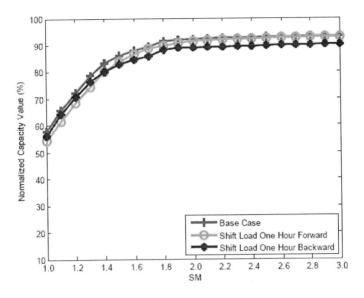

Figure 16. Average annual capacity value of a CSP plant with no TES at the Imperial Valley location based on ELCC metric with loads shifted.

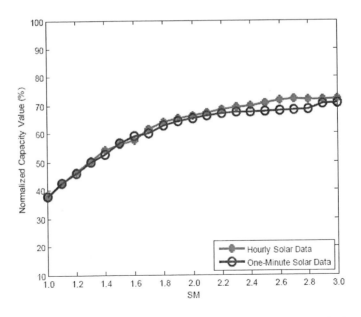

Figure 17. Capacity value of a CSP plant with no TES at the Boulder City, Nevada, location based on ELCC metric while using hourly and one-minute interval solar data.

The differences in the estimated ELCCs are maximized for plants with an SM between 2.4 and 2.8. This is because plants with this configuration have more time periods in which solar radiation variability can prevent the powerblock from starting up, which is not captured without hourly data. Despite these issues, the small difference in the ELCC values suggest that hourly data can provide relatively good capacity value estimates if sub-hourly data is not available or too computationally intensive to work with.

6. CAPACITY VALUE OF A CONCENTRATING SOLAR POWER PLANT WITH THERMAL ENERGY STORAGE

A major benefit of coupling CSP with TES is that TES will make the CSP plant more dispatchable. This is because TES allows the CSP plant to store excess energy collected by the solar field when it is not needed and discharge that energy later when solar resources are lower. Our results in Section 5 clearly show that the ability of a CSP plant to generate electricity in critical peak hours with high loads or LOLPs has a significant impact on capacity value. Therefore, adding TES to a CSP plant can increase its capacity value by allowing it to generate electricity during critical periods when solar resources are not available. As suggested earlier, adding TES to a CSP plant can also make a higher SM more economic since excess thermal solar energy collected by the solar field will not be wasted and can be stored and later used.

Estimating the capacity value of a CSP plant is more complicated when it has a TES system. This is because a proper capacity value estimate must not only account for how much energy the plant generates each hour but also how much energy it could produce using energy in storage.

One must account for energy in storage because if a system shortage event occurs, the CSP plant would, in principle, use energy in storage to help support the system. Modeling energy in storage is difficult because of the energy-limited nature of energy storage. Namely, if energy in TES is used in hour t, then it cannot be used in any hour $s > t$. A previous capacity value estimation technique for energy storage technologies was developed by Tuohy and O'Malley [23] and applied to pumped hydroelectric storage (PHS). Their technique uses operational data to determine the maximum potential output of the PHS device in each hour if the energy in storage is discharged at maximum capacity (based on the available energy in storage).

The capacity value of the PHS device is then estimated from the maximum potential output data using a capacity-factor-based approximation technique.

We apply a similar approach to estimate the capacity value of the CSP plant with TES. As in the case without TES, we assume that the operation of the CSP plant and TES is optimized to maximize the revenues that the CSP plant receives. Once the operation of the CSP plant is established, we can determine the maximum potential output of the CSP plant by first computing the maximum amount of thermal energy that can be delivered from the solar field and TES to the power block in each hour as:

$$\tau_t^{\mu} = \min\{\tau^+.\bar{\tau}, SF_t + \phi.\min\{\bar{d}, \rho.l_{t-1}\} - SU.\bar{\tau}.(1 - u_t)\}$$

$$(17)$$

Equation (17) defines the maximum thermal energy that can be delivered to the powerblock in each hour ($_{\mu}\tau$) as the minimum of the powerblock's rated capacity ($_{.+}\tau\,\tau$) and the sum of thermal energy collected by the solar field and the amount of energy available in TES ($_{1}$ .min{,.} $_{-+t\,t}SF\,dl\,\varphi\,\rho$). Equation (17) assumes that if the powerblock is offline it can be committed within the hour in case of a system shortage event [27]. We can also define how much of the $_{\mu}\tau$ MWh-t is taken from TES as:

$$d_t^{\mu} = \tau_t^{\mu} - SF_t \tag{18}$$

Finally, the maximum potential output of the CSP plant, $e_{t\,\mu,}$ is given by:

$$e_t^{\mu} = f(\tau_t^{\mu}) - P_h(d_t^{\mu}) - P_b(f(\tau_t^{\mu})) \tag{19}$$

Once we determine the maximum potential output, we estimate the capacity value using the top weighted approximation technique considering the 10 highest-load hours of each year since our results in Section 5 show this to be the most accurate approximation. We model the operations of the CSP plant under two different market settings. The first is an energy-only market, in which the CSP plant only receives payments for the electricity that it supplies to the market.

The operation of the CSP plant in the energy-only market setting is optimized using the model given in Section 3 and is represented by objective function (6) and constraints (7) through (16). The other market setting that we examine is one in which the CSP plant can receive energy and capacity payments. In this case the optimization model must be changed to co-optimize the sum of energy and capacity payments. Further details of the capacity payment model are given in Section 6.2.

6.1. Capacity Value of a Concentrating Solar Power Plant with Thermal Energy Storage in an Energy-Only Market

Figures 18 through 22 summarize the average annual capacity value of CSP plants at the different locations that we study.

The figures show that the capacity values are typically increasing with the SM and the hours of TES in the CSP plant, although this relationship is not perfectly monotonic. At all of the locations, adding some TES increases the capacity value of the plant above the no-TES case.

For instance, a CSP plant at the New Mexico location with an SM of 1.5 and no TES has a capacity value of about 78 MW-e. Adding one hour of TES to this plant addresses many of the days on which solar and load are not well correlated and increases its capacity value by 47% to 115 MW-e.

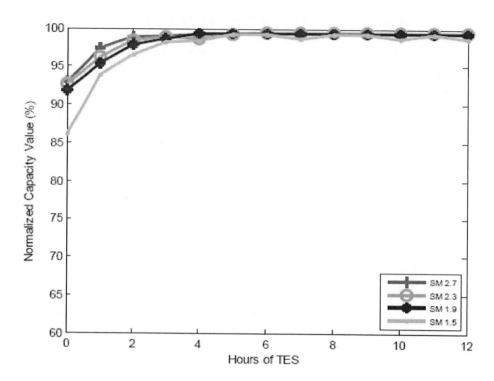

Figure 18. Average annual capacity value of a CSP plant with TES at the Imperial Valley location under an energy-only market setting.

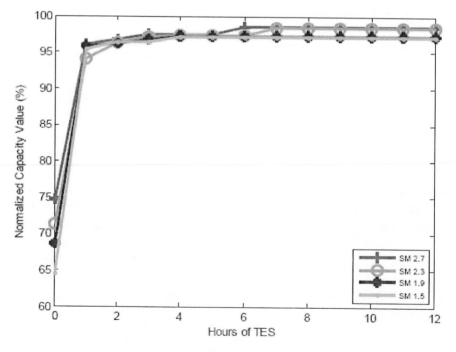

Figure 19. Average annual capacity value of a CSP plant with TES at the New Mexico location under an energy-only market setting.

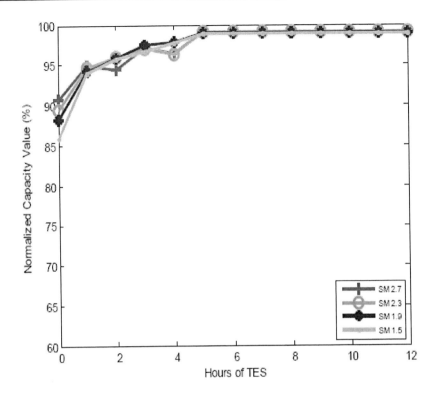

Figure 20. Average annual capacity value of a CSP plant with TES at the Death Valley location under an energy-only market setting.

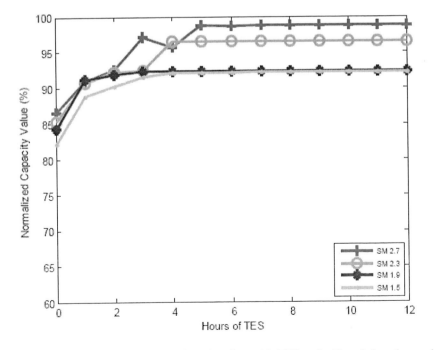

Figure 21. Average annual capacity value of a CSP plant with TES at the Nevada location under an energy-only market setting.

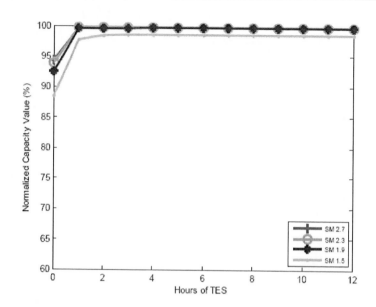

Figure 22. Average annual capacity value of a CSP plant with TES at the Arizona location under an energy-only market setting.

In some cases, however, adding an incremental hour of TES or increasing the solar field size may cause a slight reduction in the capacity value of a plant. This is because different CSP plant configurations will yield different operational decisions, and in some cases a larger CSP plant may have less energy in TES during a high-LOLP hour. For example, a CSP plant at the Nevada location with four hours of TES and an SM of 2.2 has a capacity value of 117 MW-e in 1999. The same CSP plant with an SM of 2.7 would have a lower capacity value of only 95 MW-e in 1999. This difference in the capacity value is due to less energy being in the TES of the larger CSP plant on July 12, which is the day with 5 of the 10 highest hourly LOLPs of the year. The larger CSP plant has less energy in storage because the larger solar field provided sufficient energy to operate the powerblock above its minimum operating point in the afternoon of the previous day. The smaller solar field of the CSP plant with an SM of 2.2 could not meet this minimum-load constraint, and as such the output of the solar field was stored. Thus, the CSP plant with an SM of 2.2 can, on average, generate up to 74 MW-e during the five highest-LOLP hours on July 12. The larger CSP plant with an SM of 2.7 can only generate up to an average of 54 MW-e during these hours. Figure 23 shows the amount of energy in storage and energy collected by the solar field in each hour on July 12 for these two CSP plant configurations.

It is important to note that due to weather patterns on this particular day, the solar field only collects solar energy during hour 18—the output of the field is zero in the remaining hours.

Adding TES can also, in some cases, reduce the capacity value of the CSP plant, although this is less typical. For example, a CSP plant at the Death Valley location with an SM of 2.7 and one hour of TES has a capacity value of 79 MW-e in 1999. Increasing TES by one hour for the same CSP plant reduces its capacity value to 75 MW-e. The reduction in capacity value stems from the fact that energy prices are not necessarily correlated with hours with highest LOLPs, as suggested by Figure 24, which is a scatter plot of California ISO energy prices and LOLPs in the year 1999. The operation of both of the CSP plants on July 12, which is the day on which the highest LOLPs of the year occur, is shown in Figure 25.

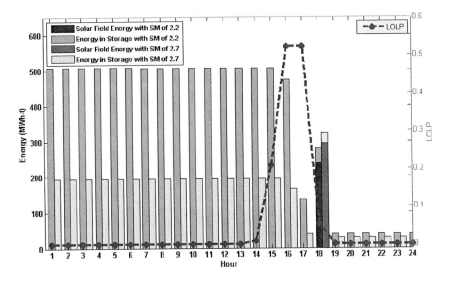

Figure 23. LOLP, energy from solar field and energy in storage for a CSP plant at the Nevada location with four hours of TES and different SM values on July 12, 1999.

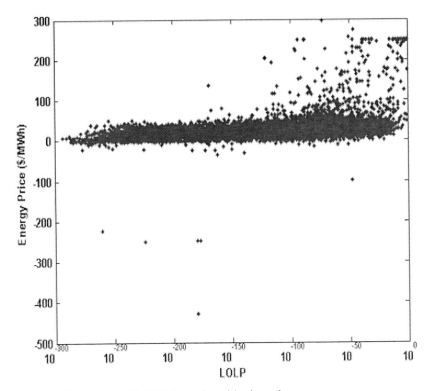

Note: The x-axis used to represent LOLPs has a logarithmic scale.

Figure 24. LOLP versus energy price for the Death Valley location in year 1999.

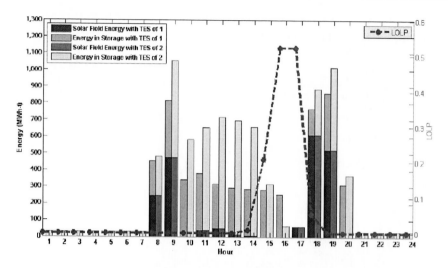

Figure 25. LOLP, energy from solar field and energy in storage for a CSP plant at the Death Valley location with an SM of 2.7 and different TES sizes on July 12, 1999.

Figure 25 shows that in hour 16, during which the LOLP is the highest, the larger CSP plant has less energy in storage compared to the smaller CSP plant. This reduces the capacity value of the larger CSP plant. The reason behind these operations is that in hours 12 through 15 of the day, the larger CSP plant will use energy in TES to generate electricity since energy prices are higher in these hours than in hours during which the highest LOLPs occur. The smaller CSP cannot do so since its smaller TES system does not have sufficient energy in storage to operate above its minimum generation point during these hours. These operational differences leave the smaller CSP plant with more energy in TES during hour 16, which yield the higher capacity value.

6.2. Capacity Value of a Concentrating Solar Power Plant with Thermal Energy Storage in a Capacity Market

In Section 6.1 we estimate the capacity value of a CSP plant with TES in an energy-only market. The results there suggest that adding TES to a CSP plant will tend to increase the capacity value of the plant, although this relationship is not monotonic. This is because energy prices and LOLPs will not always be perfectly correlated, and there can be high-LOLP hours that have lower energy prices than other hours with lower LOLPs. An example of this is demonstrated in Figure 25. An alternative market design that could help reduce the impact of such price and LOLP patterns is an energy and capacity market. Under such a market design, the CSP plant receives both payments for electricity that it generates, as well as the capacity that it provides the system. Many electricity markets have moved toward adopting capacity markets. Even in systems that do not have an explicit capacity market, such as the APS, NP, and PNM service territories, a model that maximizes the sum of energy and capacity payments may be more appropriate. This is because such integrated utilities would likely operate a CSP plant to minimize its overall energy supply costs—which would be akin to our energy revenue maximization. However, such utilities would also likely adjust the operation of their plants to have more energy available in TES during anticipated system shortage events.

The introduction of a capacity market tends to increase the capacity value of a CSP plant since capacity payments typically have performance requirements that are related to the capacity value of a generator. Most capacity markets impose financial penalties on generators that do not meet the performance requirements. Although the specific performance requirements differ from market to market, they are typically related to how much firm capacity a generator has available during system shortage events. Our capacity market model is based on the forward capacity market (FCM) used by ISO New England, although the modeling framework is sufficiently general that it can be adapted to model other markets as well.

6.2.1. Capacity Market Procedures

The objective of a capacity market is to encourage enough generating capacity to enter the system so that reliability requirements are met. This objective is met by a forward capacity auction (FCA).[8] Resources that participate and are selected in the FCA are eligible to receive capacity payments throughout the capacity commitment period based on their capacity commitment obligations. Capacity payments are subject to certain performance requirements, however. Performance requirements are set so that the capacity resources contribute to system reliability during hours in which shortage events could occur. The definition of shortage events will differ between capacity markets. Some markets, such as the FCM, define shortage events as periods during which reserves (spinning and non-spinning reserves) fall below certain levels. This definition does not necessarily imply that supply is less than demand during the shortage event hours. For instance, if the reserve level falls to 1%, generating capacity will still be greater than demand, but due to low reserve levels the probability of having a capacity deficiency is high. Based on this definition, there is a one-to-one relationship between shortage event hours and the hourly LOLPs. In this study, the 10 hours of each year with the highest LOLPs are defined as shortage event hours.

A generator that fails to provide its contracted capacity during a shortage event hour will incur financial penalties. The FCM sets penalties based on the cost of replacement capacity.

We assume that the capacity market uses the cost of a natural-gas-fired combustion turbine, which we assume to be $671/kW in 2008 dollars, to set the penalties. This cost is then translated into an annualized cost of $73.81/kW-year, using an 11% capital charge rate. We assume that the capacity market imposes a penalty that is equal to half of this annualized cost, which is reflective of the penalties imposed in the FCM. We use consumer price index data to deflate the cost of the combustion turbine to previous-year dollars.

6.2.2. Optimization Model

In order to determine the operations of a CSP plant in an energy- and capacity-market setting, our model must be adjusted to maximize the sum of energy and capacity payments and net of any capacity penalties. We follow a similar approach to that used in Section 6.1 and add variables to our optimization model that determine the maximum potential generation from the CSP plant in each hour (based on energy in TES and collected by the solar field). The difference between the firm capacity sold and this maximum potential generation is the shortfall from the capacity commitment, and these shortfalls are penalized in the objective function to reflect capacity penalties. In order to give the formulation of the model, we define the following parameters:

M^c: Market clearing price of capacity ($/MW-year)
PF: Penalty factor for unserved capacity requirements
H: Set of hours during which shortage events occur

We also define the following variables:

$Csold$: Firm capacity sold
e_t^{μ} : Maximum potential net electric energy (MWh-e) produced by powerblock in each hour μ
d_t^{μ} Maximum potential thermal energy taken out of storage (MWh-t) in each hour
τ_t^{μ}: Maximum potential total thermal energy (MWh-t) fed to powerblock in each hour
C_t^{short}: Shortfall from capacity commit t ment in each hour

The formulation of the model is then given by:

$$\max \sum_{t \in T} (M_t^e - c).e_t + M^c.C_{sold} - \sum_{t \in H} (M^c.PF.\frac{C_t^{short}}{C_{sold}}),$$

(20)

s.t. (7)-(16)

$$C_t^{short} \geq C_{sold} - e_t^{\mu} \qquad \forall t \in T$$

(21)

$$d_t^{\mu} \leq \rho.l_{t-1} \qquad \forall t \in T$$

(22)

$$-\phi.d_t^{\mu} + \tau_t^{\mu} + SU.\overline{\tau}.r_t \leq SF_t \qquad \forall t \in T$$

(23)

$$e_t^{\mu} = f(\tau_t^{\mu}) - P_h(d_t^{\mu}) - P_b(f(\tau_t^{\mu})) \quad \forall t \in T$$

(24)

$$\tau^-.\overline{\tau}.u_t \leq \tau_t^{\mu} \leq \tau^+.\overline{\tau}.u_t \qquad \forall t \in T$$

(25)

Objective function (20) maximizes the sum of net energy and capacity revenues. The last term in the objective function corresponds to penalties associated with shortfalls from capacity commitments.

Constraints (7) through (16), which are from the original energy-only model, are included since the same underlying constraints on the operation of the CSP plant apply. Constraint (21) defines the hourly capacity commitment shortfall as the difference between firm capacity sold and the maximum potential net electrical generation of the CSP plant. Constraint (22) restricts the potential thermal energy taken out of storage (MWh-t) in each hour, based on the ending storage level of the previous hour. Constraint (23) limits the total amount of potential thermal energy used in the CSP plant to not be greater than the energy collected by the solar field. Constraint (24) defines the maximum potential output of the CSP plant in each hour. Finally, constraint (25) imposes restrictions on potential capacity of the CSP plant when the powerblock is online.

Because the penalty term in the objective function is non-linear in the variables, we solve this model by fixing the value of c_{sold} and solving the model iteratively until finding a maximum. For the cases that we consider, selling 120 MW-e of capacity (the maximum net output of the CSP plant) maximizes CSP revenues.

6.2.3. Results

The model, given by objective function (20) and constraints (7) through (16) and (21) through (25), is used to determine the optimized operation of the CSP plant in each hour. We then apply the same capacity-factor-based approximation technique used in Section 6.1 to estimate the capacity value of the plant. Figures 26 through 30 summarize the average annual capacity value of the CSP plants at the different locations. Figures 26 through 30 show the benefits of implementing a capacity payment scheme, as opposed to an energy-only market. Adding capacity payments tends to slightly increase the capacity value of the CSP plant. Moreover, the capacity value is more monotonic in the size of the plant. There are still, however, some cases in which increasing the size of a CSP plant can result in a slight reduction in the capacity value.

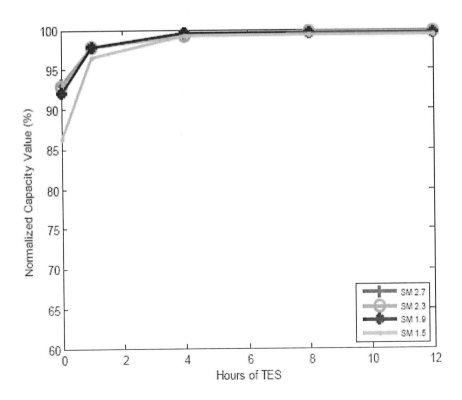

Figure 26. Average annual capacity value of a CSP plant with TES at the Imperial Valley location under an energy and capacity market setting.

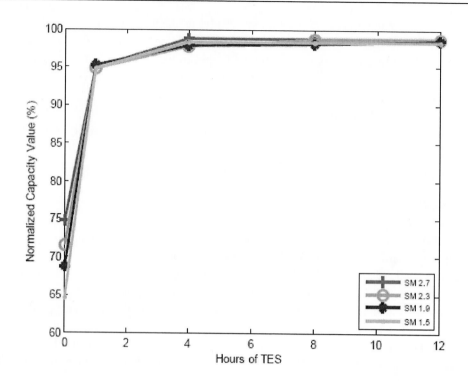

Figure 27. Average annual capacity value of a CSP plant with TES at the New Mexico location under an energy and capacity market setting.

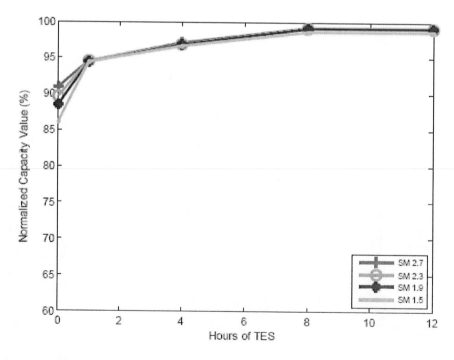

Figure 28. Average annual capacity value of a CSP plant with TES at the Death Valley location under an energy and capacity market setting.

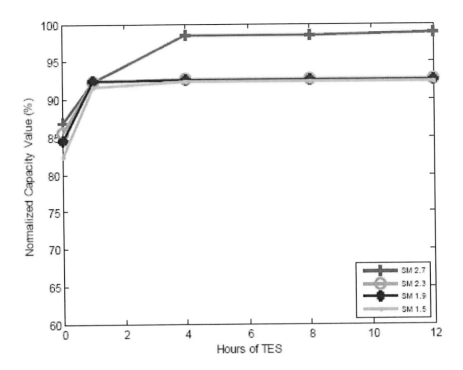

Figure 29. Average annual capacity value of a CSP plant with TES at the Nevada location under an energy and capacity market setting. [9]

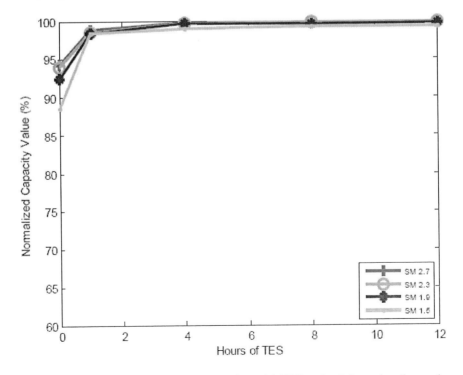

Figure 30. Average annual capacity value of a CSP plant with TES at the Arizona location under an energy and capacity market setting.

Even when the capacity payment is added, there may still be high-LOLP hours in which the value of energy (when accounting for the energy price and capacity penalty) is lower than other hours with lower LOLPs. However, these cases are rare and their magnitude (in terms of capacity value reductions) is relatively small. More broadly, contrasting these results with the energy-only market design, and Figure 23 in particular, demonstrates the benefit of capacity payments (or co-optimizing the energy and capacity value of a CSP plant) in improving the system benefits of CSP. Figure 23 shows that the larger CSP plant has a lower capacity value because of poor correlation between energy prices and LOLPs and the lack of solar resource during high-LOLP hours. If a CSP plant can anticipate potential high-LOLP periods or shortage events, the total value of the plant to the system can be drastically increased by slightly adjusting plant operations.

CONCLUSIONS

This study estimates the capacity value of a CSP plant at a variety of locations within the WECC, while accounting for rational dispatch behavior of a CSP operator. This is done by optimizing the operation of the CSP plant and by using standard reliability-based capacity value estimation techniques.

Although the ELCC metric is the most accurate estimation technique, we show that capacity-factor-based approximation methods can closely estimate the ELCC value. When introducing TES, the capacity value of the CSP plant is more difficult to estimate since one must account for energy in storage.

We apply the capacity-factor-based technique used by Tuohy and O'Malley [23] under two different market settings: an energy-only market and an energy and capacity market.

Our results show that adding TES to a CSP plant can increase its capacity value significantly at all of the locations. Adding a single hour of TES significantly increases the capacity value above the no-TES case, in most cases to above 90%. Although additional hours of TES increase the capacity value of the plant, their marginal benefit is less than the first hour of TES.

Nevertheless, Sioshansi and Denholm [19] show that a greater number of hours of TES can have incremental energy and ancillary service benefits. Since energy prices, LOLPs, and solar resource will not be perfectly correlated, the use of capacity payments (or co-optimization of energy and capacity value) can significantly increase the value of a CSP plant to the power system compared to an energy-only market.

The capacity value estimates we provide examine a single CSP plant, which will have a marginal effect on the rest of the system.

Clearly, changes in the generation mix or load patterns could affect the capacity value of a CSP plant.

Adding more CSP (or PV) plants, especially if they are concentrated at similar locations in the system, can reduce the marginal capacity value of additional CSP capacity.

Adding TES to a CSP plant can alleviate this reduction in the marginal capacity value, however, since it gives the CSP plant additional flexibility in dispatching its generation.

REFERENCES

[1]   Söder, L.; Amelin, M. "A Review of Different Methodologies Used for Calculation of Wind Power Capacity Credit." *Proceedings of the IEEE Power Engineering Society General Meeting; 2008, Pittsburgh, PA, 2008.*

[2]   Pudaruth, G.R.; Li, F. "Capacity Credit Evaluation: A Literature Review." *Third International Conference on Electric Utility Deregulation and Restructuring and Power Technologies, DRPT 2008, Nanjing, China;* pp. 2719–2724.

[3]   Milligan, M.; Porter, K. "Determining the Capacity Value of Wind: An Updated Survey of Methods and Implementation." *WindPower 2008; June 2008, Houston, Texas.*

[4]   Billinton, R.; Allan, R. *Reliability Evaluation of Power Systems.* 2nd edition. New York: Plenum Press, 1984.

[5]   Kahn, E.P. "Effective Load Carrying Capability of Wind Generation: Initial Results with Public Data." *The Electricity Journal;* Vol. 17, Iss. 10, December 2004; pp. 85–95.

[6]   Amelin, M. "Comparison of Capacity Credit Calculation Methods for Conventional Power Plants and Wind Power." *IEEE Trans. Power Syst.;* Vol. 24, No. 2, May 2009.

[7]   Ensslin, C.; Milligan, M.; Holttinen, H.; O'Malley, M.; Keane, A. "Current Methods to Calculate Capacity Credit of Wind Power, IEA collaboration." *Proceedings 2008 IEEE Power & Energy Society General Meeting; 2008,* p. 3.

[8]   Milligan, M.; Parsons, B. "A Comparison and Case Study of Capacity Credit Algorithms for Intermittent Generators." *Proceedings Solar '97; April 27–30, 1997, Washington, D.C.* NREL/CP-440-22591. Golden, CO: National Renewable Energy Laboratory, March 1997.

[9]   Keane, A.; Milligan, M.; DAnnunzio, C.; Dent, C.J.; Dragoon, K.; Hasche, B.; Holttinen, H.; Samaan, N.; S¨oder, L.; OMalley, M. "Capacity Value of Wind Power." *IEEE Trans. Power Syst.;* forthcoming.

[10] D'Annunzio, C.; Santoso, S. "Noniterative Method to Approximate the Effective Load Carrying Capability of a Wind Plant." *IEEE Trans. Energy Conv.;* Vol. 23, No. 2, June 2008; pp. 544–550.

[11] Martin, B.; Diesendorf, M. "Calculating the Capacity Credit of Wind Power." *Proceedings 4th Biennial Conference University of Queensland, August 1980, Brisbane, Queensland, Australia;* pp. 36–42.

[12] Garver, L.L. "Effective Load Carrying Capability of Generating Units." *IEEE Trans. on PAS;* Vol. PAS-85, August 1966; pp. 910–919. Hoff, T.; Perez, R.; Ross, J.P.; Taylor, M. "Photovoltaic Capacity Valuation Methods." SEPA REPORT # 02-08. Washington, DC: Solar Electric Power Association, 2008.

[14] Bernow, S.; Biewald, B.; Singh, D. "Modelling Renewable Electric Resources: A Case Study of Wind Reliability." Presented at the NARUC-DOE National Conference on Renewable Energy; Savannah, GA, October 1993.

[15] El-Sayed, M. "Substitution Potential of Wind Energy in Egypt." *Energy Policy;* Vol. 30, 2002; pp. 681–687.

[16] Milligan, M.; Parsons, B. "A Comparison and Case Study of Capacity Credit Algorithms for Wind Power Plants." *Wind Energy;* Vol. 23, Iss. 3, 1999; pp. 159–166.

[17] Milligan, M.; Porter, K. "The Capacity Value of Wind in the United States: Methods and Implementation." *The Electricity Journal;* Vol. 19, Iss. 2, March 2006.

[18] Milligan, M. *Modeling Utility-scale Wind Power Plants Part 2: Capacity Credit.* NREL/TP500-27514. Golden, CO: National Renewable Energy Laboratory, June 2000.

[19] Sioshansi, R.; Denholm, P. "The Value of Concentrating Solar Power and Thermal Energy Storage." *IEEE Trans. Sustainable Energy;* Vol. 1, October 2010; pp. 173–183.

[20] Gilman, P.; Blair, N.; Mehos, M.; Christensen, C.; Janzou, S. *Solar Advisor Model User Guide for Version 2.0.* NREL/TP-670-43704. Golden, CO: National Renewable Energy Laboratory, August 2008.

[21] Pacheco, J.E.; Gilbert, R. Overview of Recent Results of the Solar Two Test and Evaluations Program." SAND99-0091C. Albuquerque, NM: Sandia National Laboratories, January 1999.

[22] Herrmann, U.; Kelly, B.; Price, H. "Two-tank Molten Salt Storage for Parabolic Trough Solar Power Plants." *Energy;* Vol. 29, April–May 2004; pp. 883–893.

[23] Tuohy, A.; O'Malley, M. "Impact of Pumped Storage on Power Systems with Increasing Wind Penetration." *Power & Energy Society General Meeting, July 26–30, 2009.* Calgary, AB, Canada: Institute of Electrical and Electronics Engineers; pp. 1–8.

[24] U.S. Department of Energy Form 860. http://www.eia.doe.gov/cneaf/ electricity/page/eia860.html. Accessed June 20, 2011.

[25] North American Electric Reliability Corporation Generating Availability Data System. http://www.nerc.com/page.php?cid=4|43. Accessed June 20, 2011.

[26] Federal Energy Regulatory Commission Form No. 714. http://www.ferc. gov/docs-filing/forms/form-714/elec-subm-soft.asp. Accessed June 20, 2011. Ho, C.K.; Kolb, G.J. "Incorporating Uncertainty into Probabilistic Performance Models of Concentrating Solar Power Plants." *J. Sol. Energy Eng.*; Vol. 132, Iss. 3, August 2010.

In: Concentrating Solar Power
Editors: Burt J. Alexander and Ted F. Richardson

ISBN: 978-1-62081-423-9
© 2012 Nova Science Publishers, Inc.

Chapter 3

ENABLING GREATER PENETRATION OF SOLAR POWER VIA THE USE OF CSP WITH THERMAL ENERGY STORAGE[*]

Paul Denholm and Mark Mehos

1. INTRODUCTION

Falling cost of solar photovoltaic (PV) generated electricity has led to a rapid increase in the deployment of PV and projections that PV could play a significant role in the future U.S. electric sector. The solar resource itself is virtually unlimited compared to any conceivable demand for energy (Morton 2006); however, the ultimate contribution from PV could be limited by several factors in the current grid. One is the limited coincidence between the solar resource and normal demand patterns (Denholm and Margolis 2007a). A second is the limited flexibility of conventional generators to reduce output and accommodate this variable generation resource.

At high penetration of solar generation, increased grid flexibility will be needed to fully utilize the variable and uncertain output from PV generation and shift energy production to periods of high demand or reduced solar output (Denholm and Margolis 2007b).Energy storage provides an option to increase grid flexibility and there are many storage options available or under development.[1]

In this work we consider a technology now beginning to be deployed at scale − thermal energy storage (TES) deployed with concentrating solar power (CSP).PV and CSP are both deployable in areas of high direct normal irradiance such as the U.S. Southwest. From a policy standpoint, a simplistic approach to choosing a generation technology might be based simply on picking the option with the lowest overall levelized cost of electricity (LCOE). However, deployment based simply on lowest LCOE ignores the relative benefits of each technology to

---

[*] This is an edited, reformatted and augmented version of a National Renewable Energy Laboratory Technical Report NREL/TP-6A20-52978 publication, prepared under Task No. SS10.2720, dated November 2011.

the grid, how their value to the grid changes as a function of penetration, and how they may actually work together to increase overall usefulness of the solar resource. Both PV and CSP use solar energy to generate electricity, although through different conversion processes. A key difference between CSP and PV technologies is the ability of CSP to utilize high-efficiency thermal energy storage (TES) which turns CSP into a partially dispatchable resource.[2] The addition of TES produces additional value by shifting solar energy to periods of peak demand, providing firm capacity and ancillary services, and reducing integration challenges. Given the dispatchability of CSP enabled by thermal energy storage, it is possible that PV and CSP are at least partially complementary.

The dispatchability of CSP with TES can enable higher overall penetration of solar energy in two ways. The first is providing solar-generated electricity during periods of cloudy weather or at night. However a potentially important, and less well analyzed benefit of CSP is its ability to provide grid flexibility, enabling greater penetration of PV (and other variable generation sources such as wind) than if deployed without CSP.

In this work we examine the degree to which CSP may be complementary to PV via its use of thermal energy storage. We first review the challenges of PV deployment at scale with a focus on the supply/demand coincidence and limits of grid flexibility. We then perform a series of grid simulations to indicate the general potential of CSP with TES to enable greater use of solar generation, including additional PV.

Finally, we use these reduced form simulations to identify the data and modeling needed for more comprehensive analysis of the potential of CSP with TES to provide additional flexibility to the grid as a whole and benefit all variable generation sources.

2. CHALLENGES OF SOLAR DEPLOYMENT AT HIGH PENETRATION

The benefits and challenges of large scale PV penetration have been described in a number of analyses (Brinkman et al 2011). At low penetration, PV typically displaces the highest cost generation sources (Denholm et al. 2009) and may also provide high levels of reliable capacity to the system (Perez et al 2008). Figure 1 provides a simulated system dispatch for a single summer day in California with PV penetration levels from 0% to 10% (on an annual basis). This figure is from a previous analysis that used a production cost model simulating the western United States (Denholm et al. 2008). It illustrates how PV displaces the highest cost generation, and reduces the need for peaking capacity due to its coincidence with demand patterns At fairly low penetration (on an energy basis) the value of PV capacity drops. This can be observed in Figure 1 where the peak net load (normal load minus PV) stays the same between the 6% and 10% penetration curves.3 The net load in this figure is the curve at the top of the "Gas Turbine" area. Beyond this point PV no longer adds significant amounts of firm capacity to the system. Several additional challenges for the economic deployment of solar PV also occur as penetration increases. These are illustrated in Figure 2, which shows the results of the same simulation, except on a spring day. During this day, the lower demand results in PV displacing lower cost baseload energy. At 10% PV penetration in this simulation, PV completely eliminates net imports, and California actually exports energy to neighboring states.

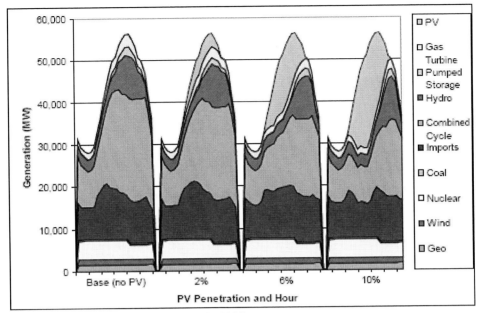

Note: Figure is modified from Denholm et al. (2008).

Figure 1. Simulated dispatch in California for a summer day with PV penetration from 0%–10%.

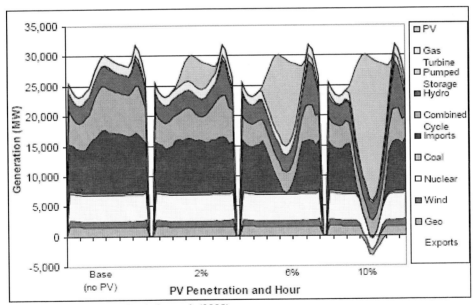

Note: Figure is modified from Denholm et al. (2008).

Figure 2. Simulated dispatch in California for a spring day with PV penetration from 0%–10%.

Several factors limit the ability of conventional generators to reduce output to accommodate renewable generation. These include the rate at which generators can change output, particularly in the evening when generators must increase output rapidly in a high PV scenario. This challenge is illustrated in Figure 3, a ramp duration curve for California covering an entire simulated year.

This is the net load ramp rate (MW/hour) for all 8,760 hours in the simulated year ordered from high to low. In the no PV case, the maximum load ramp rate is about 5,000 MW/hour and a ramp rate of greater than 4,000 MW/hour occurs less than 100 hours in the simulated year.

In the 2% PV case, the hourly ramps are actually smaller since PV effectively removes the peak demand (as seen in Figure 1). However at higher penetration, the ramp rates increase substantially, and in the 10% PV case the net load increases at more than 4,000 MW/hour more than 500 hours per year.

Another limitation is the overall ramp range, or generator turn-down ratio. This represents the ability of power plants to reduce output, which is typically limited on large coal and nuclear units. Accommodating all of the solar generation as shown in Figure 2 requires nuclear generators to vary output which is not current practice in the U.S. nuclear industry. Most large thermal power plants cannot be turned off for short periods of time (a few hours or less), and brief shutdowns could be required to accommodate all energy generated during the period of peak solar output. The actual minimum load of individual generators is both a technical and economic issue – there are technical limits to how much power plants of all types can be turned down. Large coal plants are often restricted to operating in the range of 50%–100% of full capacity, but there is significant uncertainty about this limit (GE Energy 2010). Many plant operators have limited experience with cycling large coal plants, and extensive cycling could significantly increase maintenance requirements.[4]

The ability to "de-commit" or turn off power plants may also be limited by the need to provide operating reserves from partially loaded power plants. As the amount of PV on the system increases, the need for operating reserves also increases due to the uncertainty of the solar resource, as well as its variability over multiple time scales.

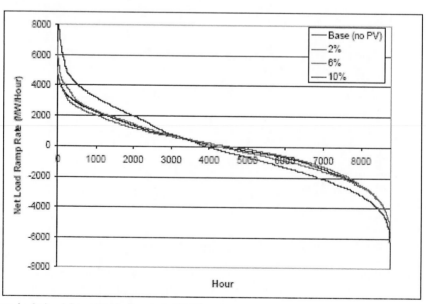

Note: Figure is derived from Denholm et al. (2008).

Figure 3. Ramp duration curve in California with PV penetration from 0%–10%.

Previous analysis has demonstrated the economic limits of PV penetration due to generator turn-down limits and supply/demand coincidence (Denholm and Margolis 2007a, Nikolakakis and Fthenakis 2011). Because of these factors, at high penetration of solar, increasing amounts of solar may need to be curtailed when its supply exceeds demand, after subtracting the amount of generation met by plants unable to economically reduce output due to ramp rate or range constraints or while providing operating reserves. Generator constraints would likely prevent the use of all PV generation in Figure 2. Nuclear plant operators would be unlikely to reduce output for this short period. Furthermore, PV generation may be offsetting other low or zero carbon sources. In Figure 2, PV sometimes displaces wind and geothermal generation, which provides no real benefit in terms of avoided fuel use or emissions.[5]

While the penetration of solar energy is currently far too small to see significant impacts, curtailment of wind energy is an increasing concern in the United States (Wiser and Bolinger 2010).

While a majority of wind curtailments in the United States are due to transmission limitations (Fink et al 2009), curtailments due to excess generation during times of low net load are a significant factor that will increase if grid flexibility is not enhanced. The resulting curtailed energy can substantially increase the levelized cost of energy (LCOE) from variable generators, because their capital costs must be recovered over fewer units of energy actually sold to the grid.

The ability of the aggregated set of generators to rapidly change output at a high rate and over a large range can be described as a grid's overall flexibility. Flexibility depends on many factors, including:

- Generator mix – Hydro and gas-fired generators are generally more flexible than coal or nuclear.
- Grid size – Larger grids are typically more flexible because they share a larger mix of generators and can share operating reserves and a potentially more spatially diverse set of renewable resources.[6]
- Use of forecasting in unit commitment –Accurate forecasts of the wind and solar resources and load reduces the need for operating reserves.
- Market structure – Some grids allow more rapid exchange of energy and can more efficiently balance supply from variable generators and demand.
- Other sources of grid flexibility – Some locations have access to demand response, which can provide an alternative to partially-loaded thermal generators for provision of operating reserves. Other locations may have storage assets such as pumped hydro.

A comprehensive analysis of each flexibility option is needed to evaluate the cost-optimal approach of enhancing the use of variable generation. In this analysis, we consider the use of thermal energy storage. Previous analysis has demonstrated the ability of a wind- and solar-based system to meet a large fraction of system demand when using electricity storage (Denholm and Hand 2011). A number of storage technologies are currently available or under development, but face a number of barriers to deployment including high capital costs[7] efficiency related losses[8], and certain market and regulatory challenges.[9] A number of initiatives are focused on reducing these barriers.[10]

An alternative to storing solar generated electricity is storing solar thermal energy via CSP/TES. Because TES can only store energy from thermal generators such as CSP, it cannot be directly compared to other electricity storage options, which can charge from any source. However, TES provides some potential advantages for bulk energy storage. First, TES offers a significant efficiency advantage, with an estimated round trip efficiency in excess of 95% (Medrano et al. 2010).[11] TES has the potential for low cost, with one estimate for the cost associated with TES added to a CSP power tower design at about $72/kWh-e (after considering the thermal efficiency of the power block).[12]

3. SYSTEM MODEL

The purpose of this analysis is to explore the potential of CSP to provide grid flexibility and enable increased solar penetration in the Southwestern United States. To perform this preliminary assessment, we use the REFlex model, which is a reduced form dispatch model designed to examine the general relationship between grid flexibility, variable solar and wind generation, and curtailment (Denholm and Hand 2011). REFlex compares hourly load and renewable resources and calculates the amount of curtailment based on the system's flexibility, defined as the ability for generators to decrease output and accommodate variable generator sources such as solar and wind.

California is a likely candidate for large-scale deployment of both PV and CSP, and has strong solar incentive programs and a renewable portfolio standard. However, modeling California in isolation ignores the fact that California has strong transmission ties to neighboring states, including Arizona and southern Nevada, which have significant potential for solar energy. Currently, power exchanges between neighboring areas in the western United States are accomplished through bilateral contracts, and typically do not occur in real time. This analysis assumes the eventual availability of real-time power and energy exchanges across California, Arizona, New Mexico and Southern Nevada to allow sharing of solar resources. It also assumes that transmission is accessible to all generation sources on a short-term, non-firm basis. This "limiting case" allows for examination of the best technical case for solar deployment without market barriers or transmission constraints.

We began our simulations by evaluating the limits of PV, given flexibility limits of the existing grid. The simulations use solar, wind and load data for the years 2005 and 2006. Load data was derived from FERC Form 714 filings. For hourly PV production, we used the System Advisor Model (SAM), which converts solar insolation and temperature data into hourly PV output (Gilman et al. 2008). Weather data for 2005 and 2006, was obtained from the updated National Solar Radiation Database (NSRDB) (Wilcox and Marion 2008). We assume that PV will be distributed in a mix of rooftop and central systems (both fixed and 1-axis tracking). Additional description of this mix, including geographical distribution is provided in Brinkman et al. (2011).

Because California has significant wind capacity installed and plans for more, we also consider the interaction between solar and wind generation. Simulated wind data for 2005 and 2006 for California/Southwest sites was derived from the datasets generated for the Western

Wind and Solar Integration Study (WWSIS) (GE Energy 2010). We started with a base assumption that wind provides 10% of the region's energy based on the "In-Area −10% Wind" scenario from the WWSIS. These data sets were processed through the REFlex model to establish base relationships between grid penetration of PV, curtailment, and grid flexibility. The overall system flexibility was evaluated parametrically, starting with a base assumption that the system is able to accommodate PV over a cycling range of 80% of the annual demand range. This corresponds to a "flexibility factor" of 80%, meaning the aggregated generator fleet can reduce output to 20% of the annual peak demand (Denholm and Hand 2011). This value is based on the WWSIS study and corresponds roughly to the point where all on-line thermal units have reduced output to their minimum generation levels and nuclear units would require cycling.

The actual flexibility of the U.S. power system is not well defined, and this value is not intended to be definitive, but is used to represent the challenges of solar and wind integration and the possible flexibility benefits of CSP/TES.[13]

Figure 4 illustrates the framework for this analysis, showing the simulated dispatch over a 4-day period (April 7-10). It demonstrates a case where 10% of the annual demand is met by wind and 20% is met by solar. The figure shows both the simulated solar profile and its contribution to meeting load. Because of relatively low load during this period, PV generation exceeds what can be accommodated using the assumed grid flexibility limits. This typically occurs in the late morning, before the demand increases to its maximum in the afternoon. In these four days about 16% of all PV generation is curtailed and about 5% of the annual PV generation is curtailed.[14]

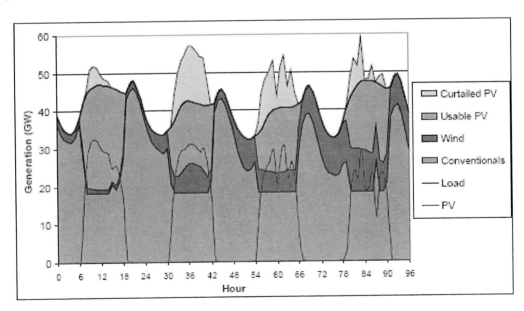

Figure 4. Simulated system dispatch on April 7-10 with 20% contribution from PV generation and resulting curtailment due to grid flexibility constraints.

Figure 5 illustrates the average and marginal PV curtailment rates as a function of PV energy penetration for this initial scenario. It should be noted that the x-axis shows penetration of only solar PV. Because wind provides 10%, the total penetration of variable generation is 10% plus the penetration of solar. The average curve shows the total curtailment of all PV at a certain generation level. At the overall assumed system flexibility level, by the time PV is providing 22% of total demand, about 6% of all potential PV generation is curtailed.

The actual allocation of curtailment strongly influences the economics of PV and other variable generation. Figure 4 also shows the marginal curtailment rate, or the curtailment rate of the incremental unit of PV installed to meet a given level of PV penetration. If curtailment were assigned on an incremental basis at the point where PV is providing 22% of total demand, only about 50% of this additional PV would be usable, with the rest curtailed.

In this analysis we "assign" all incremental curtailment to solar, partially based on the federal production tax credit which incentivizes wind generation, while the primary federal incentive for solar is an investment tax credit that incentivizes installations but not generation.[15] Curtailment of solar may also occur if wind is installed "first" and a "last in, first curtailed" rule applies. The actual allocation of curtailment is, and is likely to continue to be, a contentious issue. Regardless of allocations rules, increased grid flexibility will be needed to minimize curtailment if solar is expected to play a "primary" role in reducing fossil-fuel use in the electric sector.

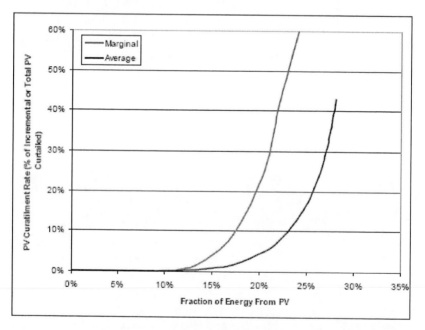

Figure 5. Marginal curtailment rates of PV in a base scenario in the southwestern United States assuming an 80% system flexibility.

The estimation of the marginal curtailment rate is important because it helps establish the optimal mix of generators serving various portions of the load. This can be observed in Figure 6, which translates curtailment into a cost of energy multiplier. This multiplier— equal to 1/(1-curtailment rate) —can be applied to the "base" LCOE of electricity generation (no curtailment). This represents how much more would need to be charged for electricity based on the impact of curtailment and the corresponding reduction in electricity actually provided to the grid.

Both the average and marginal multipliers are shown in Figure 6. The average multiplier is applied to all PV generators. The marginal multiplier is applied to the incremental generator, and is more important when determining the role of storage or other load-shifting technologies. For example, at the point where PV is providing 25% of the system's energy, the curtailment of all PV (average curtailment) is about 17% and the resulting cost multiplier is 1.2. If the base cost of PV is $0.06/kWh, the overall, systemwide cost of PV would be $0.06 x 1.2 or $0.072/kWh. This overall cost may be acceptable, but the costs are greater at the margin. For example, the last unit of PV installed to reach the 25% threshold has a curtailment rate of about 68% and a cost multiplier of 3.1. At a $0.06/kWh base price, this incremental unit of PV generation would have an effective cost of more than $0.18 per kWh. This would likely result in examining options to both increase grid flexibility (to accommodate more PV with lower curtailment rates) and improve the solar supply/demand coincidence.

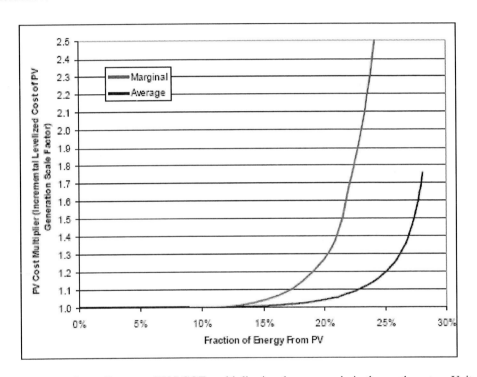

Figure 6. Impact of curtailment on PV LCOE multiplier in a base scenario in the southwestern United States assuming an 80% system flexibility.

4. INCREASING SOLAR DEPLOYMENT USING CSP

While there are many options to increase grid flexibility, in this work we focus on the potential use of CSP with TES. Thermal storage extends the contribution of solar electricity generation by shifting generation to improve its coincidence with normal demand, and by improving system flexibility. The latter is accomplished by reducing constraints of ramping and minimum generation levels.

CSP was added to REFlex using hourly generation values produced by SAM. SAM uses the direct normal irradiance (DNI) to calculate the hourly electrical output of a wet-cooled trough plant (Wagner and Gilman 2011). The choice of technology was based primarily on data availability at the time of analysis as opposed to any presumption regarding CSP technology or economics. The results should be applicable to any CSP technology able to deploy multiple hours of thermal energy storage. For our base case, we assume 8 hours of storage and that the electrical energy produced by the plant can be dispatched with an effective 95% efficiency. In this initial analysis we did not consider the effects of part loading or multiple starts on plant efficiency. Distribution of locations was based on the study described by Brinkman et al. (2011).

Figure 7 illustrates the importance of dispatchability at high solar penetration. This scenario is identical to Figure 4, except PV provides 15% of annual demand and CSP meets 10% (so the contribution of solar technologies in total is greater in the PV/CSP case in Figure 7). The figure shows two CSP profiles. This first "non-dispatched CSP" is the output of CSP if it did not have thermal storage. It aligns with PV production, and would result in significant solar curtailment. The other curve is the actual dispatched CSP, showing its response to the net demand pattern after wind and PV generation is considered. It shows how a large fraction of the CSP energy is shifted toward the end of the day. In the first day, this ability to shift energy eliminates curtailment. On the other days, the wind and PV resources exceed the "usable" demand for energy in the early part of the day, resulting in curtailed energy even while the CSP plant is storing 100% of thermal energy. However, overall curtailment is greatly reduced. Solar technologies provide an additional 5% of the system's annual energy compared to the case in Figure 4, but the actual annual curtailment has been reduced to less than 2%, including the losses in thermal storage.

Figure 8 shows how the addition of CSP/TES can increase the overall penetration of solar by moving energy from periods of low net demand in the middle of the day to morning or evening. In this figure there is an equal mix of CSP and PV on an energy basis and the PV-only curves are identical to those in Figure 5.

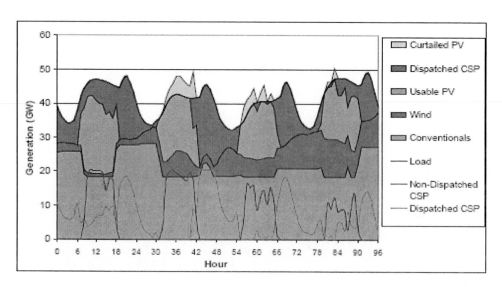

Figure 7. Simulated system dispatch on April 7-10 with 15% contribution from PV and 10% from dispatchable CSP.

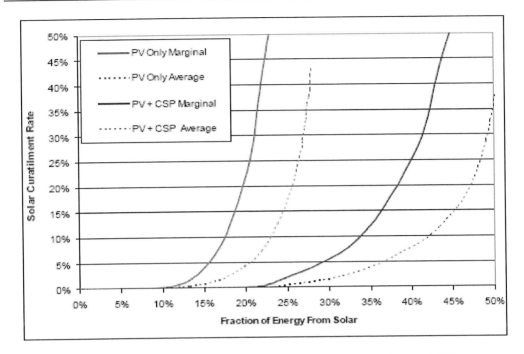

Figure 8. Curtailment of solar assuming an equal mix (on an energy basis) of PV and CSP.

Figure 8 demonstrates the importance of dispatchability to reduce curtailment and increase the overall penetration of solar via the ability to shift solar energy over time. However, the analysis to this point assumes that CSP and PV are complementary only in their ability to serve different parts of the demand pattern. We have not yet considered the additional benefits of CSP to provide system flexibility by replacing baseload generators and generators online to provide operating reserves.

The importance of system flexibility can be observed in Figure 4, where conventional generators must ramp up rapidly to address the decreased output of PV during peak demand periods. In order to meet this ramp rate and range (along with sufficient operating reserves) a significant number of thermal generators will likely need to be operating a part-load, creating a minimum generation constraint during periods of solar high output. This is represented by the flat line occurring in the middle of each day when the aggregated generator fleet is at their minimum generation point. Comparing the CSP/PV case in Figure 7 to the PV only case in Figure 4, we see that the CSP is dispatched to meet the peak demand in the late afternoon/early evening, and the overall ramp rate and range is substantially reduced. In Figure 4 conventional generators need to ramp from about 18 GW to over 45 GW in just a few hours, while in Figure 7 the generators need to ramp from 18 GW to less than 30 GW.

Adding a highly flexible generator such as CSP/TES can potentially reduce the minimum generation constraint in the system. In the near term, this means that fewer conventional generators will be needed to operate at part load during periods of high solar output. In the longer term, the ability of CSP to provide firm system capacity could replace retiring inflexible baseload generators.

CSP plants with TES add system flexibility because of their large ramp rate and range relative to large baseload generators. Many CSP plants, both existing and proposed, are essentially small steam (Rankine-cycle) plants whose "fuel" is concentrated solar energy. Few of these plants are deployed, so it is not possible to determine their performance with absolute certainty. However, historical performance of the SEGS VI power plant provides some indication of CSP flexibility. Figure 9 provides a heat rate curve based on an hourly simulation model to assess the performance of parabolic trough systems, and validated by comparing the modeled output results with actual plant operating data (Price 2003). It indicates a typical operating range over 75% of capacity, with only a 5% increase in heat rate at 50% load. Figure 9 also provides historical data from small gas-fired steam plants which also indicates high ramp rate and range and fairly small decrease in efficiency at part load (about a 6% increase in heat rate at 50% load).[16] These plants also often operate as low as 25% of capacity, although with lower efficiency.[17] This provides a strong indication that CSP plants should be able to provide high flexibility.

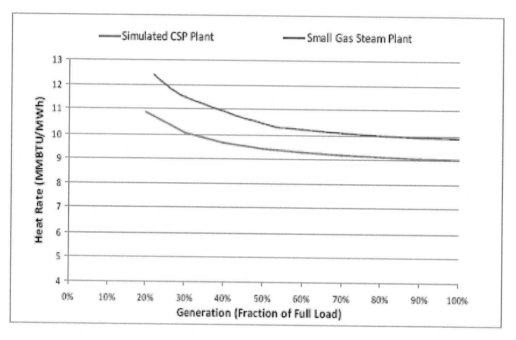

Figure 9. Part load heat rate of a CSP parabolic trough Rankine cycle power block and historic performance of small gas steam plants.

The change in minimum generation constraints is dependent on both the flexibility of CSP plants and the flexibility of generators supplemented or replaced with CSP. As discussed previously, nuclear plants are rarely cycled in the United States, while coal plants are typically operated in the range of 50%-100%. Because it is not possible to determine the exact mix of generators that would be replaced in high renewables scenarios, we consider a range of possible changes in the minimum generation constraints resulting from CSP deployment. For example, deployment of a CSP plant which can operate over 75% of its capacity range could allow the de-commitment of a coal plant which normal operates over 50% of its range. In this scenario each unit of CSP could reduce the minimum generation constraint by 25% of the plant's capacity. This very simplistic assumption illustrates how the dispatchability of a CSP plant should allow for a lower minimum generation constraint. Reducing this constraint should allow for greater use of wind and PV. As a result, as CSP is added, the system can actually accommodate more PV than in a system without CSP.

This is illustrated conceptually in Figure 10, which shows the same 4-day period as in Figures 4 and 7. CSP still provides 10% of the system's annual energy, but now we assume that the use of CSP allows for a decreased minimum generation point, and the decrease is equal to 25% of the installed CSP capacity. In this case about 21 GW of CSP reduces the minimum generation point from about 18 GW to 13 GW.

This generation "headroom" allows for greater use of PV, and enough PV has been added to meet 25% of demand (up from 15% in Figure 7).[18] As a result, the total solar contribution is now 35% of demand, significantly greater than the PV-only case shown in Figure 4, and total curtailment is less than the 6% rate seen in Figure 4. By shifting energy over time and increasing grid flexibility, CSP enables greater overall solar penetration AND greater penetration of PV.

Figures 11 and 12 show the potential overall impact of the flexibility introduced by CSP and the corresponding opportunities for increased use of PV. Figure 11 builds on Figure 8 by adding the flexibility benefits of CSP. The figure assumes that each unit of CSP reduces the minimum generation constraint by 25% of its capacity, and an equal mix of PV and CSP on an energy basis. In this case, the addition of CSP allows PV to provide 25% of the system's energy with very low levels of curtailment.

Figure 12 more directly illustrates the relationship between the reduction in minimum generation constraint and potential increase in PV penetration. The figure shows how much more PV could be incorporated at a constant marginal curtailment rate of 20% when CSP is added. In this scenario, the *x*-axis represents the fraction of annual system energy provided by CSP. Increased penetration of CSP results in a linear decrease in minimum generation constraints. The figure illustrates two CSP flexibility cases.

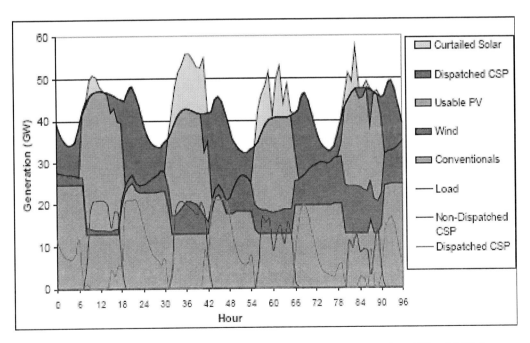

Figure 10. Simulated system dispatch on April 10-13 with 25% contribution from PV and 10% from dispatchable CSP where CSP reduces the minimum generation constraint.

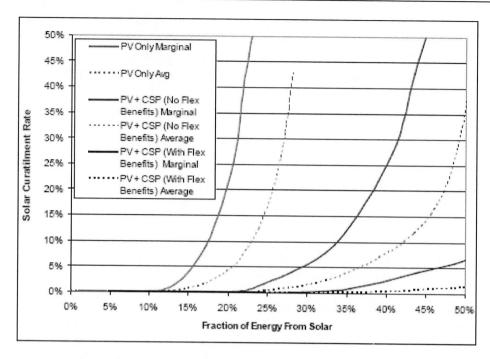

Figure 11. Curtailment of solar assuming an equal mix (on an energy basis) of PV and CSP and impact of CSP grid flexibility.

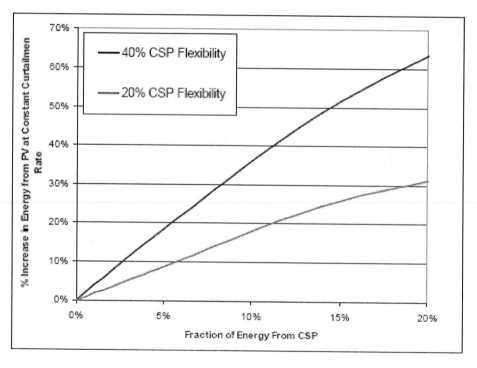

Figure 12. Increase in PV penetration as a function of CSP penetration assuming a maximum PV marginal curtailment rate of 20%. CSP flexibility is defined as the fraction of the CSP rated capacity that is assumed to reduce the system minimum generation constraint.

In one, each unit of CSP reduces the minimum generation constraint by 20% of its capacity; in the other, the rate of reduction is 40%. These amounts are not meant to be definitive, but represent a possible impact of CSP in reducing minimum generation constraints.

Overall, this analysis suggests that CSP can significantly increase grid flexibility by providing firm system capacity with a high ramp rate and range and acceptable part-load operation. Greater grid flexibility could increase the contribution of renewable resources like solar and wind. This demonstrates that CSP can actually be complementary to PV, not only by adding solar generation during periods of low sun, but by actually enabling more PV generation during the day. This analysis also suggests a pathway to more definitively assess the ability of CSP to act as an "enabling" technology for wind and solar generation.

5. FURTHER QUANTIFYING THE BENEFITS OF CSP DEPLOYMENT

This analysis is a preliminary assessment of the potential benefits of CSP in providing grid flexibility using reduced form simulations with limited geographical scope and many simplifying assumptions. Gaining a more thorough understanding of how CSP can enable greater PV and wind penetration will require detailed production simulations using security-constrained unit commitment and economic dispatch models currently used by utilities and system operators.

These simulations should consider the operation of the entire power plant fleet including individual generator characteristics and constraints, and the operation of the transmission system. The geographical footprint should cover the entire Western interconnect including possible transmission expansion to take advantage of greater spatial diversity of the wind and solar resources as well conventional generators.

To date, production simulations have not considered CSP operations in detail. Both the WWSIS and the first phase of the California 33% Renewable Portfolio Standard integration studies (CAISO 2011) included CSP, but assumed fixed schedules for CSP dispatch. This assumption limits CSP's ability to shift generation to when needed most and to provide grid flexibility to enable PV and wind. Future and ongoing studies, including the second phase of both the California study and the WWSIS will evaluate the benefits of TES in more detail. To perform these simulations, production cost models will need to include the ability of CSP to optimally dispatch the solar energy resource, and not rely on heuristics or schedules often used to estimate the operation of conventional storage plants such as pumped hydro. However, the ability to optimize CSP, including scheduling both its energy and ability to provide operating reserves, is limited by lack of certain data sets needed for a more detailed simulation. A greater understanding of the predictability and variability of the solar resource, including the sub-hourly variation and the effects of spatial diversity in mitigating variability, is needed. This data will also be needed to determine any required increase in operating reserves over various time scales as a function of solar penetration. In addition, more data is needed on the actual characteristics of CSP plants—those now being deployed and under development— including ramp rates, turn-down ratio, part-load efficiency, and start times under various conditions.

CONCLUSIONS

While it will be some time until solar technologies achieve very high penetrations in the U.S. grid, international experience in wind deployment demonstrates the importance of increasing overall grid flexibility. Key factors in improving grid flexibility include increasing the ramp range and rate of all generation sources and the ability to better match the supply of renewable resources with demand via increased spatial diversity, shiftable load, or energy storage. The use of thermal energy storage in concentrating solar power plants provides one option for increased grid flexibility in two primary ways. First, TES allows shifting of the solar resource to periods of reduced solar output with relatively high efficiency. Second is the inherent flexibility of CSP/TES plants, which offer higher ramp rates and ranges than large thermal plants currently used to meet a large fraction of electric demand. Given the high capacity value of CSP/TES, this technology could potentially replace a fraction of the conventional generator fleet and provide a more flexible generation mix. This could result in greater use of nondispatchable solar PV and wind meaning CSP and PV may actually be complementary technologies, especially at higher penetrations.

The preliminary analysis performed in this work requires advanced grid simulations to verify the actual ability of CSP to act as an enabling technology for other variable generation sources. Complete production simulations using utility-grade software, considering the realistic performance of the generation fleet, transmission constraints, and actual CSP operation will be an important next step in evaluating the benefits of multiple solar generation technologies.

REFERENCES

Brinkman, G.L.; Denholm, P.; Drury, E.; Margolis, R.; Mowers, M. (2011). "Toward a Solar-Powered Grid—Operational Impacts of Solar Electricity Generation." *IEEE Power and Energy* (9); pp. 24–32.

California Independent System Operator (CAISO) (2011). "Track I Direct Testimony of Mark Rothleder on Behalf of the California Independent System Operator Corporation." Testimony for the Public Utilities Commission of the State of California, Order Instituting Rulemaking to Integrate and Refine Procurement Policies and Consider Long-Term Procurement Plans, Rulemaking 10-05-006, Submitted July 11.

Denholm, P.; Hand, M. (2011). "Grid Flexibility and Storage Required to Achieve Very High Penetration of Variable Renewable Electricity." *Energy Policy* (39); pp. 1817–1830.

Denholm, P.; Ela, E.; Kirby, B.; Milligan, M. (2010). *The Role of Energy Storage with Renewable Electricity Generation.* NREL/TP-6A2-47187. Golden, CO: National Renewable Energy Laboratory.

Denholm, P.; Margolis, R.M.; Milford, J. (2009). "Quantifying Avoided Fuel Use and Emissions from Photovoltaic Generation in the Western United States." *Environmental Science and Technology* (43); pp. 226–232.

Denholm, P.; Margolis, R.M.; Milford, J. (2008). *Production Cost Modeling for High Levels of Photovoltaics Penetration.* NREL/TP-581-42305. Golden, CO: National Renewable Energy Laboratory.

Denholm, P.; Margolis, R.M. (2008). "Land Use Requirements and the Per-Capita Solar Footprint for Photovoltaic Generation in the United States." *Energy Policy* (36); pp. 3531–3543.

Denholm, P.; Margolis, R.M. (2007a). "Evaluating the Limits of Solar Photovoltaics (PV) in Traditional Electric Power Systems." *Energy Policy* (35); pp. 2852–2861.

Denholm, P.; Margolis, R.M. (2007b). "Evaluating the Limits of Solar Photovoltaics (PV) in Electric Power Systems Utilizing Energy Storage and Other Enabling Technologies." *Energy Policy* (35); pp. 4424–4433.

Electric Power Research Institute (EPRI). (December 2010). "Electricity Energy Storage Technology Options: A White Paper Primer on Applications, Costs, and Benefits." 1020676. Palo Alto, CA: EPRI.

Fink, S.; Mudd, C.; Porter, K.; Morgenstern, B. (2009). *Wind Energy Curtailment Case Studies: May 2008 - May 2009*. SR-550-46716. Golden, CO: National Renewable Energy Laboratory.

GE Energy. (2010). *Western Wind and Solar Integration Study*. SR-550-47434. Golden, CO: National Renewable Energy Laboratory.

Gilman, P.; Blair, N.; Mehos, M.; Christensen, C.; Janzou, S.; Cameron, C. (2008). *Solar Advisor Model User Guide for Version 2.0*. TP-670-43704. Golden, CO: National Renewable Energy Laboratory.

Johnson, M. (2 March 2011). "Overview of Gridscale Rampable Intermittent Dispatchable Storage (GRIDS) Program." Washington, DC: U.S. Department of Energy.

Kearney, D.; Miller, C. (15 January 1998). "Solar Electric Generating System VI - Technical Evaluation of Project Feasibility." Los Angeles, CA: LUZ Partnership Management, Inc.

Kolb, G.; Ho, C.; Mancini, T.; Gary, J. (2011). *Power Tower Technology Roadmap and Cost Reduction Plan*. SAND2011-2419. Albuquerque, NM: Sandia National Laboratories.

King, J.; Kirby, B.; Milligan, M.; Beuning, S. (2011) *Flexibility Reserve Reductions from an Energy Imbalance Market with High Levels of Wind Energy in the Western Interconnection*. NREL/TP-5500-5233. Golden, CO: National Renewable Energy Laboratory.

Lefton, S.A.; Besuner, P. (2006). "The Cost of Cycling Coal Fired Power Plants." *Coal Power Magazine*, Winter 2006.

Medrano, M.; Gil, A.; Martorell, I.; Potau, X.; Cabeza, F. (2010). "State of the Art on High-Temperature Thermal Energy Storage for Power Generation. Part 2 – Case Studies." *Renewable and Sustainable Energy Reviews* (14); pp. 56–72.

Morton, O. (2006). "Solar Energy: A New Day Dawning?: Silicon Valley Sunrise." *Nature* (443); pp. 19–22.

Nikolakakis, T.; Fthenakis, V. "The Optimum Mix of Electricity from Wind- and Solar-Sources in Conventional Power Systems: Evaluating the Case for New York State." *Energy Policy*, (39); 6972-6980.

Perez, R.; Taylor, M.; Hoff, T.; Ross, J.P. (2008). "Reaching Consensus in the Definition of Photovoltaic Capacity Credit in the USA: A Practical Application of Satellite-Derived Solar Resource Data." *IEEE Journal of Selected Topics In Applied Earth Observations And Remote Sensing* (1:1); pp. 28–33.

Price, H. (2003). *A Parabolic Trough Solar Power Plant Simulation Model*. CP-550- 33209. Golden, CO: National Renewable Energy Laboratory.

Sioshansi, R.; Denholm, P. (2010). "The Value of Concentrating Solar Power and Thermal Energy Storage." *IEEE Transactions on Sustainable Energy* (1:3); pp. 173–183.

Wagner, M. J.; Gilman, P. (2011). *Technical Manual for the SAM Physical Trough Model.* TP-5500-51825. Golden, CO: National Renewable Energy Laboratory.

Wilcox, S.; Marion, W. (2008). *Users Manual for TMY3 Data Sets.* NREL/TP-581- 43156. Golden, CO: National Renewable Energy Laboratory.

Wiser, R.; Bolinger, M. (August 2010). *2009 Wind Technologies Market Report.* LBNL-3716E. Berkeley, CA: Lawrence Berkeley National Laboratory.

End Notes

[1] The only storage technology with large scale deployment to date is pumped hydro, with about 20GW of capacity in the United States. Other storage technologies deployed in the United States include a single 110 MW CAES facility, and a number of relatively small battery and flywheel installations (Denholm et al. 2010).

[2] The degree of dispatchability is based largely on the amount of storage in the plant. For additional discussion see Sioshansi and Denholm (2010).

[3] When evaluating the impact of wind and solar, net loads typically remove both sources from the normal load. We just show the load minus the solar output to isolate the impact.

[4] "Cycling operations, that include on/off startup/shutdown operations, on-load cycling, and high frequency MW changes for automatic generation control (AGC), can be very damaging to power generation equipment." However, these costs can be very difficult to quantify, especially isolating the additional costs associated with cycling above and beyond normal operations (Lefton and Besuner 2006).

[5] We discuss the tradeoff in curtailment in more detail in Section 3.

[6] This includes both the size of a balancing authority area (the area in which supply and demand resources are balanced) and the connections between a balancing authority and its neighbors. Larger balancing authority areas can utilize a greater set of generation resources. Absent a large balancing authority area, there is the potential to exchange supply and demand resources with neighboring areas, but requires both the transmission capacity and the market or other regulatory mechanisms to efficiently schedule and exchange resources (King et al. 2011).

[7] Estimates of storage costs vary widely. However a cost of $2,000/kW for an 8-hour (usable) storage device appears to be on the low end of estimates for commercially available storage technologies with the exception of compressed air energy storage (EPRI 2010).

[8] The AC-AC round trip efficiency of new pumped hydro and some batteries (such as lithium-ion) is expected to exceed 80%, but many battery technologies such as sodium sulfur and most flow batteries have round-trip efficiencies of 75% or below (EPRI 2010).

[9] These include difficulty in valuing and recovering the value for the multiple services that storage can provide. (Denholm et al 2010).

[10] Examples include R&D efforts to reduce costs such as the ARPA-E Grid-Scale Rampable Intermittent Dispatchable Storage (GRIDS) program with a goal of $100/kWh, or $800/kW for an 8-hour device (Johnson 2011).

[11] This efficiency value represents the ratio of useful energy recovered from the storage system to the amount of energy extracted from the heat source, and is restricted to this application. A more rigorous definition of round-trip efficiency would include the loss of availability associated with a reduction in temperature at the outlet of a thermal storage system This as occurs for indirect storage systems where a temperature drop exists across heat exchangers transferring thermal energy from the solar field working fluid to the storage medium and again from the storage medium to the power block.

[12] Assumes base case total capital cost for storage of $30/kwh (thermal) and 42% Rankine power cycle efficiency. (Kolb et al. 2011)

[13] For more discussion of grid flexibility and its relationship to minimum generation levels see Denholm et al. (2010)

[14] This "assigns" all curtailment to PV as discussed later in this section.

[15] As a result of the production tax credit, wind generators can bid negative values into wholesale markets and still receive positive operating revenues.

[16] This curve represents the capacity weighted average of 298 gas steam plants operating in the year 2008. Data is derived from the U.S. Environmental Protection Agency continuous emission monitoring database at www.epa/gov/ttn/emc/cem/html

[17] The difference in heat rates between CSP plants and gas steam plants is likely due to a variety of factors. The steam plant data includes many old plants, including plants constructed before 1960. The CSP curve represents a parabolic trough plant including a power block consisting of a two-stage reheat turbine and multiple feedwater heaters to improve efficiency (Kearney and Miller 1988).

[18] All additional PV and CSP have the same mix of locations and types. In all cases the hourly solar profiles are simple scaled to obtain the desired penetration.

In: Concentrating Solar Power
Editors: Burt J. Alexander and Ted F. Richardson

ISBN: 978-1-62081-423-9
© 2012 Nova Science Publishers, Inc.

Chapter 4

Summary Report for Concentrating Solar Power Thermal Storage Workshop: New Concepts and Materials for Thermal Energy Storage and Heat-Transfer Fluids[*]

G. Glatzmaier

Introduction

The US Department of Energy (DOE), National Renewable Energy Laboratory (NREL), and Sandia National Laboratories hosted a workshop on thermal energy storage for concentrating solar power (CSP) on May 20, 2011, at NREL in Golden, Colorado. The objective for this workshop was to engage the university and laboratory research communities to identify and define research directions for developing new high-temperature materials and systems that advance thermal energy storage for CSP technologies. Desired outcomes for the workshop were to 1) inform the workshop participants of CSP technology challenges, specifically with respect to materials, and 2) generate and document new ideas for advancing materials development for CSP thermal energy storage.

The workshop agenda featured introductory presentations by DOE, NREL and Sandia staff that provided overviews of the DOE CSP Program goals and CSP technologies. Emphasis for the presentations was on the role and impact of thermal energy storage when it is incorporated into an operating CSP plant. These were followed by featured presentations given by invited speakers. Topics for these talks were 1) new heat transfer fluids for CSP technologies, 2) sensible thermal energy storage systems, and 3) thermochemical cycles for thermal energy storage. The presentations were followed by three parallel breakout sessions that covered 1) heat transfer fluids, 2) sensible and latent storage, and 3) thermochemical storage. For each session, participants were asked to identify system/material challenges and

---

[*] This is an edited, reformatted and augmented version of a National Renewable Energy Laboratory Technical Report NREL/TP- 5500-52134 publication, Contract No. DE-AC36-08GO28308, Prepared under Task No. CP09.2201, dated May 20, 2011.

promising research directions for the topic area. The workshop concluded with summary presentations of the findings from the breakout sessions. All findings from the workshop are documented in this summary report.

SunShot Initiative

This workshop was motivated, in part, by the DOE SunShot Initiative, which was established in 2010.[1] This initiative sets a very aggressive cost goal for CSP technologies. The primary goal is to reach a levelized cost of energy (LCOE) of 6¢/kWh by 2020 with no incentives or credits.

Because CSP is the only solar technology that is capable of significant energy storage, this cost goal applies to CSP plants that have several hours of thermal energy storage (TES) included in their design and operation.[2] As such, the cost and performance of the TES system are critical to meeting the overall cost goal for the CSP technology. The target cost for the TES system depends on other cost and performance factors for the power plant, but the initial cost target for TES system components under SunShot has been established at $15-$20/kWhth. Furthermore, this cost target assumes the TES system integrates with the solar field and power block components in a fashion that does not reduce the efficiency of their operation.

Figure 1 shows qualitatively the collection, conversion, and overall efficiencies for a general CSP plant. The temperature at which the overall efficiency reaches its maximum depends on many factors, including material properties of the CSP plant components. Increasing the operating temperature of the power generation system generally leads to higher thermal-toelectric conversion efficiency. In a CSP system, higher operating temperature leads to greater thermal losses. These two effects combine to give an optimal system-level operating temperature that may be less than the upper operating temperature limit of system components. System-level efficiency may be improved by developing materials, power cycles, and system-integration strategies that enable operation at elevated temperature while limiting thermal losses.

This is particularly true for a TES system and its components. Meeting the SunShot cost goal will require new materials for the TES system and heat-transfer fluid (HTF) that allow the CSP power plants to operate at higher temperatures and with greater efficiency than current parabolic trough and power tower plants.

CSP Technology Description

CSP plants offer an attractive means for near-term, utility-scale, dispatchable, renewable electricity generation. More than 400 megawatts (MW) of capacity are currently in place in the US southwest.[3] With 650 MW currently under construction in Arizona and California, [4,5] CSP technologies will play an increasingly significant role in providing sustainable power generation.

All CSP technologies have similar components – solar collectors, receivers, and thermal power conversion systems. They are grouped into two general types according to their collector/receiver geometries: point-focus and line-focus.

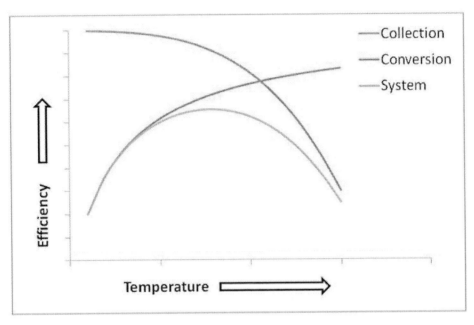

Figure 1. Collection, conversion, and total system efficiencies as functions of temperature.

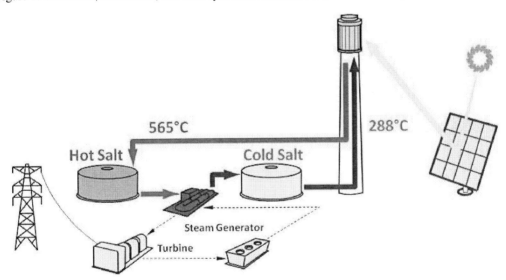

Figure 2. Schematic of power tower with direct, two-tank molten-salt thermal storage.

Point-focus geometries are the power tower and parabolic dish. The power tower consists of a single receiver that is located at the top of a tower (Figure 2). The tower is surrounded by a field of two-axis tracking mirrors, or heliostats, that reflect and concentrate sunlight to the receiver. An HTF circulates to the receiver, collects thermal energy contained in the concentrated sunlight, and returns to the power block where it is used to generate steam for the turbine power cycle. Power towers using molten salt HTF normally store the hot and cold salt in tanks that allow for separation of the solar collection and power generation cycles.

The most common HTF is molten nitrate salt that is a thermally stable liquid in the temperature range of 220° to 565°C. This type of configuration is a direct system because the HTF and storage fluids are the same. Some power towers send water to the tower, generate steam in the receiver, and send it directly to the turbine.

The parabolic dish is a modular design in which each module consists of a two-axis tracking, point-focus concentrator that has a receiver/engine/ generator located at its focal point (Figure 3). A Stirling engine is typically used to convert thermal energy to mechanical power for electricity generation. The working fluid is hydrogen or helium and is heated directly in the receiver. The Stirling engine operates nominally at 800°C and has a high thermal-tomechanical conversion efficiency. Heat transfer to the working fluid occurs isothermally at the operating temperature of the working fluid.

The most common line-focus geometry is the parabolic trough design. Its collector field consists of single-axis parabolic mirrors that reflect and concentrate sunlight to a focal line (Figure 4). The concentrated sunlight is absorbed by an HTF that flows through receiver tubes located at the focal line. Most trough plants use a synthetic oil for the HTF. Thermal energy within the heated HTF is used to generate steam for the turbine power cycle or can be stored within a separate storage fluid for later use. The storage fluid for this design is molten salt and the storage system is referred to as indirect because the HTF and storage fluids are distinct and require a heat exchanger to transfer thermal energy between them.

Figure 3. Schematic of parabolic dish with Stirling engine.

Line- and point-focus power plants are currently operating at commercial scale in the US southwest and Spain. Commercial-scale plants of both types are currently under construction in the US and Europe. However, broad implementation of CSP technologies historically has been limited by the cost of electricity produced by these plants, which is greater than electricity costs from conventional power generation. The purpose of the SunShot Initiative is to significantly increase broad-base implementation of solar-to-electricity technologies. Key thrusts of this initiative are dramatic performance improvements and cost reductions in all of the components that make up a CSP plant and the use of TES to increase the plant's capacity factor and dispatchability. Both thrusts will make CSP plants more attractive for utility-scale implementation. Power towers in particular are thought to have greater potential for wide-scale implementation because of their higher thermal conversion efficiency and greater stored energy densities. Both of these features are due to their higher operating temperatures.

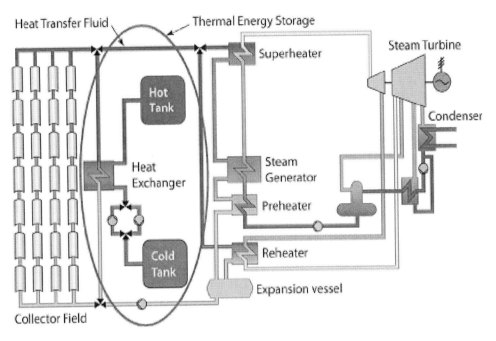

Figure 4. Schematic of parabolic trough power plant with two-tank, molten-salt thermal storage.

CSP THERMAL ENERGY STORAGE

CSP plants are unique among renewable technologies in that they provide utility-scale, dispatchable electricity to the power grid. Dispatchable delivery means power is reliably available when it is needed to meet the utility load demand. This feature is due to the incorporation of TES into the power plants.

TES allows electricity to be generated consistently at times when sunlight is not available, including momentary cloud transients, which otherwise disrupt electricity generation and cause widely varying power output. For longer time scales, TES allows CSP plants to generate electricity well into the evening hours when electricity is highly valued, making the power plant more cost effective. TES also allows greater use of the turbine and other power-block components. These features provide an economic incentive for the addition of TES.

Without TES, CSP solar power is an intermittent power resource that depends on sunlight availability. In addition to enhancing CSP dispatchability, TES enables increased deployment of renewables in general by adding flexibility to a grid with photovoltaic and wind power systems.

Types of Thermal Energy Storage

Figure 5 lists a variety of TES options for CSP plants. They fall into three general categories: sensible, latent, and thermochemical storage. A book published in the mid 1980s provides a comprehensive survey of the fundamentals of the storage options, examples of systems, and the issues that must be addressed for technologies in the range from low to high temperatures.[6] The only TES system that currently operates with multiple hours of storage is the sensible, two-tank, molten-salt system. This system is used because the components associated with molten-salt handling—pumps, valves, tanks, and heat exchangers—have demonstrated reliable operation at commercial scale.

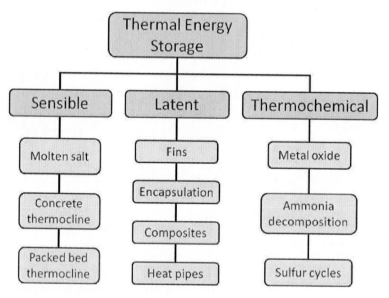

Figure 5. Thermal energy storage options for CSP technologies.

The molten-salt storage fluid is a mixture of $NaNO_3$ and KNO_3. This fluid is liquid in both the charge and discharge states, so there are minimal heat-transfer limitations, making the heat-exchanger design relatively straight-forward. One drawback for this system is the relatively low stored energy density, which results in a large storage medium inventory, requiring large insulated storage vessels. Implementation of this TES system into parabolic trough power plants requires an indirect configuration—distinct heat-transfer and storage fluids—because the storage salt has a high freezing point (220°C) and could possibly freeze in the solar collectors if used as the HTF. The indirect system requires a heat exchanger for transferring thermal energy between the HTF and storage fluid (Figure 4). This heat exchanger reduces the performance of the storage system and adds cost to the plant. This approach has been demonstrated commercially in Spain at the Andasol plants.

Implementation of this TES system into power towers can use a direct configuration—common heat-transfer and storage fluids—because steps can be taken to prevent the freezing of molten salt in the receiver and transfer lines within the vertical tower that are not possible in a parabolic trough configuration. This type of system was demonstrated during the Solar Two project in Barstow, California.

The stored energy density of the two-tank system can be increased in two ways. First, increasing the maximum operating temperature of the power plant increases the temperature drop across the turbine. Higher temperature drops increase the efficiency of the turbine power-cycle and the stored energy density of the sensible portion of the TES system. Second, increasing the heat capacity of the storage medium also directly increases the stored energy density. These effects are important to reducing size, and therefore the capital cost of the two-tank TES system.

Thermoclines that use low-cost storage materials offer an opportunity for reducing TES costs. The benefit of thermoclines is significant, especially if the storage material is self-supporting. In this case, the structural requirements of the containment vessel can be reduced. At very high temperatures, the cost of the containment vessel(s) for the storage system may negate the cost benefit from increased temperature drop. Thermoclines have more complex operating requirements than the two-tank, molten-salt system, which creates the potential for utilization and performance losses.

Alternatives to the two-tank, molten-salt storage system are being considered to increase the stored energy density and, ultimately, to reduce the cost of the TES system. The most developed alternative is the use of phase-change materials (PCMs) to increase stored energy density. PCMs have both latent and sensible enthalpies that contribute to the stored energy density, providing a benefit over purely sensible systems. PCM systems suffer from a limitation in heat transfer during the discharge process due to the generally low thermal conductivity of the solid phase. This limitation results in low power density for PCM systems and will need to be overcome if PCM storage is to become a viable alternative. PCM storage is the most compatible storage system for the parabolic dish/Stirling concentrator because thermal energy delivery to the engine is isothermal.

The third option, thermochemical storage offers perhaps the greatest benefit due to the large quantity of stored energy associated with the heat of reaction. Practical implementation of these systems is often limited by the loss of system performance as it is put through many charge/discharge cycles. System performance depends on maintaining consistent physical and chemical properties of the chemical components and of any solid-phase materials used in the system over many cycles. Over time, degradation of these material properties may result in reducing both the system heat-transfer rate and storage capacity. In addition, some cycles require the handling of gas-phase reactants that may require compression or corrosive substances that require special materials of construction. The benefits of very high energy densities and the possibility of storing reaction products at ambient temperature keep thermochemical storage under consideration for CSP technologies.

SYSTEM AND MATERIAL CHALLENGES FOR THERMAL ENERGY STORAGE

Meeting the SunShot cost target will require cost and performance improvements in all systems and components within a CSP plant. Solar collector field hardware will need to decrease significantly in cost with no loss in performance and possibly with performance improvements. As higher temperatures are considered for the power block, new working fluids, heat-transfer fluids, and storage fluids will all need to be identified to meet these new operating conditions. Figure 6 shows thermodynamic conversion efficiency as a function of temperature for the ideal Carnot cycle and 75% Carnot, which is considered to be the practical efficiency attainable by current power cycles. Current conversion efficiencies for the parabolic trough steam cycle, power tower steam cycle, parabolic dish/Stirling, Ericsson, and combined air-Brayton cycles are shown at their corresponding operating temperatures. Efficiencies for supercritical steam and CO_2 are also shown for their operating temperature ranges.

Figure 6 makes clear the benefit of increased power-cycle operating temperature. Moving in this direction requires the use of working fluids other than subcritical steam for parabolic troughs and power towers. Supercritical steam and CO_2 are options that correspond to power cycles in the 600° to 800°C range. Air is being considered for air-Brayton cycles operating above 1,200°C. These working fluids will impact the requirements for the heat-transfer fluid. In some cases, the HTF and working fluid may by the same, as in the case of a supercritical CO_2 power cycle that uses a supercritical CO_2 receiver or an air-Brayton cycle that uses an air receiver. These cycles also dictate the requirements for the heat exchanger and TES system that will couple to the power cycle and receiver. A temperature greater than 565°C will be required, and whether that temperature falls into the 565°–800°C range or is closer to 1,300°C will depend, to a large extent, on the feasibility of developing a TES system able to operate at the corresponding temperature while keeping to a minimum the system losses associated with high-temperature operation (Figure 1).

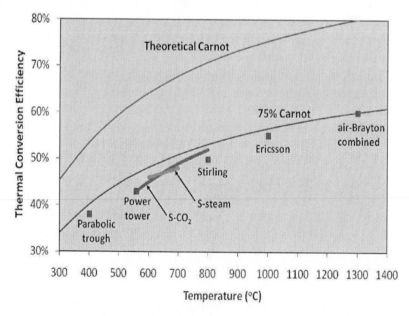

Figure 6. Power-cycle efficiencies for CSP technologies.

Participants in the breakout sessions identified the following needs and challenges for thermal energy storage.

Heat-Transfer Fluids

Reaching the higher temperatures required for the SunShot goal will require new HTFs that possess a very wide liquid temperature range. In the extreme, new HTFs could be identified that have liquid temperatures in the range of $0°$ to $1,300°C$. Practically, the temperature range will be narrower, depending on the power cycle. In addition to having a wide liquid temperature range, a suitable fluid will require combination of the following properties, depending on heat-transfer and storage media: 1) low cost, 2) environmentally safe, 3) compatible with piping and tank wall materials, and 4) high-temperature stability, possibly in air. Preferred properties that will make any new HTF more attractive for particular systems are 1) high heat capacity, 2) high thermal conductivity, 3) low viscosity, 4) high fluid density, 5) low thermal expansion coefficient, 6) high extinction coefficient, 7) high heat-transfer coefficient, and 8) low vapor pressure over the operating range.

Needs and Challenges

When considering a fully integrated power plant, use of a single fluid for heat transfer and storage is preferred because the heat exchanger and associated thermodynamic penalties can be eliminated. This arrangement results in lower power-plant capital costs and greater thermodynamic efficiency. Developing a low-cost fluid that meets all the technical requirements for both functions may not be possible, in which case the use of two distinct fluids may be the only practical configuration for a plant.

There is a need to develop guidelines and standards for high-temperature thermophysical properties measurements and a figure of merit for high-temperature performance of new heat-transfer fluids. High-temperature measurements were recognized as being very difficult to make, and a large amount of high-temperature data already exist in the literature.

There is a need to better characterize the structure of nanofluids and identify the role of radiative heat transfer in high-temperature systems. Additionally, hysteresis of the melting and freezing points can generate uncertainty in the behavior of the fluid at low temperatures where freezing in the plant piping may occur; this effect needs to be better understood. Compatibility with materials of construction must also be determined. The measurement of properties requires very careful analysis of the chemical composition of the samples tested and documentation of the methods of measurement.

Sensible Energy Storage

The effectiveness of TES systems depends critically on the thermophysical properties of the storage materials. Thermal conductivity, density, viscosity, melting and freezing points, and enthalpies of fusion or reaction all impact the design, performance, and cost of the TES system, as well as the fully integrated power plant. Part of current work is to identify the impact of these properties, along with operating conditions, on TES system performance. The following analysis for storage-fluid heat capacity is given as an example of the analyses that will help define new research directions.

Cost Benefit from Improved Heat Capacity of Sensible Storage Fluids

The simplicity and efficiency of direct two-tank storage makes it an appealing approach to TES. A relatively easy way to improve the economics of this system is to improve the heat capacity of the storage fluid. The minimum required heat capacity for a sensible storage material is a function of the temperature drop across the turbine. The heat capacity and temperature drop together determine the stored energy density of the TES system. Other factors are the costs of the storage material, tank, and piping materials that are required for the TES system. For the two-tank storage system, the low-temperature tank is normally at 300°C (as specified by the steam-cycle pinch point), so the temperature drop across the power block is determined by the maximum operating temperature.

Analysis was performed in which the cost of TES was estimated as a function of the maximum operating temperature from 400°C to 1,100°C. Heat capacities for the storage fluid varied from 1.5 J/g-K, which is the heat capacity of the binary NaNO3/KNO3 mixture that is currently used in the two-tank storage system, to 4.5 J/g-K or a factor of 3 greater than the binary salt. The cost of the tank wall material varies with temperature. From 400°C to 450°C, carbon steel can be used as the wall material for the hot tank. From 450°C to 650°C, stainless steel is required and above 650°C, a nickel-based alloy is required. The cost difference between these materials significantly impacts the cost of the TES system as a function of operating temperature. The analysis determined the cost of the TES system in the temperature range accounting for the increased cost of the tank wall material as temperature increases.

Results of the analysis indicate that the TES cost goal of $15–$20/kWhth can be reached at temperatures in the range of 450°C and at 650°C if the heat capacity of the storage fluid is between 3–4.5 J/g-K. For temperatures greater than 650°C, the high cost of nickel-based alloys makes it difficult to meet the cost target using this type of storage system. This analysis assumes that the storage medium needs to be contained in a two-tank type storage system. If thermochemical TES is used, the high-energy products from the charging process may be stored at low temperature. The stored energy in the products can then be released at high temperature. Also, if the storage medium is self supporting, such as a ceramic matrix material in a thermocline, then the requirements for the high-temperature tank material may not be as strict and its associated cost may be less. In both of these cases, operating temperatures well above 650°C still offer performance and cost benefits.

Similar analyses have been performed for the other thermophysical properties including conductivity, density, and viscosity. The impacts of these properties on the performance of TES systems and the complete plant have been characterized. High viscosities for either the HTF or storage fluid lead to unacceptably high pumping power within the plant. This power requirement is subtracted from the total generated power to get the net power produced. Limits for viscosity have been established to minimize this parameter.

Increasing HTF and storage-fluid densities actually improve plant performance and cost. Higher storage-fluid density decreases the required storage volume and decreases tank costs. Higher HTF density reduces HTF velocities in the piping, thereby reducing frictional losses and pumping power.

Minimum values for storage fluid and HTF thermal conductivities have also been established to ensure adequate heat transfer within the receiver and heat exchangers.

Needs and Challenges

There is significant overlap of needs in sensible-heat storage materials and heat-transfer fluids. These include the need for integrated systems modeling to determine costs, requirements, and relative needs for various fluids and components within an operating power plant. The point was made that the requirements for the HTF vary depending on the specifications and performance of other components within the plant. Fully integrated system models are able to determine the dependence and trade-offs between these factors and set bounds of the properties that are required for the HTF and other components.

There is a need to learn more from members of the nuclear community because they have been working in this area of high-temperature HTFs for many years and have accumulated much information on this topic. The laboratories need to develop high-temperature materials characterization methods so new fluids can be accurately characterized. These methods include high-temperature materials compatibility testing and properties measurements.

Several needs were identified relating to systems and components for the heat-transfer fluid. Eliminating the heat exchanger between either the HTF and storage fluid or HTF and working fluid reduces capital cost and exergy losses. For the air-Brayton power cycle, means for efficient heat transfer between the air and storage medium need to be modeled and developed. New alloys need to be developed that are inexpensive, strong at high temperatures, and compatible with potential heat-transfer fluids.

Phase-Change Storage

Needs and Challenges

The same capability needs that were identified for sensible storage are applicable to phase-change storage, as well. For phase-change storage, it is particularly important to develop new materials with high thermal conductivity to improve heat-transfer rates upon discharging (freezing) of the PCM. Fully integrated systems modeling is essential to determine the specifications and performance for PCM storage because its behavior is more complex than that of sensible-storage systems. Of specific interest is the need to better model heat transfer between the heat transfer fluid and PCM in complex geometries. New approaches must be found to overcome the losses due to build up of solid phase at heat-exchange surfaces.

Encapsulation of phase-change media at scales from nano to macro must be developed to improve heat transfer and construction of a cascade of PCMs that cover the operating range of the power cycle. High-temperature materials characterization is also essential for PCM storage. PCM storage matches well to Stirling engines because energy transfer to the Stirling engine is isothermal. There is a need to develop PCMs that are specific to this application.

Also, the need for high heat-transfer rates and adequate power density is required and may be met by the use of heat pipes integrated with the receiver and Stirling engine components.

Thermochemical Storage

Thermochemical storage offers the greatest volumetric stored energy density of any of the thermal energy storage options.[7, 8, 9] In some cases, the stored energy density may be an order of magnitude greater than that available from sensible or phase-change storage systems. In thermochemical storage systems, thermal energy from sunlight is absorbed by a forward reaction, A → B (Figure 8).

The reaction product, B, preheats the reactant, A, and is stored at ambient temperature. To recover thermal energy, the reverse reaction generates product A and is used to preheat the reactant B for this reaction. Because A and B can be stored at ambient temperature, this approach creates the potential for long-term storage.

For any thermochemical cycle, design considerations must include the minimization of exergy losses. For the general storage system in Figure 7, the heat exchangers should be designed to have minimal temperature drop. The reverse reaction, B → A, should occur at a temperature as close as practical to the temperature of the forward reaction, A → B. Parasitic losses due to pumping and/or compressing reactants and/or products also need to be minimized.

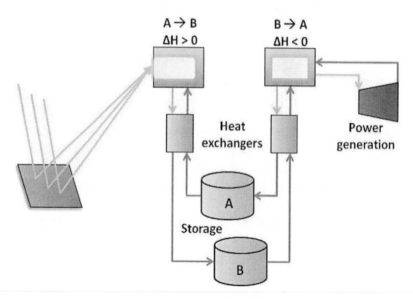

Figure 7. Schematic of generalized thermochemical storage cycle for CSP technologies.[10]

Needs and Challenges

Comparisons were made to the development of thermochemical cycles for the nuclear industry and high-temperature solar fuels applications. These are predominantly directed to water splitting to produce hydrogen as an energy carrier.[11,12] The multi-step thermochemical cycles proposed in the temperature range of $600°$ to $>1,000°C$ will present a challenge to integrate into CSP technologies where operation may be subject to repeated start up and shut down. Further, integration of thermochemical reactions into CSP systems will require receivers that are quite different compared to current receiver designs, which have HTF flowing through them. Systems will have to be designed that can meet the requirements for both generating electricity and charging the storage system with high efficiency.

Thermochemical cycles will need to be simpler and unaffected by the variable energy input that is characteristic of solar power generation.Much discussion related to the need to always evaluate any thermochemical system from the standpoint of exergy losses. On an energy basis, TES efficiency may be very high, but if the thermal energy ultimately is delivered to the power block at a low temperature, then the exergy efficiency will be unacceptably low. Exergy losses can be minimized by minimizing heat-exchange steps in the system and operating the reverse chemical process at the highest possible temperature.Other practical challenges are the need to minimize loss of surface area or activity for catalysts or solid-phase reactants, if present, over many thermal cycles due to sintering or poisoning. Reaction kinetics are proportional to these properties, so they need to be preserved to maintain adequate power densities. There is a need to identify chemical reaction rates that are fast enough to match the solar or heat flux that is supplied to the chemical reactors—whether the chemical reactor is directly driven by the solar heat in a dedicated receiver designed for the chemical process (direct solar thermal chemistry) or is driven by some fraction of heat from the same HTF stream used for driving the power cycle (an indirect solar thermal process). Gas-phase reactants or products from the chemical system may require compression for storage and contribute to parasitic losses. For example, identifying chemical cycles in which gas-phase reactants are oxygen or water would be advantageous because the system could be open and not require compression for storage of these gases.

RESEARCH DIRECTIONS FOR THERMAL ENERGY STORAGE

Participants in the breakout sessions identified the following research directions for thermal energy storage.

Heat-Transfer Fluids

1. Develop advanced capabilities in modeling of mechanistic, multi-physics systems and new standards for high-temperature stability and properties measurements. Both of these efforts will help define the requirements for performance and reliability for HTFs in fully integrated power plants.
2. Develop single heat-transfer/storage fluid, preferably a fluid that has improved radiative properties. Possible fluid types include liquid metals (Na, Al/Sn), gases (nitrogen), nanofluids, high-temperature non-nitrate salts, ionic liquids, or sulfur. Liquid Na has already been studied for use in nuclear power plants, so there are existing data that may be applicable to CSP.
3. Explore surface modification for improved heat transfer to fluids. Characterization of the structure of nanofluids is important for understanding enhancements due to adding nanoparticles to fluids.
4. Examine the use of particles for direct absorption of solar radiation. Such systems could use the same particles for TES.
5. Develop barrier coatings to prevent hydrogen permeation for Stirling engines and evaluate variations of the HTF for Brayton systems that include particles, air, liquid, or helium.

Sensible Storage

New directions for sensible storage include:

1. Additives that will lower the freezing point of molten salts to near-ambient temperature.
2. Lower-cost containment materials for high-temperature storage. One approach is to develop protective coatings that allow containment of potentially corrosive storage fluids with lower-cost wall materials.
3. Consideration of materials that have not previously been considered for storage applications. These materials include inter-metallic materials, nanofluids, and high-temperature storage materials derived from natural sources such as lava, rocks, sand, and cements.

Phase-Change Storage

New directions in phase-change storage materials include:

1. Investigation of metal alloy PCMs. There is also a need to fully characterize chlorates, sulfates, and carbonates for high-temperature storage and to develop materials or composites with higher thermal conductivity, particularly in the solid state.
2. Methods to encapsulate micro- or nano-sized PCMs that may be integrated into an HTF. Encapsulation of PCMs is needed to reduce heat-transfer losses are encountered in the charging and discharging of the storage material.
3. The development of PCMs specific to dish/Stirling applications. Also, the development of heat pipes integrated with the receiver and Stirling engine components will increase the high heat-transfer rate and power density required for this system.

Thermochemical Storage

Many thermochemical cycles were discussed and identified as potential candidates for solar thermochemical storage. These cycles include the following:

1. Solid-based reactant plus a gas-phase reactant: $MO + CO_2 = MCO_3$
2. Reactions that use other gases: SO_2, SO_3, H_2O
3. Systems that have liquid reactant(s) and liquid product(s)
4. Organic reactions that could be possible below $400^{\circ}C$, e.g., deploy merization = polymerization conversion
5. Inorganic reactants possible at higher temperatures: polymerization/depolymerization reactions based on siloxane chemistry $[-S(CH_3)_2O-]_n$
6. Polymerization/depolymerization of sulfur
7. Metallurgical conversions involving molten metals and metal oxides

8. Gas reactants to liquid or gas products
9. Reforming reactions and the corresponding reverse
10. Methanation with catalysts from $600^\circ-700^\circ C$
11. Gas reactants to gas products:
    $$SO_2 + y_2O_2 = SO_3 \quad CO + y_2O_2 = CO_2$$
12. Identifying and screening new cycles for solar thermal energy storage will require a general capability that 1) uses high-level chemical process modeling software for screening chemical storage cycles and 2) takes into account thermodynamics, kinetics, by-products, heat recovery, separations, and more.

SUMMARY

CSP technologies need to make significant cost and performance improvements to meet the SunShot Initiative cost target of 6¢/kWh LCOE. In addition, thermal energy storage will be an essential component of next-generation power plants because these plants will need to deliver reliable, consistent power during daylight hours and into the evening. Meeting the cost target will require significant performance improvements and cost reductions for all components and subsystems that make up a CSP plant. With respect to TES, new heat-transfer fluids and storage materials will be required that are stable at high temperature and have high stored energy density due to high heat capacities and/or multiple phase changes. Thermochemical storage may provide the ultimate solution to the TES challenge if a suitable system can be identified and developed for high-temperature CSP applications.

REFERENCES

[1] US Department of Energy. (2011). "SunShot Initiative." Website. www1.eere.energy. Accessed July 7, 2011.

[2] U. Herrmann, D. Kearney. (2002). *J. Solar Energy Eng.* 124, 145.

[3] Acciona North America. (2011). "Nevada Solar One." Website. www.acciona-na.com/About-Us/Our-Projects/U-S-/Nevada-Solar-One.aspx. Accessed July 7, 2011.

[4] Abengoa Solar. (2011). "Solana: The world's largest solar plant." Website. www. abengoa solar.com/corp/web. Accessed July 7, 2011.

[5] BrightSource Energy. (2011). Ivanpah Project Overview. Website. www. Brightsource energy. Accessed July 7, 2011.

[6] H.P. Garg, S.C. Mullick, A.K. Bhargava; (1985). *Solar Thermal Energy Storage*, D. Reidel Publishing Company, Dordrecht, Holland 642 pp.

[7] R.D. Smith. (1979). Chemical Energy Storage for Solar Thermal Conversion, Final Report. SAND79-8198, Livermore: Sandia National Laboratories, 190 pp.

[8] T.T. Bramlette, R.M. Green, J.J. Bartel, D.K. Ottesen, C.T. Schafer, T.D. Brumleve. (1976). Survey of High Temperature Thermal Energy Storage, SAND75-8063, Livermore: Sandia National Laboratories.

[9] E.A. Fletcher. (2001). *J. Solar Energy Eng.* 123, 63-74

[10] Steinfeld, R. Palumbo (2001). *Solar Thermochemical Process Technology, Encyclopedia of Physical Science and Technology,* 237-256.

[11] S. Yalcin. (1989). *A Review of Nuclear Hydrogen Production, International Journal of Hydrogen Energy* 14(8), 551-561.

[12] Steinfeld. (2005). *Solar Thermochemical Production of Hydrogen A Review, Solar Energy* 78(5), 603-615.

In: Concentrating Solar Power
Editors: Burt J. Alexander and Ted F. Richardson

ISBN: 978-1-62081-423-9
© 2012 Nova Science Publishers, Inc.

Chapter 5

POWER TOWER TECHNOLOGY ROADMAP AND COST REDUCTION PLAN*

Gregory J. Kolb, Clifford K. Ho, Thomas R. Mancini and Jesse A. Gary

ABSTRACT

Concentrating solar power (CSP) technologies continue to mature and are being deployed worldwide. Power towers will likely play an essential role in the future development of CSP due to their potential to provide dispatchable solar electricity at a low cost.

This Power Tower Technology Roadmap has been developed by the U.S. Department of Energy (DOE) to describe the current technology, the improvement opportunities that exist for the technology, and the specific activities needed to reach the DOE programmatic target of providing competitively-priced electricity in the intermediate and baseload power markets by 2020.

As a first step in developing this roadmap, a Power Tower Roadmap Workshop that included the tower industry, national laboratories, and DOE was held in March 2010. A number of technology improvement opportunities (TIOs) were identified at this workshop and separated into four categories associated with power tower subsystems: solar collector field, solar receiver, thermal energy storage, and power block / balance of plant.

In this roadmap, the TIOs associated with power tower technologies are identified along with their respective impacts on the cost of delivered electricity. In addition, development timelines and estimated budgets to achieve cost reduction goals are presented.

The roadmap does not present a single path for achieving these goals, but rather provides a process for evaluating a set of options from which DOE and industry can select to accelerate power tower R&D, cost reductions, and commercial deployment.

---

* This is an edited, reformatted and augmented version of a Sandia National Laboratories publication, SAND2011-2419, dated April 2011.

1. INTRODUCTION

In recent years there has been a resurgent interest in concentrating solar power (CSP) power tower technologies, with at least five companies currently pursuing the development of commercial power tower projects: Abengoa Solar, BrightSource Energy, eSolar, SolarReserve, and SENER. One of the reasons for the renewed interest in power tower technology is that power towers offer high efficiencies and, therefore, the opportunity for low-cost electricity. In addition, power towers can readily integrate thermal energy storage into their operation to achieve high capacity factors, which can provide for cost-effective, dispatchable electricity to serve the needs of the intermediate and baseload power markets.

In March 2010, the U.S. Department of Energy (DOE) and Sandia National Laboratories hosted a Power Tower Roadmap Workshop that included participation of the power tower industry, the national laboratories, and DOE.

At the workshop, areas of discussion included the current status of power tower technology, a number of Technology Improvement Opportunities (TIOs), and cost-reduction goals for power tower systems and subsystems. After the workshop, further evaluation of the TIOs was performed, resulting in a levelized cost of energy (LCOE) analysis that identified the potential for a 40% reduction in power tower LCOE by the end of the decade. If this LCOE reduction can be achieved, power towers will likely become competitive with newly constructed conventional fossil-fired power plants in both the intermediate and baseload power markets.

Commercial power tower plants with power ratings greater than 100 MW$_e$ or more are now being pursued and constructed in the USA. These tower projects are more than ten times larger than the 10 MW$_e$ Solar One and Solar Two power tower demonstrations sponsored by DOE in the 1980s and 1990s. The success of these first projects should lead to investment in future power tower projects. For commercial power tower projects to be successful, close cooperation will be required among all stakeholders, including the power tower industry, DOE, national laboratories, international partners, utilities, and the financial community.

1.1. Power Tower Background

The Solar One project — a joint undertaking of the U.S. DOE, Southern California Edison Company (SCE), Los Angeles Department of Water and Power, and the California Energy Commission — was a 10 MW$_e$ water-steam solar power tower facility built in Barstow, CA. Solar One was instrumental in helping to prove that central receiver technology is effective, reliable, and practical for utility-scale power generation. It operated from 1982 to 1988 and ultimately achieved 96% availability during hours of sunshine [1].

A few years later, the Solar One steam-receiver plant was redesigned into a power tower plant named Solar Two, which employed a molten-salt receiver and thermal energy storage system. The change from steam to a molten-salt working fluid was made primarily because of the ease of integrating a highly efficient (~99%) and low-cost energy storage system into a molten-salt plant design.

The project was developed by the U.S. DOE along with a consortium of utilities led by SCE.

Solar Two operated from 1996 to 1999 and helped validate nitrate salt technology, reduce the technical and economic risks of power towers, and stimulate the commercialization of CSP power tower technology. The baseline power tower used in this roadmap utilizes the data generated by the Solar Two project.

Due to budget constraints, DOE removed most power tower activities from the CSP Program portfolio after the decommissioning of Solar Two. As a result, virtually no work was performed on power towers in the U.S. for nearly a decade. Recent increases in budgets and a renewed interest in power towers have led the DOE CSP Program to reintroduce power towers into its portfolio.

As mentioned above, the primary reasons for this reintroduction are the broad interest among industry to develop power towers, the potential for high-temperature operation, and the ability to effectively integrate thermal energy storage, thereby producing dispatchable electricity.

Experimental power tower test facilities are currently located at Sandia's National Solar Thermal Test Facility (NSTTF) in Albuquerque, New Mexico, USA; the Plataforma Solar de Almeria in Spain; the Julich Solar Tower in Germany; the Weizmann Institute of Science in Israel; the CSIRO National Solar Energy Centre in Australia; and the Odeillo and THEMIS Solar Power Towers in France. In addition, private industry has built small-scale tower demonstration facilities in the USA, Spain, and Israel.

Commercial electricity-generating power tower plants in operation today include Abengoa's PS10 (11 MW$_e$) and PS20 (20 MW$_e$) steam towers in Spain and eSolar's Sierra SunTower (5 MW$_e$) steam towers in California. Commercial electricity-generating power tower plants under construction include BrightSource Energy's Ivanpah (392 MW$_e$) steam towers in California and Torresol Energy's (SENER and Masdar) Gemasolar (17 MW$_e$) molten-salt tower in Spain. SolarReserve has also announced their intention to construct utility-scale, molten-salt power towers near Tonopah, Nevada, and Palm Springs, California.

1.2. Roadmap Approach

As outlined in the DOE Solar Energy Technologies Program (SETP) Multi-Year Program Plan 2007-2011, the development of a technology roadmap consists of four steps:

1. Determine baseline and goals for component costs and performance;
2. Identify technology improvement opportunities (TIOs);
3. Assess and prioritize TIOs; and
4. Develop a multi-year task portfolio.

The first three steps of this process were initiated at a Power Tower Roadmap Workshop held at Sandia's NSTTF in Albuquerque, NM on March 24-25, 2010. Participants were asked to discuss costs, performance, and research needs for the following subsystems:

1. Solar Collector Field (Heliostats);
2. Solar Receiver;
3. Thermal Energy Storage; and
4. Power Block / Balance of Plant.

During the workshop, facilitators led group discussions in each of these four areas. Current and future costs were collectively discussed, and R&D needs associated with component performance and cost reductions were identified. At the end of the two-day workshop, participants prioritized the topics they thought were most important for cost reduction and could be supported by DOE, and the results were then tabulated. After the workshop, Sandia conducted a more detailed assessment of the potential impact of the identified TIOs on LCOE.

1.3. Purpose and Objectives

One of the goals of the DOE CSP Program is to achieve large-scale deployment of CSP technologies, including power tower systems, so that they become major contributors to domestic energy supply. Of course, deployment will be encouraged by lower power tower system costs, higher costs of the competition (e.g. carbon pricing), or a combination of the two. However, large-scale deployment will also require that utilities and investors observe the successful operation of power tower plants and recognize the value of energy storage and dispatchability of electricity. There are currently Power Purchase Agreements (PPAs) for approximately 8,200 MW of new CSP plants in the U.S. and, of these, approximately 3,100 MW involve power towers [2]. For even a fraction of these plants to be financed and built, it is critically important that the first round of new plants be successful. DOE and the national laboratories can provide support for these first commercial power tower projects, including component testing, systems analysis, process optimization, and rapid feedback to industry. DOE has developed this Power Tower Technology Roadmap to describe the current technology, the improvement opportunities that exist for the technology, and the specific activities needed to reach the DOE programmatic target of providing competitively-priced electricity in the intermediate and baseload power markets by 2020. The roadmap will be used to evaluate the current DOE CSP Program portfolio and guide future funding areas and budget allocations. Furthermore, it will be a source of input for the next Solar Energy Technologies Program (SETP) Multi-Year Plan. The remainder of this roadmap is broken into the following three main sections:

- Power Tower Cost and Performance Goals: describes the baseline system, current costs, and cost goals for power tower systems;
- Technology Improvement Opportunities: identifies and discusses specific TIOs that will lead to the required cost reductions; and
- Recommended Activities and Spend Plan: provides a 10-year schedule of potential programmatic activities, costs, and their impact on LCOE.

2. POWER TOWER COST AND PERFORMANCE GOALS

In 2009, the DOE CSP Program set a goal to reduce the LCOE of CSP technology of a hypothetical 100 MW plant from today's costs of approximately 15¢/kWh to a value in 2020 of 9¢/kWh or less.[1] In other words, the goal was to cut the cost by 40% over ten years.

Although a 30% investment tax credit (ITC) is in effect until 2016, this analysis uses a 10% ITC for both present and future costs to reveal the actual improvement that is necessary.

Table 1 summarizes the baseline costs and future cost goals for power tower subsystems.

Table 1. Baseline costs and Roadmap Workshop cost goals for commercial power towers

	Solar Field	Solar Receiver	Thermal Storage	Power Block	Steam Generation	O&M
Today's Baseline	$200/m2	$200/kWt	$30/kWht	$1000/kWe	$350/kWe	$65/kW-yr
Workshop Goal	$120/m2	$170/kWt	$20/kWht	$800/kWe	$250/kWe	$50/kW-yr

The baseline costs identified above are based on information from four sources:

- responses to a confidential questionnaire that was distributed by Sandia to power tower developers;
- escalation to 2010 dollars of power tower subsystem costs reported in the 1988 U.S. Utility Study [3];
- a recent study by Abengoa Solar that included molten-salt power towers [4]; and
- a 2007 study of heliostat costs by Sandia National Laboratories [5].

The baseline power tower used in this roadmap is a 100 MW$_e$ plant assumed to have a solar multiple of 2.1, a heliostat field size slightly larger than 1,000,000 m^2, a 540 MWt surround receiver, and 9 hours of thermal storage. The receiver and field size represent a direct scale-up of the technology demonstrated at DOE's Solar Two project. Furthermore, this baseline is only 15% larger than the plant that was chosen for the U.S. Utility Study, allowing for a more direct use of the cost data that was developed in that study. Given a power tower plant with a 540 MWt receiver and a 100 MW$_e$ turbine, the System Advisor Model (SAM) predicts the lowest LCOE to result with 9 hours (i.e. 2340 MWht) of 2-tank, sensible heat, molten-salt thermal storage.

It should be noted that the majority of U.S. utilities do not presently value storage beyond a few hours; however, the focus of this analysis is reaching the lowest possible LCOE[2]. Using the baseline subsystem costs shown in Table 1, SAM models were run to predict the performance of a baseline plant with a direct capital cost of $552M and an indirect cost of $192M, yielding a total installed cost of $744M, or $7400/kW.

The annual capacity factor of the baseline plant is 48%. As shown in Figure 1, the LCOE for this plant with a 10% ITC is 15.0¢/kWh. Figure 1 also includes the LCOE impact of realizing the cost goals displayed in Table 1. If these targets are reached, power tower systems can achieve a real LCOE of less than 8¢/kWh.

The total installed cost is the sum of direct and indirect costs; direct costs are essentially the capital costs of the plant, and indirect costs are obtained by multiplying direct costs by a given percentage. For the 2013 10% ITC case in Figure 1, direct costs alone account for 8.8¢/kWh of the 15.0¢/kWh total. Of this 8.8¢/kWh, direct costs break out into 3.3¢/kWh (38%) for heliostats, 1.8¢/kWh (20%) for power plant, 1.7¢/kWh (19%) for receiver/tower, 1.1¢/kWh (13%) for storage, 0.6¢/kWh (7%) for balance of plant, and 0.3¢/kWh (3%) for site preparation. The cost breakdowns for the four main subsystems—solar collector field, solar receiver, thermal energy storage, and power block / balance of plant—are detailed in the following sections of this roadmap.

It is important to note that the predicted baseline LCOEs for steam and molten-salt power tower technologies are nearly identical.

Although the analysis presented in Figure 1 is based on a molten-salt power tower with several hours of energy storage, modeling a steam tower system with little to no storage results in an LCOE prediction within 1¢/kWh of the 2013 values shown in Figure 1. In addition, much of the cost reduction potential identified for molten-salt power towers also applies to steam receiver towers.

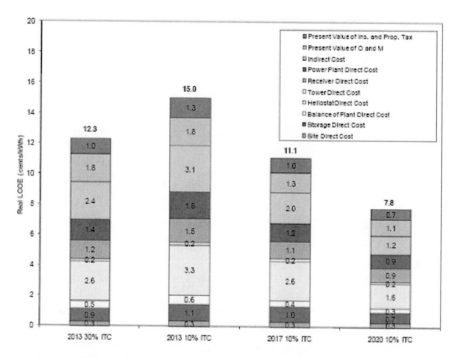

Figure 1. Projected LCOE (real 2010 dollars) and associated costs of individual components (The 2013 case is shown with both a 30% and 10% ITC).

3. TECHNOLOGY IMPROVEMENT OPPORTUNITIES (TIOs)

From a technical standpoint, the LCOE of a power tower can be reduced in two ways: 1) by increasing annual performance of the plant (both initial and long-term) and 2) by lowering costs of the plant (both capital and O&M). This roadmap addresses both avenues to power tower plant cost reduction.

Power tower performance can be increased by:

- improving plant availability;
- improving the optical efficiency (including tracking accuracy) of the heliostat field;
- reducing the thermal losses of the receiver;
- increasing receiver operating temperature to power higher-efficiency power cycles;

- increasing thermal storage efficiency; and/or
- reducing parasitic losses and improving operational efficiency.

One way to characterize the annual performance of a power tower plant is through annual solarto-electric conversion efficiency. This metric includes all of the energy losses that affect the annual electricity produced by the plant, including optical, thermal, electrical parasitics, and equipment unavailability losses.

During Solar One's final year of operation (1988), the annual efficiency was 10.7% gross and 7.7% net (including parasitics) given the achieved plant availability of 96% [1]. Solar Two did not operate long enough to achieve a reliable daily operation; while Solar One operated for 10,000 hours, Solar Two operated for less than 2,000 hours. Thus, it is difficult to estimate an annual efficiency for Solar Two. During PS10's second year of operation (2008), the annual efficiency was 11.5% gross.[3] Since parasitics were not reported, a net annual efficiency could not be estimated.

Due to their small size, the power blocks for Solar One and PS10 did not incorporate a reheat loop, which resulted in a relatively low thermal-to-electric conversion efficiency of approximately 31%. However, reheat will be incorporated into each of the three steam power towers at Ivanpah, which will raise turbine thermal-to-electric conversion efficiency to approximately 42%.

If Solar One or PS10 had used reheat, the gross annual efficiencies would have been approximately 15%, which may represent a good target for future water-steam power towers.[4]

The annual efficiency predicted using SAM (Beta version) for the baseline 100 MW$_e$ molten-salt power tower plant operating in Barstow, California is 16.0% gross and 14.8% net assuming a plant availability of 90%.

These values are nearly identical to the efficiency values (16.3% gross and 14.6% net) predicted using the SOLERGY code in 1999 for a commercial molten-salt power tower based on lessons learned from Solar Two [1]. Thus, these values are used as the annual efficiencies for the baseline molten-salt power tower.

Power tower cost can be reduced by:

- reducing equipment capital cost via reduced material content, lower-cost materials, more efficient design, or less expensive manufacturing and shipping costs;
- reducing field assembly and installation costs via simpler designs and minimization and/or ease of field assembly;
- lowering operation and maintenance costs through improved automation, reducing need (as with more reliable components), and better O&M techniques;
- building larger systems that provide economies of scale; and/or
- deploying more systems to benefit from learning-curve effects.

The cost of electricity generated by a solar power tower system is dependent on the capital cost, the annual performance, and the annual operations and maintenance cost.[5] The capital equipment for a power tower plant consists of solar components (heliostats, solar receivers, steam generators, and storage) and the use of more-or-less conventional Rankine-steam-cycle components. While current tower projects utilize subcritical Rankine steam cycles, it is feasible for power towers to transition to supercritical Rankine steam cycles that operate at higher temperatures and convert solar heat at a much higher efficiency (50% thermal-to-electric efficiency for supercritical versus 42% for subcritical).

This roadmap focuses on improvements to the solar-specific components; however, the need to adapt existing supercritical Rankine plant equipment for power tower applications is also addressed.

In the following sections, potential opportunities for performance improvement and cost reduction in the four subsystem areas, as well as O&M, are described.

3.1. Solar Collector Field 3.1.1 Current Status

There is no consensus among power tower developers regarding the optimum size of a heliostat, and heliostats ranging between 1 m^2 and 130 m^2 are being developed. Simplified heliostat-scaling theory, described in Sandia's Heliostat Cost Reduction Study [5], indicates that capital costs can be proportional to Area$^{1.5}$, which would favor smaller heliostats. However, the more detailed investigation described in the same study (including O&M, field wiring, and some manufacturing quotes on heliostat subcomponents) show that lowest life-cycle cost may ultimately be achieved with heliostats larger than 50 m^2. The optimum heliostat size — if in fact one exists — will be better understood as the power tower industry continues to deploy and operate more systems.

As shown in Table 2, the current cost of the solar field is dominated by four components for both large and small heliostats. For large heliostats, the major cost drivers are drives (27%); manufacturing facilities / profit (23%); mirror modules (22%); and pedestal / mirror support structure / foundation (19%). For small heliostats, the major cost drivers are drives (30%); manufacturing facilities / profit (23%); field wiring and controls (19%); and mirror modules (16%). It is interesting to note that "pedestal / mirror support structure / foundation" costs impact large heliostats more than small heliostats, as large heliostats experience higher wind loads and require more structural steel (per m2 of surface area) to maintain a rigid structure and survive worst-case wind storms. It is also interesting to note that "field wiring and controls" costs impact small heliostats more than large heliostats, as small heliostats require more complex field wiring and controls due to the increased number of heliostats in the field.

As mentioned above, the Roadmap Workshop Baseline cost is a "rolled-up" value based primarily on responses obtained during the Roadmap Workshop. Columns 1 and 2 of Table 2 were estimated in year 2000, and columns 3 and 4 were estimated in year 2006. Due to minor changes in certain aspects of the cost categorization between 2000 and 2006, a normalization using the year 2000 categories was performed.[6] The values in Table 2 indicate that large heliostats may have lower capital and O&M costs when supplying heliostats for a single plant (comparing columns 1 and 2).[7]

However, small heliostats display better optical performance than large heliostats and, with a performance improvement value of $10/m^2 or more, the cost differential is narrowed [5]. Table 2 also indicates that multi-plant / multi-year-production scenarios can significantly reduce the cost for a given heliostat design (comparing columns 2 and 3) and that ramping up to a highly automated production line also has a significant impact on cost reduction (comparing columns 3 and 4).

Table 2. Cost of solar collector field subsystem [$/m2] expressed in 2010 dollars [5]

Heliostat Component	30 m² size 235,000 m² 7800 helios one time	148 m² size 235,000 ₘ2 1600 helios one time	148 m² size 740,000 m²/yr 5,000 helios/yr	148 m² size 7,400,000 m²/yr 50,000 helios/yr	Roadmap Workshop Baseline
Mirror Modules	39	43	29	25	–
Drives	71	52	52	29	–
Pedestal, Mirror Support Structure, Foundation	17	38	48	44	–
Controls and Wired Connections	27	8	5	4	–
Field Wiring	18	8	9	8	–
Manufacturing Facilities and Profit	54	45	26	20	–
Installation and Checkout	11	4	8	7	–
Total Capital Cost	$237/m²	$196/m²	$177/m²	$137/m²	$200/m²
O&M Cost (life-cycle cost)	$16/m²	$7/m²	–	–	–

3.1.2. Future Improvement Opportunities

The solar collector field (materials plus labor) is the largest single capital investment in a power tower plant, and thus represents the greatest potential for LCOE cost reduction among capital equipment costs. Unfortunately, a comprehensive DOE R&D plan for power tower solar fields is complicated by the variations in heliostat designs among industry. As described above, each commercial power tower company is developing their own heliostat, ranging in size from 1 m² to 130 m². Thus, the solar field TIOs identified attempt to focus on common areas that would be beneficial to the industry at large. These include:

- Drives and controls: The most expensive part of the heliostat is the azimuth drive, and therefore next-generation, low-cost drives that employ less conservative or alternative designs must be developed. Control algorithms that maintain less than 1 milliradian pointing accuracy are also needed for accurate positioning of heliostats at long slant ranges (i.e. for large fields).
- Heliostat support structure: Survival wind-loads dominate heliostat design criteria, and therefore experimental validation of models is necessary to optimize future heliostat designs that are more material-efficient. The optical and structural performance of today's heliostats must be fully characterized during operating and high-wind conditions through both analytical modeling and empirical experimentation.
- Manufacturing facilities: Highly-automated facilities and equipment to support the low-cost manufacture and installation of heliostats will lead to cost reduction. Improved construction, assembly, and installation methods can reduce construction time, which in turn reduces financial risk and improves time to market.
- Reflectors, coatings, and cleaning techniques: Optical efficiency is critical to overall plant performance, and a highly reflective facet surface — in terms of both total

hemispherical and specular reflectance — is the first step in minimizing optical losses. In addition, passive (e.g. anti-soiling coatings) and active (e.g. optimized low-to-no water cleaning techniques) methods of keeping the reflector surface clean play a key role in reducing the O&M of the solar field. Developing low-cost reflectors — both glass and non-glass — with increased reflectivity and durability is also imperative to reducing the cost of heliostats.

Figure 2 shows the potential impact of solar collector field cost reductions and performance improvements on LCOE. Results are based on the baseline power tower model with individual parameters varied one at a time in SAM.[8]

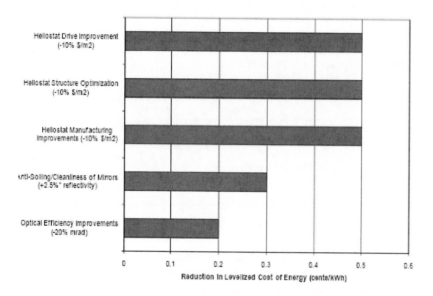

Figure 2. Potential impact of solar collector field cost reductions and performance improvements on LCOE (*absolute percentage improvement).

3.2. Solar Receiver 3.2.1 Current Status

The baseline solar receiver is a scaled-up version of the receiver used at Solar Two. The external receiver used at Solar Two consisted of 24 panels of thin-walled, metal tubes through which salt flowed in a serpentine path. The panels formed a cylindrical shell that surrounded the associated piping, structural supports, and control equipment. The external surfaces of the tubes were coated with a black Pyromark paint that provided an absorptivity of 95% and an emissivity of 88%.

The receiver was designed to accept a maximum amount of solar energy in a minimum area to reduce heat losses due to convection and radiation. In terms of function and basic description, a steam receiver is similar to a molten-salt receiver; however, steam receivers are a more mature technology than molten-salt receivers.

Table 3 identifies the costs associated with a typical molten-salt solar receiver system using a single tower. The cost of the receiver system is dominated by two components: the solar receiver (59%) and tower (21%). The calculations are based on the Utility Study plant since it is closer in size to the baseline plant. As mentioned above, the Roadmap Workshop Baseline cost is a "rolled-up" value based primarily on responses obtained during the Roadmap Workshop. Whereas columns 1 and 2 are from single studies, column 3 represents a consolidated value from numerous individuals and organizations, which may explain the discrepancy in receiver costs. Furthermore, the discrepancy in receiver costs may also be attributable to different receiver sizes.

Table 3. Cost of solar receiver subsystem [$/kWt] expressed in 2010 dollars

Receiver System Component	Utility Studies 470 MWt	Abengoa Study 910 MWt	Roadmap Workshop Baseline
Receiver	71	58	–
Tower	25	27	–
Riser/Downcomer	16	13	–
Cold Salt Pumps	6	7	–
Controls and Instruments	1	1	–
Spare Parts and Other Directs	1	3	–
Contingency	18	16	–
Total Capital Cost	$138/kWt	$125/kWt	$200/kWt

3.2.2. Future Improvement Opportunities

Smaller and simpler receivers will result in higher efficiencies (due to reduced heat-loss area) and improved reliability. For advanced central receivers, this translates into a durable, high-temperature absorber (solar spectrum) with reduced thermal emissivity (infrared) that is capable of operating unprotected in ambient air conditions. Specific TIOs identified to achieve these design characteristics include:

- High thermal conversion efficiency and receiver materials database: One way to increase thermal-to-electric conversion efficiency is by interfacing a power tower with a supercritical Rankine cycle, which can be accomplished by raising the receiver outlet temperature to approximately 650°C. Thus, receiver tube materials that can reliably operate above 650°C with incident flux concentrations exceeding 1000 suns must be developed or identified, evaluated, and catalogued.

- Solar selective absorbers and coatings: Current receiver surfaces possess a high solar absorptivity but do not possess low infrared emissivity. New materials and formulations must be examined that exhibit the desired thermal/optical properties and are resistant to oxidation or degradation when operating in air. Thermal cycling testing is also required to ensure candidate materials can operate over a wide range of temperatures for many years.

- Receiver thermal loss and flux measurements: Characterization of thermal losses and incident fluxes for a thermal receiver will lead to optimized receiver designs. Thermal losses from a receiver are primarily the result of radiation and convection to the environment. A rotating flux mapper for characterizing the solar flux incident on the receiver is currently under development at Sandia, and other advanced measurement techniques are necessary to accurately characterize and evaluate receiver designs and optical surface characteristics at high temperatures.

- Steam receiver studies and optimization: Current steam receivers are based on mature steam boiler technology and designs. Further development of direct steam receivers can be achieved through studies, monitoring, and optimization of initial commercial steam-receiver power tower plants.

- Tall tower acceptance: Towers that exceed 100 meters in height are typically used in commercial power tower projects. As can be expected, public opinion of such tall structures is mixed; while some have a positive reaction to the aesthetics of power towers, others take a more negative view. The U.S. Air Force (USAF) has also expressed concern that power towers may encroach on their flight testing grounds in the desert Southwest. The USAF and DOE are working together to address these concerns. In addition, Sandia currently performs glint and glare studies and participates in public meetings to support power tower acceptance.

Figure 3 shows the potential impact of solar receiver cost reductions and performance improvements on LCOE. Results are based on the baseline model with individual parameters varied one at a time in SAM.[9]

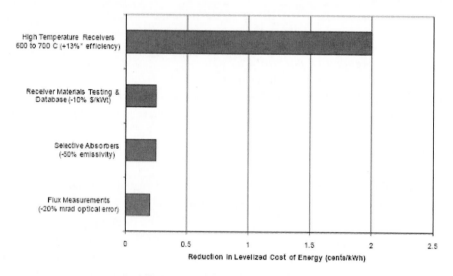

Figure 3. Potential impact of solar receiver cost reductions and performance improvements on LCOE (*absolute percentage improvement).

3.3. Thermal Energy Storage

3.3.1. Current Status

The 2-tank, sensible-heat molten-salt thermal storage system is the current state-of-the-art for power towers. This storage configuration was originally demonstrated at Solar Two and has been adapted for use in commercial trough systems deployed in Spain. As shown in Table 4, the cost of this type of storage system is dominated by two components: salt media (57%) and tanks (29%). The calculation is based on the Utility Study plant since it is closer in size to the baseline plant.

As mentioned above, the Roadmap Workshop Baseline cost is a "rolled-up" value based primarily on responses obtained during the Roadmap Workshop. Whereas columns 1 and 2 are from single studies, column 3 represents a consolidated value from numerous individuals and organizations, which may explain the discrepancy in storage costs. Furthermore, the discrepancy in storage costs may also be attributable to different storage sizes.

Table 4. Cost of thermal energy storage subsystem [$/kWht] expressed in 2010 dollars

Storage System Component	Utility Studies 1560 MWh	Abengoa Study 8140 MWh	Roadmap Workshop Baseline
Tanks	6	6	–
Foundations	0.7	1	–
Salt Media	12	11	–
Piping and Small Support Pumps	1	0.2	–
Controls and Instrumentation	0.5	0.1	–
Spare Parts and Other Directs	1	0.9	–
Contingency	4	3	–
Total Capital Cost	$25/kWht	$22/kWht	$30/kWht

3.3.2. Future Improvements Opportunities

In support of advanced heat transfer fluid and thermal storage research, a molten-salt component testing facility is currently under development at Sandia to test hardware at operating conditions.

In addition, the DOE CSP Program is currently supporting multiple projects that are exploring a number of thermal storage techniques, including thermoclines, phase change materials, nanoparticle fluids, thermochemical and solid-state storage. Specific TIOs identified in the area of thermal energy storage include:

- Salt valves and other hardware: Valves and other flow-loop hardware need to be improved relative to the experience at Solar Two. There is a particular need for materials suitable for use as valve packing and flange gaskets, as well as for instrumentation (e.g. flow and pressure sensors) capable of operation in a high-temperature molten-salt environment. In addition, the melting of large volumes of salt during facility start-up, along with the NO_x emissions that can occur, is a significant challenge. Sandia will leverage its molten-salt test loop and high-temperature corrosion test facility to evaluate components under realistic conditions.

- High-temperature operation: Thermal storage cost is inversely proportional to the hot and cold temperature differential; in other words, as the temperature differential increases, the capital cost of the storage subsystem is reduced because of the increase in sensible heat capacity, which leads to a reduction in storage media volume and tank size. The baseline 2-tank, molten-salt storage system operates at temperatures of 565°C in the hot tank and 290°C in the cold tank. An increase in temperature to 650°C may be feasible with nitrate salts [8] but will necessitate the use of higher-temperature containment designs. Higher temperature storage also supports high-efficiency power cycles.

- High-temperature, single tank thermal storage: Replacing the 2-tank storage approach with a 1-tank, thermocline system using liquids or particles has the potential to reduce the cost of the thermal energy storage subsystem. However, thermal ratcheting resulting in increased tank stresses (i.e. thermal cycling causing the thermocline inside the tank to slump, placing excessive pressure on the tank walls) is a serious challenge that must be resolved before the predicted cost reduction can be realized. This problem is exacerbated in power tower thermoclines due to the high temperature differential between the top and bottom of the tank (as high as 300°C). Potential solutions such as tank inserts or sloping tank walls, as well as new materials for fluids and tanks, must be sought.

- Advanced high temperature heat transfer fluids: Power towers can potentially operate at very high temperatures (>1000°C), but available, low-cost, non-exotic engineering materials are required to increase the practical upper temperature limit. These advanced heat transfer fluids will enable high-temperature receivers and high-efficiency power cycles.

- Storage systems for steam towers: Future direct steam power towers will likely include at least a few hours of thermal storage to increase the value of electricity produced and increase capacity factor. Many of the storage options for steam towers are similar to molten-salt towers; however, they must be specifically adapted for compatibility with a direct steam system. Prior research at Sandia has been devoted to studying a variety of storage options for DSG systems [9].

Figure 4 shows the potential impact of thermal energy storage cost reductions and performance improvements on LCOE. Results are based on the baseline model with individual parameters varied one at a time in SAM.[10]

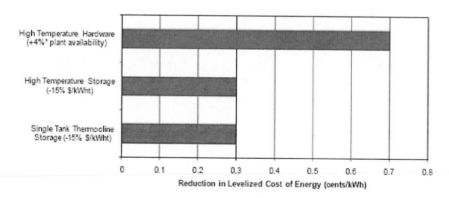

Figure 4. Potential impact of thermal energy storage cost reductions and performance improvements on LCOE (*absolute percentage improvement).

3.4. Power Block / Balance of Plant

3.4.1. Current Status

The current power tower power blocks used in both steam and molten-salt power tower designs have been promoted since the 1980s and utilize steam Rankine cycle components representative of a conventional fossil-fired plant. The baseline power block consists of a molten-salt steam generator that feeds a subcritical Rankine cycle with reheat.

The inlet steam temperature is 540°C, and the turbine thermal-to-electric conversion efficiency is approximately 42% with a wet-cooled condenser [1]. While subcritical Rankine cycles are already commercially available in the 100-200 MW$_e$ size range and employ conventional turbomachinary, the molten-salt steam generator is solar-specific hardware that has only been demonstrated at a relatively modest scale.

As shown in Table 5, the cost of the steam generator system is dominated by a single class of components: salt heat exchangers (85%). The calculation is based on the Utility Study plant since it is closest in size to the baseline plant.

As mentioned above, the Roadmap Workshop Baseline cost is a "rolled-up" value based primarily on responses obtained during the Roadmap Workshop. Whereas columns 1 and 2 are from single studies, column 3 represents a consolidated value from numerous individuals and organizations, which may explain the discrepancy in steam generator costs. Furthermore, the discrepancy in steam generator costs may also be attributable to different power block sizes.

Table 5. Cost of steam generator subsystem [$/kWe] expressed in 2010 dollars

Steam Generator System Component	Utility Studies 100 MWe (260 MWt)	Abengoa Study 400 MWe (1000 MWt)	Roadmap Workshop Baseline
Heat Exchangers	214	110	–
Structures/Foundations	1	0.5	–
Piping	22	12	–
Hot Salt Pumps	10	12	–
Auxiliary Equipment	3	2	–
Spare Parts and Other Directs	1	9	–
Contingency	38	22	–
Total Capital Cost	$290/kWe	$168/kWe	$250/kWe

3.4.2. Future Improvement Opportunities

Many of the issues surrounding the power block and balance of plant are non-solar in nature and are beyond the scope of the DOE CSP Program; however, "exceptions" do exist. TIOs identified during the Roadmap Workshop include:

- Advanced power cycles: Three advanced power cycles applicable to power towers — supercritical steam Rankine, high temperature air Brayton, and supercritical CO_2 Brayton — offer the potential to increase the efficiency of the power block to nearly 50% relative to today's subcritical steam Rankine cycle efficiency of 42%. The "next step" power cycle is likely supercritical steam Rankine since this cycle readily exists at commercial utility-scale fossil plants. However, existing systems are 400 MW$_e$ or larger and may need to be scaled down to better accommodate power tower systems.
- Parasitic power reduction: Parasitic power consumption at Solar One and Solar Two were relatively high. Although most of the consumption can be attributed to the small size of the plants, studies of proposed commercial-scale plants suggest that parasitics will consume 10% or more of the gross annual electricity. Receiver pumps are a major source of consumption, and thus head-recovery options should be explored to

reduce their impact. A campaign to reduce plant-wide parasitics in early commercial plants should also be implemented.[11]

- Hybridization: A promising lower-cost market-entry strategy is augmentation of existing fossil-fired plants with power tower systems. Integration with existing natural-gas combined cycle and coal-fired plants is being studied by EPRI and the national laboratories, among others. Hybridization of power towers and existing fossil-fired plants holds several distinct advantages, including reduction in capital and O&M costs through the use of existing power block hardware and O&M crews, respectively. In addition, new "solar-only" power tower plants can benefit from a small amount of fossil backup to ensure dispatchability by increasing capacity factor.

- Dry cooling: Power towers are typically built in desert areas where water is a scarce resource. A standard power tower power blockthat employs wet cooling requires approximately 650 gallons of water to produce one megawatt-hour of solar electricity [10]. The issue of water use will likely require power towers to transition to dry or hybrid cooling; therefore, a dry cooling system that does not significantly reduce the efficiency of the power block is needed.

- Designs for rapid temperature change: Initial steam receiver power towers will not incorporate a thermal energy storage system. Thus, cloud transients affecting the solar receiver will rapidly impact the operation of the turbine generator. If cloud duration lasts more than a few minutes, steam conditions will degrade and the turbine generator may trip offline. When sun returns, the turbine must be able to quickly restart to mitigate energy losses. The inability to quickly restart the turbine at Solar One led to significant energy losses, and the problem is only intensified in commercial plants.

Figure 5 shows the potential impact of power block cost reductions and performance improvements on LCOE. Results are based on the baseline model with individual parameters varied one at a time in SAM.[12]

3.5. Operation and Maintenance Costs

3.5.1. Current Status

Very little data exists on the annual O&M costs for power towers; the best data available to the DOE CSP Program is from Solar One, which operated in a daily power-production mode for approximately four years after the test and evaluation phase was completed. As time progressed at Solar One, fewer O&M personnel were required to maintain a high degree of plant availability.[13] During the final years of Solar One's operation, the SEGS I parabolic trough plant, located near Solar One, began its early phase of commercial operation. Both Solar One and SEGS I produced approximately 10 MW$_e$ of solar power. Based on discussions between key staff from the two plants, it was discovered that the number of O&M staff required for a tower and trough plant is very similar. Thus, to a first order, O&M costs for towers and troughs should be comparable. Sandia worked with the SEGS III-VII trough plants (150 MW$_e$ total) at Kramer Junction, CA throughout the 1990s to reduce O&M costs

[9]. Table 6 shows estimated O&M costs for towers (columns 1, 2, and 4) and troughs (column 3).

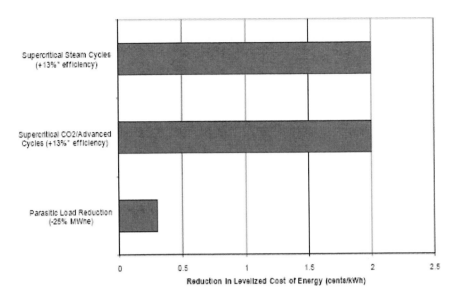

Figure 5. Potential impact of power block and balance of plant cost reductions and performance improvements on LCOE (*absolute percentage improvement).

As mentioned above, the Roadmap Workshop Baseline cost is a "rolled-up" value based primarily on responses obtained during the Roadmap Workshop. Whereas columns 1 and 2 are from single studies, column 4 represents a consolidated value from numerous individuals and organizations, which may explain the discrepancy in O&M costs. Furthermore, the discrepancy in O&M costs may also be attributable to different plant sizes.

Table 6. Cost of O&M [$/kW-yr] expressed in 2010 dollars

	Utility Studies 100 MWe	Abengoa Study 400 MWe	Trough 150 MWe	Roadmap Workshop Baseline
Annual O&M Costs	$87/kW-yr	$67/kW-yr	$100/kW-yr	$65/kW-yr

One reason for the discrepancy between the O&M costs shown for towers and troughs in Table 6 is that the 150 MW$_e$ plant at Kramer Junction is actually composed of five 30 MW$_e$ plants, each with its own turbine and operating crew. If the Kramer Junction facility had only one turbine and operating crew, O&M costs would likely be more in agreement with the tower values.

3.5.2. Future Improvement Opportunities

As the first commercial power towers come online in the USA, the actual O&M costs should be closely monitored, which in turn should lead to plant optimization and O&M cost reduction. As mentioned, the O&M costs of the SEGS plants at Kramer Junction were reduced through collaboration between the plant owner and DOE. The Kramer Junction

SEGS plants initially experienced high O&M costs, and a joint project with DOE was established to address the problem. Over a six year period, O&M improvements were made in 28 technical areas, resulting in O&M LCOE cost reductions of over 35% [9].

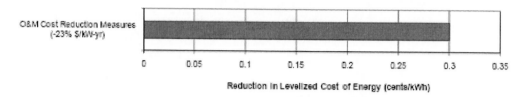

Figure 6. Potential impact of O&M cost reductions and performance improvements on LCOE.

Figure 6 shows the potential impact of O&M cost reductions and performance improvements on LCOE. Results are based on the baseline model with individual parameters varied one at a time in SAM.

3.6. Summary of TIO Impacts

In summary, all four subsystems should be the focus of a cost reduction plan for power towers. The relative importance of each cost category can be identified using the percentage breakdowns described in the preceding sections, which is shown in Table 7. The top three capital-cost categories identified are 1) heliostat drives for both large and small heliostats; 2) receiver module; and 3) manufacturing facilities for both large and small heliostats. In Table 7, the percentages in column 3 result from the multiplication of the values in columns 1 and 2.

Table 7. Relative ranking of capital cost categories per subsystem[14]

Subsystem Impact on LCOE	Subsystem Capital Cost Breakdown	Total Relative Impact on LCOE
38% Large Heliostats	27% Drives	10.3%
	23% Manufacturing	8.7%
	22% Mirror Modules	8.4%
	19% Structure support	7.2%
38% Small Heliostats	30% Drives	11.4%
	23% Manufacturing	8.7%
	16% Mirror Modules	6.1%
	19% Field Wiring/Control	7.2%
19% Receiver System	59% Receiver Module	11.2%
	21% Tower	4.0%
13% Storage System	57% Salt media	7.4%
	29% Tanks	3.8%
7% Steam Generator	85% Salt Heat Exchangers	6.0%

Figure 7 summarizes the impact of the TIOs on LCOE. It is important to emphasize that each TIO was evaluated independently of the others, and therefore the incremental impact of each TIO on LCOE cannot be added together to determine the cumulative impact of all TIOs on the system LCOE.

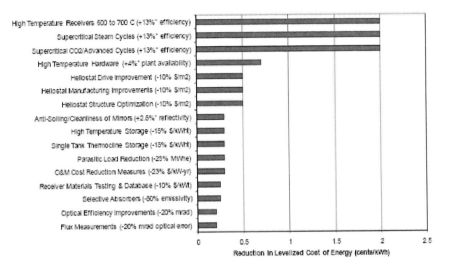

Figure 7. Potential impact of power tower cost reductions and performance improvements on LCOE (*absolute percentage improvement).

4. RECOMMENDED ACTIVITIES AND SPEND PLAN

In this section, specific potential activities to achieve the cost reductions outlined in this roadmap are listed. These activities are largely the product of the TIOs identified during the Roadmap Workshop. SAM simulations were used to estimate the impact of each activity on LCOE.

Table 8Table 8, which served as an input into Figure 1, shows projected performance and cost improvement scenarios for years 2013 (improvements "in the pipeline"), 2017, and 2020. The year 2013 case is shown with both a 30% and 10% ITC.

A potential multi-year task and spend plan for DOE-funded power tower R&D from FY12 through FY22 is shown in Table 9. Table 9 includes the following for each activity:

- the activity title,
- the activity participants,
- whether it is a new (N) or existing (E) activity,
- the relevant section of this plan to which the activity applies,
- the priority of the activity: high (IT), medium (M), or low (L),
- an appropriate metric for the activity,
- the potential improvement in the metric,
- the potential impact of the activity on the levelized cost of electricity (LCOE),
- the time frame: Near, Mid, or Long Term,

- the recommended funding for each activity from FY12 through FY22, and
- a description of the activity.

It should be noted that each activity is individually evaluated; in reality there will be overlap in the contributions of the various activities to LCOE reduction, and thus the potential improvements in the metrics and LCOE cannot simply be added together. The identification of activities as high, medium, or low, as well as near, mid, or long term, was designated through a voting and ranking process during the Roadmap Workshop. *Only high and medium priority activities are displayed in Table 9*. The content of the multi-year task and spend plan in Table 9 is organized to aid DOE in allocating a finite budget. The plan will be periodically revisited and updated based on industry feedback, programmatic objectives, and budget allocations. It is important to recognize that not all activities in the plan are necessary to achieve the target cost goals; the purpose of the plan is to list the R&D options available, from which the activities that will have the highest impact can be selected.

5. POWER TOWERS
AND THE SUNSHOT INITIATIVE

On February 4, 2011, United States Secretary of Energy Steven Chu officially unveiled the U.S. Department of Energy's **SunShot Initiative, an aggressive R&D plan to make large-scale solar energy systems cost competitive without subsidies by 2020.** The SunShot Initiative takes a systems-level approach to revolutionary, disruptive (as opposed to incremental) technological advancements in the field of solar energy. The overarching goal of the SunShot Initiative is reaching cost parity with baseload energy rates, estimated to be 5-6¢/kWh without subsidies, which would pave the way for rapid and large-scale adoption of solar electricity across the United States.

Table 8. Projected performance and cost improvement scenarios

Power Tower Inputs	Case 1 2013 Sandia & Industry Studies	Case 1.1 2013 Sandia & Industry Studies	Comments on Case 2.1 Values	Case 2.1 2017	Comments on Case 3.1 Values	Case 3.1 2020
Design Assumptions: Turbine MWe (gross/net)	110/100	110/100		165/150		165/150
Receiver Outlet Temperature (degC)	565	565	Raise salt temperature	600	Raise salt temperature some more	650
Solar Multiple	2.1	2.1		2.6		2.9
Receiver Design Point Rating MWt	540	540		1000		1000
Thermal Storage hours	9	9		13		14
Investment Tax Credit	30%	10%		10%		10%
Cost/Performance Assumptions: System Availability	90	90	Learning	94		94
Turbine efficiency	0.425	0.425	Higher operating temperature gain is negated by switch to dry cooling	0.425	Switch to supercritical Rankine cycle	0.48
Heliostat reflectivity	0.935	0.935		0.95		0.95
Heliostat cleanliness	0.95	0.95		0.95		0.975

Power Tower Inputs	Case 1 2013 Sandia & Industry Studies	Case 1.1 2013 Sandia & Industry Studies	Comments on Case 2.1 Values	Case 2.1 2017	Comments on Case 3.1 Values	Case 3.1 2020
Heliostat image error (mrad)	1.53	1.53		1.31		1.25
Heliostat Field ($/m2)	200	200		170		120
Receiver emissivity	0.88	0.88		0.88	Selective surface	0.4
Receiver System ($/kWht)	200	200	Plant scale reduces cost	165	Optimized design	150
Thermal Storage ($/kWht)	30	30	Optimized 2 tank, higher temperature	25	Thermocline 1 tank, higher temperature	20
Steam Generator ($/kWe)	350	350	Plant scale reduces cost	300	Optimized design	250
Power Block ($/kWe)	1000	1000	Plant scale reduces cost	900	Optimized design	800
O&M ($/kW-yr)	65	65	Start O&M cost reduction project, plant scale	57	Complete O&M cost reduction project	50
EPC, Project, land (% of direct costs)	35	35		30	Modular plant, learning, lower project risk	25
Outputs						
Total Installed Cost ($/kW)	7427	7427		7403		5677
Debt Fraction (optimized)	41.1	54.2		54.2		54.1
Capacity factor	48.1	48.1		64.5		72
Annual Efficiency (Enet/Q_DNI*SF_area)	14.8%	14.8%		15.7%		17.8%
LCOE (c/kWh, real)	12.3	15.0		11.1		7.8
PPA Price (c/kWh, 1st year)	14.1	17.2		12.7		8.9
LCOE (c/kWh, nominal)	15.6	19.0		14		9.8

For the SunShot Initiative, CSP provides the following benefits:

- *Thermal Energy Storage*: CSP offers a firm, dispatchable solar solution to meet utility demand for power, offsetting some of the intermittency and ramp-rate issues surrounding PV.
- *Hybridization*: Combined with thermal storage, a small amount of natural gas hybridization in a CSP plant can increase capacity to 75-85%, which would allow CSP to displace conventional (e.g. fossil) power plants.
- *Supply Chain*: The CSP supply chain is overwhelmingly domestic, from materials to manufacturing, including significant domestic job creation. Most, if not all, materials necessary to build a CSP plant can be found in the US.
- *Plant Size*: The size of utility-scale CSP facilities is consistent with the SunShot goal of large-scale solar installations. Two CSP plants (BrightSource Energy's Ivanpah and Abengoa Solar's Solana) currently under construction in the U.S. will be the largest and second largest solar plants in the world.

Table 9. Potential multi-year activities and budgets for DOE-funded power tower R&D

AGIP Power Tower R&D Activity	Participant(s)	New/Exist Plan ID Section	Priority	Metric	Metric Impact	LCOE Impact	Time-frame	FY12	FY13	FY14	FY15	FY16	FY17	FY18	FY19	FY20	FY21	FY22	Description
Heliostats																			
Other	Sandia/Industry	N 9.1.2	H				Near	650	750	750		500	1050						450	
Optical Methods and Testing	Sandia/NREL	E 8.1.2	H	optical error (mrad)	-10%	0.1 ¢/kWh	Near	200	200	200			100		0	0	0	0	
Wind Loads Measurement and Mitigation	Sandia/NREL	E 8.1.2	M		-20%	0.1 ¢/kWh	Near/Mid	200	200	200								200	
Manufacturing FOA	Sandia/Industry	N 9.1.2	M	$/m2	-10%	0.1 ¢/kWh	Near	500	750	750						0	0	0	
Anti-Soiling/Cleaning of Mirrors	NREL/Industry	N 9.1.2	M	Cleanliness	2.5%	0.5 ¢/kWh	Near	0	500	500		500	100			0	0	0	
Basic Structure Optimization	Sandia/Industry	E 9.1.2	M	$/m2	-10%	0.5 ¢/kWh	Mid	200	200	200			200		200	200	200	200	
Receiver System																			
Receiver Materials Testing & Database	Sandia	N 9.2.2	H		-10%	Note 1	Near/Mid	200	200	200			200						
Steam Receivers and Helio	Sandia/Industry	N 9.2.2	H	$/kWt Plant Availability	4%	Note 1	Near/Mid	0	500	500		500	500					0	
Selective Absorbers	Sandia/NREL	E 9.2.2	H	Emissivity Thermal-to-Electric Conversion	-50%	0.25 ¢/kWh	Mid	200	200	200		200	200	1000		200	200	200	
High Temperature Receivers (600 to 700 C)	Sandia/Industry	E 9.2.2	M	Efficiency	13%	2.6 ¢/kWh	Mid/Long	150	500	1000		4500	1500	1500		1500	1500	1500	
Flux Measurements	Sandia/Industry	E 9.2.2	M	optical error (mrad)	-20%	0.1 ¢/kWh	Near	150	500	500		500	0			0	0	0	
Tall Tower Acceptance	Sandia	E 9.2.2	M	Public Acceptance	N/A		Mid	100	100	100		100	100	0		0	0	1500	
Thermal Storage System								1000	1000	1000		6000	6500	1500		1500	1500	1500	
High Temperature Storage	Sandia	N 9.3.2	H	$/kWth	15%	0.1 ¢/kWh	Mid/Long	0	0	500		5000	500	500		500	500	500	
Valves and Iron-Welded Flanges	Sandia	E 9.3.2	M	Plant Availability	4%	0.1 ¢/kWh	Near/Mid	500	500	500		500	500	500		500	500	500	
Single Tank Thermocline Storage	Sandia/University	E 9.3.2	M	$/kWth	15%	0.5 ¢/kWh	Mid	200	200	200		200	5000	500		500	500	0	
Alternative Fluids at 700 C+	Sandia/NREL	E 9.3.2	M	$/kWth	7		Mid/Long	500	900	900		900	900	900		900	900	900	
Power Block/GOP								250	225	375		1000	900	900		100	100	100	
Low-Water Cooling	NREL/Sandia	N 3.4.2	H	gal/MWh water usage	-75%		Near/Mid	50	50	50		50	50	50		0	0	0	
Hi-Efficiency Hybrid Configurations	Industry/Sandia/NREL	E 9.4.2	H	$/kWe	-25%	3 ¢/kWh	Near/Mid	50	50	50		50	50	50		0	0	0	
Designs for Rapid Temperature Change	Sandia/Industry	N 3.4.2	M	Annual Efficiency	1st	Note 1	Near/Mid	0	0	50		500	500	500		0	0	0	
Parasitic Load Reduction	Sandia/Industry	N 3.4.2	M	MW/hr Thermal-to-Electric Conversion	-25%	0.1 ¢/kWh	Near/Mid	0	0	100		100	100	100		0	0	0	
Supercritical Steam Cycle	Sandia/Industry	E 3.4.2	M	Efficiency Thermal-to-Electric Conversion	13%	2.6 ¢/kWh	Mid/Long	100	500	100		500	500	500		50	50	50	
Supercritical CO2/Advanced Cycles	Sandia/NREL	E 9.4.2	M	Efficiency	19%	2 ¢/kWh	Long	50	50	50		50	50	50		50	50	50	
O&M Cost Reduction								0	500	500		1100	1100	1100		1100	1100	1100	
O&M Analysis of Initial Commercial Plants	Industry/Sandia/NREL	N 9.5.2 H Note 2		$/kW-yr			Near	0	100	100		100	100	100		100	100	100	
O&M Support	Industry/Sandia/NREL	9.5.2 H Note 2		$/kW-yr	-25%	0.5 ¢/kWh	Near	0	0	0		1000	1000	1000		1000	1000	1000	
Baseload FOA Support	Industry/Sandia	E 3	Front LCOE	-20%	Note 1	Near	50	50	0		0	0	0		0	0	0	
TOTALS								3350	4925	6725		14300	16595	5100		5100	4600	4600	

Note 1: The improvement in this metric assumes the base case power tower is a steam receiver without storage. Base case LCOEs have not been calculated for this type of power tower.

Note 2: Plant-wide O&M cost reduction was not discussed during the Roadmap Workshop. Sandia believes this is an important activity based on our experience with early commercial trough projects.

The SunShot Initiative goal for CSP is 6¢/kWh or less. While many of the TIOs identified in this roadmap are applicable to the SunShot cost reduction goal, it is clear that an "extra step" is necessary to move from the power tower roadmap projections — 7.8¢/kWh with a 10% ITC (or 8.6¢/kWh with a 0% ITC) — to the SunShot Initiative goal of 6¢/kWh with no ITC (as shown in Figure 8).

Therefore, the DOE CSP Program is currently in the process of defining a corresponding R&D path forward. SunShot-level cost reductions for power towers likely includes an increase in system efficiency by moving to higher temperature operation (i.e. maximize conversion efficiency) without sacrificing efficiency elsewhere in the system (i.e. minimize collection efficiency losses).

Likewise, reducing the cost of the solar field and developing high-temperature storage compatible with high-efficiency, high-temperature power cycles are critical to driving costs down.

Based on industry comments, including a DOE-CSP Industry Meeting held in conjunction with SEIA on March 8-9, 2011 in Arlington, VA, the following list outlines TIOs in addition to those already mentioned that could potentially lead to SunShot-level cost reductions for power towers.

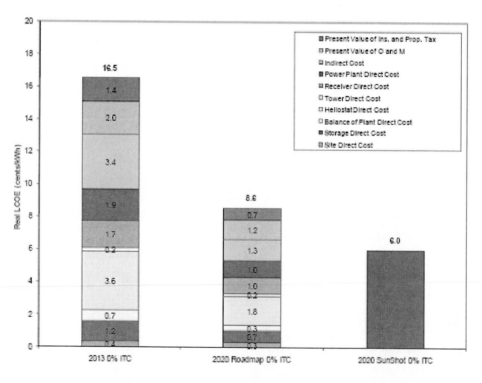

Figure 8. LCOE reduction (real 2010 dollars) pathway to SunShot Initiative goal (all cases are shown with a 0% ITC).

Solar Collector Field

- Alternative heliostat designs that use significantly less material.
- Non-steel-based support structures.
- Reliable wireless methods for heliostat power and communication.

- Advanced, self-aligning control systems.
- Closed-loop tracking.
- Curved heliostat facet optimization.
- Low-profile heliostats that are subject to less wind-loading.
- Utilization of secondary concentrator designs with improved optics.
- Automatic soiling detection and reflectivity assessment.
- Driven-pylon or ground-mounted pedestals.
- Minimal field grading and site preparation.
- Increase in volume production.

Solar Receiver

- High-temperature materials capable of reliable operation over many thermal cycles.
- Cavity receiver designs or other alternative concepts (e.g. particle, beam down, volumetric, modular) that enable efficient solar collection at high temperature.
- Appropriate models to simulate receiver performance at part-load conditions.
- Coverings for receiver designs that employ quartz windows.
- Integration of the tower as a container for the thermal energy storage system.
- For modular designs, lightweight towers that can be rapidly assembled and installed.

Thermal Energy Storage

- High-temperature storage concepts with enhanced thermal stability and increased storage density, such as novel inorganic liquids, solid particles, phase change materials, or thermochemical approaches.
- Additives that augment the heat capacity of existing fluids such as 60% $NaNO_3$ / 40% KNO_3 solar salt.
- Non-nitrate salts capable of operation at higher temperatures.
- Lightweight, compact thermal storage systems that could potentially be integrated with the tower (located within or on top).

Power Block / Balance of Plant

- Advanced power cycles "beyond" supercritical steam, such as supercritical CO_2 or air Brayton.
- Industrial micro-turbines that lead to reduced turbomachinery size and cost.
- Combined-cycle power systems that lead to higher efficiency cycles.
- Development of high-temperature metal or ceramic heat exchangers that are compatible with advanced power cycles.
- Corrosive-resistant hardware (e.g. piping, structure, valves, valve packing, flanges, ducting, blowers, dampers, insulation, pressure and flow measurement devices) that can reliably operate at elevated temperatures.
- Efficient absorption chilling systems to cool compressor inlet for gas turbines.
- Modular plant designs that can be replicated and combined to create larger systems.
- Non-electricity applications (e.g. solar fuels, desalination, cogeneration, enhanced oil recovery).

CONCLUSIONS

Since the inception of the Power Tower Technology Roadmap, the DOE CSP Program budget distribution has significantly shifted to include an increased emphasis on advanced R&D and power towers. This is primarily due to the selection and funding of a group of CSP industry projects that are evaluating and designing complete power tower baseload systems. As Figure 9 shows, power towers jumped from 4% to 20% of total DOE CSP budget as a result of the Baseload Funding Opportunity Announcement (FOA) solicitation project awards.

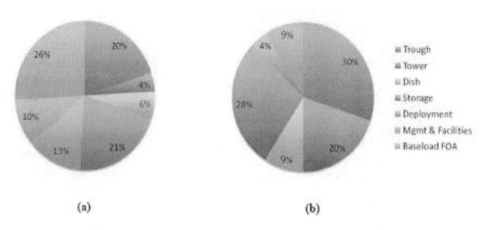

Figure 9. 2010 DOE CSP budget activity levels ($49.7M USD) (a) before and (b) after the Baseload FOA project award announcements [12].

Moving forward, it is anticipated that power tower R&D will continue to receive funding through competitive solicitations to industry and universities, as well as through activities at the national laboratories. During this ramp-up phase for power towers within the DOE CSP Program, the Power Tower Technology Roadmap will continue to be utilized as a tool to guide DOE towards those tasks that will create the most benefit and have the highest impact on reducing the cost of power tower systems.

Reducing the cost of power tower systems by up to 75% by the end of the decade is clearly a significant challenge; however, pursuing these aggressive goals will enable considerable advancements in power tower technology. This roadmap has outlined multiple pathways to achieve these ambitious cost reduction targets. DOE is poised to work alongside industry to make power towers competitive with fossil fuels through both technology activities (e.g. RDD&D, modeling, studies, testing) and non-technology activities (e.g. manufacturing, transmission, land, permitting, financing).

ACKNOWLEDGMENTS

In addition to the U.S. Department of Energy, Sandia National Laboratories, and National Renewable Energy Laboratory, representatives from the following organizations have contributed to the content of this Power Tower Technology Roadmap: Abengoa Solar, Black

& Veatch, BrightSource Energy, the Electric Power Research Institute (EPRI), eSolar, EZKlein Partners, Pratt & Whitney Rocketdyne, Sargent & Lundy, SENER, Solaflect Energy, SolarReserve, Wilson SolarPower, and WorleyParsons. The authors would also like to thank Nathan Siegel and Brian Iverson for their contributions during the Roadmap Workshop at Sandia.

Sandia National Laboratories is a multi-program laboratory managed and operated by Sandia Corporation, a wholly owned subsidiary of Lockheed Martin Corporation, for the U.S. Department of Energy's National Nuclear Security Administration under contract DE-AC04-94AL85000.

REFERENCES

[1]   Reilly, H. E. and G. J. Kolb, Evaluation of Molten Salt Power Tower Technology Based on Experience at Solar Two, SAND2001-3674, Albuquerque, NM, November 2001.

[2]   Greentech Media, list compiled and maintained by Brett Prior (prior@gtmresearch.com), updated 10/19/2010.

[3]   Pacific Gas & Electric Company, Solar Central Receiver Technology Advancement for Electric Utility Applications, Phase 1 Topical Report – Vol 1 and 2, Report No. 007.2-88.2, San Francisco, CA, September 1988.

[4]   Abengoa Solar, Inc., Advanced Thermal Storage for Central Receivers with Supercritical Coolants, Grant DE-FG36-08GO018149, Lakewood, CO, June 15, 2010.

[5]   Kolb, G. J., S. Jones, M. Donnelly, D. Gorman, R. Thomas, R. Davenport, and R. Lumia, Heliostat Cost Reduction Study, SAND2007-3293, Albuquerque, NM, June 2007.

[6]   Fernandez, V., et. al., PS10, The First Year Operation Experience, SolarPACES 2009 Book of Abstracts, September 15-18, 2009, Berlin, Germany.

[7]   Personal email from Manuel Blanco (CENER) to Greg Kolb (Sandia), October 11, 2010.

[8]   Bradshaw, R. W., and S. H. Goods, Accelerated Corrosion Testing of a Nickel-Based Alloy in a Molten Salt, SAND2001-8758, Sandia National Laboratories, Livermore, CA, November 2009.

[9]   De Laquil III, C. T. Schafer, and S. E. Faas, A Cost-Performance Comparison of Water Steam Receivers for Solar Central Electric Power Plants, SAND80-8245, December 1980.

[10] U.S. Department of Energy. Concentrating Solar Power Commercial Application Study: Reducing Water Consumption of Concentrating Solar Power Electricity Generation, Report to Congress, 2008.

[11] Cohen, G. E., D. W. Kearney, and G. J. Kolb, Final Report on the Operation and Maintenance Improvement Program for Concentrating Solar Power Plants, SAND99-1290, Sandia National Laboratories, Albuquerque, NM, June 1999.

[12] Wilkins, F (2010). Overview of CSP, presentation to the SETP Peer Review, Washington, DC, May 24, 2010.

End Notes

[1] In 2011, this goal was updated to a value of 6¢/kWh or less with no subsidies by the end of the decade as part of the DOE SunShot Initiative. For more information, see Section 5.

[2] If the same 540 MWt receiver is coupled with a 200 MWe turbine, the optimum amount of storage is only a few hours.

[3] PS10 produced 21,400 MWh (gross) in 2008 [6]. The plant is allowed to burn 15% natural gas. Annual DNI in Sevilla near the plant was approximately 2.1 MWh/m2 in 2008 [7]. Heliostat field area is 74,880 m2. Thus, $21400*0.85/(74880*2.1) = 11.5\%$.

[4] Peak efficiencies (i.e. design point) for power towers typically exceed 22%. However, annual efficiency is used here rather than peak efficiency because annual efficiency is more relevant for LCOE calculations. Some power tower developers predict annual efficiencies of 18% or higher; however, such analyses usually assume 100% equipment availability and/or perfectly clean mirrors. The values contained in this roadmap assume outages and other real-world effects.

[5] Electricity cost is also dependent on financial assumptions. The financial assumptions used in this analysis are the SAM default values assuming plant ownership by an independent power producer.

[6] See Appendix A of [5] to fully understand the cost categories defined in year 2000. A few relatively small inconsistencies can be seen between the year 2000 and year 2006 studies; for example, mirror support structure and installation and checkout costs increased in year 2006 even though production rates were higher in the 2006 study.

[7] Reflector area would power an early-deployment plant on the order of 30 MWe.

[8] The results shown in Figure 2 are not additive; in other words, the overall impact of simultaneously implementing all of the TIOs is less than and not the sum of the individual cost reductions.

[9] The results shown in Figure 3 are not additive; in other words, the overall impact of simultaneously implementing all of the TIOs is less than and not the sum of the individual cost reductions.

[10] The results shown in Figure 4 are not additive; in other words, the overall impact of simultaneously implementing all of the TIOs is less than and not the sum of the individual cost reductions.

[11] Simulations with SOLERGY suggest a 50/40/10 parasitics split between turbine plant/solar plant/offline sources for a baseload plant. For a peaking plant without storage, the parasitic split is approximately 20/30/50.

[12] The results shown in Figure 5 are not additive; in other words, the overall impact of simultaneously implementing all of the TIOs is less than and not the sum of the individual cost reductions.

[13] The O&M staff numbered approximately 25 in the third year of operation, compared to 15 in the fourth year.

[14] Only the most significant capital cost categories within each subsystem are shown. Thus, totals do not add to 100%.

INDEX

D

E

F

T